EMOTIONAL PROBLEMS OF LIVING

Books by Drs. English & Pearson

EMOTIONAL PROBLEMS OF LIVING

COMMON NEUROSES OF CHILDREN AND ADULTS

EMOTIONAL PROBLEMS OF LIVING

Avoiding the Neurotic Pattern

By

O. SPURGEON ENGLISH, M.D.

Professor of Psychiatry
Temple University Medical School

AND

GERALD H. J. PEARSON, M.D.

Director, Philadelphia Psychoanalytic Institute

W · W · NORTON & COMPANY · INC · *New York*

PRINTED IN THE UNITED STATES OF AMERICA
FOR THE PUBLISHERS BY THE VAIL-BALLOU PRESS

CONTENTS

of the Absence of the Mother · The Effect on the Girl of the Absence of
the Father.· The Effect on Either Boy or Girl of Separation from Both
Parents · The Effect on the Child of Prolonged, Painful or Crippling
Illness · The Effect on the Child of the Birth of a Sibling · The Effects
of Adverse Parental Attitudes · Parental Rejection · Parental Overprotection · Parental Indulgence · The Effect of Premature or Excessive
Sexual Stimulation · The Effects of a Traumatic Experience · The Emotional Illnesses of the Phallic Period · Irrational Fears and Phobias ·
Temper Tantrums

PREFACE

A PREVIOUS book entitled *Common Neuroses of Children and Adults* was written by the authors primarily for the physician and psychiatrist. They feel that with the passing of time a need has arisen for a more inclusive book dealing with personality problems, which could be used by the medical student, teacher, clergyman, nurse, social worker and others working in the field of interpersonal relations. As the reader will note, much that is stated in these chapters is directed toward the medical student and the young physician. However, an attempt has been made to have the book readable by and understandable to a large number of interested lay people. We see no incongruity but rather an advantage in this, since in that field of medicine which deals with the problems of children and psychoneurosis and psychosomatic disease there is a great need for the doctor and layman to have an understanding of many of the same facts concerning the functioning of human beings. The better these groups of interested people understand the fundamentals of human personality the quicker they will understand each other. They will have a common language for expressing what they mean and thus be better able to work together to bring about a cure of the disorder. In this book we have tried to follow the development of the personality and its many activities in reasonably logical sequence through the life span.

This book is orientated to psychoanalytic thinking, since we feel that Freudian psychoanalysis is the best approach to understanding personality. Consequently we are deeply in debt to Sigmund Freud and all of his fellow workers and pupils who have made contributions to the many facets of human personality and the problems that arise in connection with it. We have made specific reference to some of these contributions. If we have also omitted some who have made contributions to the subjects under discussion in this book we hereby acknowledge that lack of space or some other reason did not make it possible to include every reference.

We have discussed the development of the personality chronologically from birth to old age and in so doing we have followed the normal or

Neuroses of Children and Adults afterward, as this volume is more introductory and the earlier volume more of a textbook.

We have discussed the development of the personality chronologically from birth to old age and in so doing we have followed the normal or average phenomena of emotional growth with a discussion of the commoner deviations from the normal occurring at each particular phase of development.

We found upon writing such a book how difficult it was to make a book even on the commoner emotional disturbances all inclusive. Lack of space made it impossible for us to include material on the war neuroses in children and adults or on psychoses in children and adolescents.

We acknowledge with gratitude the invaluable help of Mrs. Marguerite Haines and Mrs. Herbert Meyers for their contribution in helping to prepare material and for the conscientious labor connected with bringing the original manuscript to its final form.

O. S. E.
G. H. J. P.

INTRODUCTION: THE MEANING OF A NEUROSIS

ONE hears more and more talk these days about neuroses. We hear of the neurosis of civilization and the neurosis of peoples of other countries and within our own country. We hear of a better world we must create, with security for all, greater advantages for all. We hear that a greater maturity on the part of everyone will be necessary to create that healthier, happier, more useful, effectual life.

Books are written and papers are delivered on national psychoses, on the lack of logic and reason in civilization. War has done much to convince us all that there must be some good reason for the growing murmur that we are not individually or collectively "using our heads" to the extent we should. In short, we must be either childish or a little sick that we do not manage better. Mother earth gives us abundant advantages and we either fail to use them or we misuse them. We suffer too much, we become ill too often. We have conquered the potent force of a few bacteria and have learned how to keep the body functioning with various surgical skills. But even though we apply the old drugs and many new ones, we cannot easily find the secret to health, happiness and a richer, fuller life. Too often we struggle anxiously from the cradle to the grave in order to enjoy briefly a questionable success before we begin to dread the loss of what we have acquired through illness, separation or death.

No one wants to have things work this way, but a satisfactory remedy is not easily forthcoming. The great religious leaders of all time have only helped, not saved, the situation. Philosophers and literary men have exposed human weaknesses and made suggestions for their improvement, but few people have read or listened.

Medical science reached out and took a hand in the problem in the person of Sigmund Freud nearly a half century ago. He was the first to make a scheme or chart of the fundamentals in human personality development and to make a working plan of treatment. As time went on he modified his original ideas to some degree, and his colleagues and pupils have also modified and revised them. But the bulk of his original framework remains as a guide to the study of the human mind and how to influence it. He tried to set down what he believed to be the structure of the human personality and what caused people to behave the way they do.

If we read the history of Freud's career, we can probably understand why no doctor reached out earlier to take hold of this problem. Freud got his knuckles rapped for doing what he did; a great deal of hostility arose and was directed against him and his theories about human beings. He was regarded as immoral, fantastic and unscientific. People claimed he was being articulate about things better left unsaid. He went on many years before he achieved recognition for his work. Human beings did not and still do not want to face the truth about themselves. Human beings prefer to live in a blind, self-deluded way, ignoring their fundamental impulses. So any study of human personality proceeds very slowly.

The reader may nevertheless ask, "If a means of understanding and influencing human nature was discovered fifty years ago, why has not more been done about it?" The answer cannot be given tersely and glibly. One might say flippantly that "nobody cares about improving," and there would be a great deal of truth in that statement. Yet this does not represent the whole truth by any means, for we believe that actually people do want to behave better, more nobly, more generously, less selfishly. But to do so requires effort—an effort that cannot be put forth because the feelings and ideas that would make that effort possible are not a large enough part of the emotional and ideational nourishment of the average human being to make such effort possible in his everyday life.

For nearly two thousand years a large portion of the world has given lip service to Christian principles, yet how many professed Christians have had the inspiration to actually live from day to day according to Christ's principles? A part of the answer must lie in the fact that man is not easily inspired to such behavior as following the golden rule. Perhaps Christ seemed too far away and man needed inspiration from closer range. At any rate, the example of religion indicates that man finds it difficult to achieve his ideals. Some force holds him back, makes him indolent, selfish, cold, indifferent to a more friendly, enjoyable, co-operative existence.

Frustration and Progress

Freud observed that the force that holds the individual back from achieving the best of his potentialities is the result of the frustration of pleasure needs early in life, resulting in hostility, pain and hatred. This pain of frustration and the resulting hatred engendered gradually form a wall, a barrier within an individual so that the friendship and joy of living which he surely must encounter some day are unable to get to him and give him the happiness, peace, comfort, and desire to do for others. This same frustration and resulting hatred build up to form the *wall* of pessimism, depression of spirits, indifference and lack of generosity, and even active cruelty and oppression of others, which retard human progress and postpone the day of the better world.

While we believe a great deal of truth lies in these sentences, we realize that to many they seem like a formula or at best an explanation to be intellectually grasped but not necessarily understood in the deepest and best sense of understanding. At any rate, the authors wish in this book to take the reader chapter by chapter through certain common life experiences, so that by a process of *living with* the forces that go to make up a human personality (as well as we can make personality live in these chapters) he will emerge toward the end of the book a little closer to an understanding of human nature.

Psychiatry has taught us that the neurotic person is immature, that he is childish, that he has not grown up, that he has conflicts, all of which are true even though the facts need amplification. Growing up is a very difficult process. The human being is born into the world with certain needs which must be met by those about him. The journey through life is long and difficult, and it is the lucky person who can start under as auspicious circumstances as possible. Grownups have the responsibility for taking care of the young human being and for seeing that he is comfortable and emotionally contented in so far as possible.

If the human being from the start of life is made physically comfortable, if he is made happy, and if he has a chance to express himself without too much unnecessary frustration, he is a fortunate individual indeed, because it is the person with this kind of start who becomes the optimistic, hopeful individual, the one who can contribute something to the world at large and to those nearest to him. The human being whose needs are not met when he comes into the world, who is an unwelcome addition to the family, who is neglected and who lives in an environment that is indifferent and cold toward him will develop hostility, resentment, hate, pessimism—all of which makes it very difficult for him to function.

So when Freud as a physician directed our attention to the early life of the individual and turned our thoughts to the needs of the newborn human being, he was making an extremely important contribution to human progress. However, people did not like what he said. They did not like to be reminded of their childhood, they did not like to be reminded of their asocial impulses and they wished Freud would not say any more about it. However, psychoanalysis has continued to spread and has come to occupy a very prominent place in psychiatry, medicine and education. More and more the theories of Freud are coming to be used in the field of social work, psychology, sociology and anthropology and, in short, in any field where people are attempting to understand human behavior with a keener insight and a more human approach.

The Physician and the Personality

It is important for doctors to study human behavior as carefully as possible, not only in order to cure those persons who have a gastric distress or indigestion but also because they are depressed in spirit. Doctors are in a profession that carries considerable prestige in the community, and what the doctor says as he practices medicine from day to day will influence greatly the thinking of the community at large. So whatever truth exists about human personality as we know it now, this knowledge is important for the doctor to gain and to use. The public has always regarded the doctor as a man who knows a great deal about human nature. He was supposed to have gathered this knowledge because in the course of his practice he came close to the human body and to the minds of individuals in sickness and trouble. But the demand today is for the doctor to know more than the knowledge that can be picked up by way of individual observation, inclination and initiative. The study of medicine has so broadened that the doctor must spend considerable time learning about human personality in order to treat disease and help his patients.

As we said, man is being unnecessarily thwarted in his goals of happiness and health. He does not seem to get the right start toward a free exercising of his potentialities for happiness, peace of mind and constructive social and personal effort. He becomes fearful, doubtful, perplexed, in conflict, confused. In this state of mind he cannot act simply and constructively and his body may distress him as well as his mind. When he is in this state we say he has a neurosis.

A neurosis does not mean one single thing. It means several things. It means deprivation of love and interest as a child. It means an inadequate acquaintance with the realities of the world about him. It means an inadequate set of values for participation in the world around him. It means an inability to love and hate effectively. It means that the individual has not matured or developed emotionally and ideationally to meet life. He may have poor control of his emotions, possibly reacting too passively or too violently. He may be either too prejudiced or have no opinions at all. He is either too sensitive to certain experiences or has too little feeling for them. He often gets distresses in his body. In short, his personality, that tool for social adjustment, is not well integrated to function smoothly, and the unnecessary emotional friction generated results in unhappiness, unpopularity, spiritual emptiness, strife with his fellow men, or illness.

In the succeeding chapters we shall endeavor to describe how these different frictions can generate within the self or through contacts of the individual with his environment. We shall also try to give a point of view and a therapeutic approach which will reduce to a minimum these conflicts that produce the neurotic pattern.

Chapter I

DEVELOPMENT OF PERSONALITY DURING THE ORAL PERIOD

SINCE personality develops simultaneously with physical growth, the factors that enter into personality development are also linked up rather definitely with physiological processes much more than is commonly supposed. This makes for a physiological psychology, an approach that is best suited to medical thinking and to the solution of medical problems, and one, moreover, that is best suited to the understanding of personality whether one is a doctor or not. We repeat that human beings do not want to think about themselves; they have a considerable feeling of anxiety—even shame, disgust and prejudice against their own body and its functions. People want to forget about their former helplessness and about their needs of childhood. Yet if they are ever going to understand themselves adequately, they must turn back and look at what they went through as children and accept it as natural and normal, and do away with their embarrassment and rejection of it.

The first phase of personality development is referred to as the *oral* period of development. It is not a particularly attractive or exciting name to give to this first development period, but it does convey meaning, and we hope sooner or later the reader will agree it is a good one to use since the needs and interests of the newborn human being center around this particular part of the body, his desires being satisfied largely in the area of the mouth, esophagus and stomach. The taking of food, being fed, being made comfortable through the nursing process are to a great extent what satisfy and make life endurable and bearable for the child—assuming, of course, that he is wanted and loved, that his skin is kept warm and comfortable. It has been clearly shown that the newborn child needs fondling and affection in much the same rhythm that he is fed. Being wanted, being loved and played with are an important part of the diet, so to speak. The intake of nourishment and the intake and acceptance of goodwill should proceed simultaneously, the latter being no less important in the eventual well-being of the person than the former.

Constitution and Personality

Before going too far with the oral period, we ought to think for just a moment about the physical makeup of the individual who goes through the experiences that have so much to do with the forming of personality.

A person's physical makeup is referred to as his *constitution*. We say people are born with a certain constitution, which means several things. It means that people are born destined to have a certain type of stature which may be tall or short, thin or obese; it means they have light skin or dark skin; it means they have a brain with a cellular structure that is capable of absorbing and handling much factual knowledge or one that is capable of absorbing very little. In other words, they may be potentially intelligent individuals or they may be feeble-minded. They may be born with a cardiovascular system that fulfills its function with a certain strength until well into old age, or they may be born with a weaker cardiovascular system that develops sclerosis (hardening of the arteries) or some other disease of the cardiovascular system early in life. In some the cardiovascular system will begin to wear out as early as thirty-five or forty and in others it will still be functioning well when the individual is ninety. The lungs may have a tendency to break down easily and become infected with an organism like the tubercular bacillus. In some families the kidney structure seems not to endure so long as in others. In other families the glandular system seems to have its own limited potentialities which are transmitted from generation to generation. This tendency to have varying strengths in the various systems of the body is transmitted through the germ plasm, and these varying physical factors in human beings we allude to as their constitutional endowment.

The more we observe human behavior in its beginnings the more we observe things which when combined with the world outside the child are important to consider in personality formation. These observations are that some children are more sensitive than others to stimuli such as light, sound, heat, cold, being moved, etc., while some are phlegmatic as regards these things; that some children by their very earliest life reaction have a great "will to live and get"—a great tenacity to struggle for what they want and need. Others have a weak will to live and get and enjoy (possibly related to the sensitivity alluded to above) and easily turn away from frustrating experiences into apathy, inertia and even death. What determines this quality we do not know but it is probably constitutional to some degree. Moreover, while we feel this quality is modifiable by environmental events after birth, it should be further studied and reckoned with in the whole problem of personality formation.

Conflict in Life

Throughout the world there is a constant struggle being waged. On the one hand there are living creatures constantly striving to remain alive and to keep their species alive, and on the other the elemental forces whose action is inimical to life. Each living creature is forced constantly to wrest its livelihood and protect its life and the life of its species from these inimical forces, and its survival depends on its ability to accomplish this struggle successfully.

Not only must the living creature wage an unceasing struggle with these hostile forces but at the same time it must contend with forces within itself whose action is to break down the complex molecule consistent with life into simpler, nonliving molecular constellations in order that the energy required for life itself may be liberated. We do not understand just what constitutes life; therefore we do not understand the nature of the forces that strive to preserve life, both personally and racially, or the nature of the forces within the organism that tend to destroy it. We can only observe the manifestations of their presence. Freud referred to these forces as instinctive and classified them into two groups: (1) the erotic or life instincts, whose presence is coexistent with life, and whose purpose is to maintain the life of the individual and to create and maintain the life of the species, and (2) the death or aggressive instincts, whose presence is also coexistent with life, and whose purpose is to reduce the complex living molecule to simpler, inorganic ones.

Thus all life is subject to two groups of conflicts, those between the living creature and the elemental forces of the physical world, and those between the opposing instinct drives within the living organism itself. In these struggles the living organism eventually succumbs and is reduced to inorganic substance. Life is maintained only by the propagation of new individuals, often differing in some degree from their parents and so gradually becoming new species.

As one ascends the biological scale from the vegetable to the animal life, a new conflict is encountered. Most animals cannot maintain their existence without assimilating molecules that are or have been alive themselves. Except for water and salt, the human being feeds exclusively on substances that are or have recently been alive. Therefore, the third conflict is the struggle for existence between the various forms of life. In this struggle the species, race or individual that is better equipped at the time is victorious and continues to live, while the vanquished dies.

A fourth conflict is found among the higher animals, including man. These animals tend to live in a social organization, whose purpose is better to protect their existence against the inimical forces of the physical world and of other living creatures. Such a social organization can only function if each individual comprising it is willing to inhibit certain of his needs at those times when their immediate gratification would injure another member of the group or interfere too seriously with the gratification of his needs. To accomplish this inhibition, certain rules of conduct are formulated by the group, and each individual must learn to conform to them lest he lose the protection and assistance of the group organization. At the very best, these rules curtail the individual's freedom in living and maintaining the life of the species. There arises a conflict between the individual's instinctive drives and the group's rules of conduct. This conflict becomes most marked in the case of man, whose social organization has formulated a large number of rules of conduct which are handed down from generation to generation. In this conflict the basic rules of conduct that preserve the existence of the social organization must always be victorious, and the conflict results in the individual's curtailing his liberty of action at the expense of some pain and suffering to himself for which he tries to find compensations. If he will not do this, he may be excluded from the benefits of group life or be killed.

Every human being, therefore, is exposed to these four conflicts, and his happiness and success throughout his life depend on his ability to deal adequately with them all. This ability at any given point will be a complex of his biological inheritance, his physical and intellectual constitution, and the skills he has developed as a result of the conditioning experiences because of the nature of his actual contacts with the physical world, with other forms of life, and with the other people of his social organization. It is our purpose in this book to discuss this ability during the various periods of life from childhood to mature age.

Experience and Personality

We used to blame a great many diseases on constitution when we did not know what caused the malady. However, as we gained more knowledge about the cardiovascular diseases, the respiratory diseases, the mental diseases, we put less and less blame on the constitutional factors in disease. In other words, we hide less of our ignorance under the cloak of constitution. The constitutional factor in disease grows smaller as our knowledge grows larger, though it is unlikely that it will ever come to the point where the factor of the constitution does not exist. Therefore, we have to consider the factor of the constitution but we must not use it as a catch-all, a convenient label for things we cannot explain.

A great deal that occurs in personality formation comes by way of the human experience that is due to environmental factors and very little to the constitution. For instance, we used to say glibly that if a man were irritable, or if he were depressed, the reason was perfectly understandable because his father was that way. Today we look upon the matter differently, and doubt if he inherited anything of his depression and irritability from his father. Certainly he *did inherit* his brain from his father but we do not now say that he inherited his irritability and moody experiences. If he is like his father, it is because of his *contact with* his father, because he was never helped to be cheerful by his father and because he imitated his father, and not because he inherited being a depressed individual through the germ plasm.

A person, for example, who spends an evening with friends who talk about the gruesome aspects of the war, about the high cost of living, about the difficulties of food rationing, etc., may come away with a rather pessimistic attitude. He has been affected—some would say infected—with the gloominess and pessimistic attitude of those around him. Had the conversation centered around the current art exhibit or some recent good books, the effect upon the spirits of those present would have been more toward the cheerful.

Let us discuss some of the early life experiences and the effects produced upon the young mind. Our first experience in extrauterine living is birth itself. Birth is an experience of short duration but it is worth mentioning because it is one of the first shocks the human being receives and is the first conscious impression as far as we know. Of course, it is probably not as vivid and as complicated an impression as one would get if he were in a serious accident, but as an experience it is registered along with many others that follow to make up a person's impression of life. Birth *is* definitely a trauma to the young organism and comes as a shock and requires some quick physiological readjustments—the use of the lungs, a change in circulation of the blood and the taking of food in a new way. All these new factors in the environment of the newborn child bring about tension within him. Some people have been inclined to put a great deal of stress upon birth as having maximum importance in the causation of neuroses, and have put forth the theory that birth paves the way for a great many anxieties in later life. The psychologist Otto Rank believed that birth is a kind of primary experience which starts the individual off badly by giving him an early anxiety from which he never completely recovers; he believed birth anxiety to be the prototype of all later anxieties.

The reader may think this to be carrying things back too far, that the theory is a little fantastic. Yet the idea is no more fantastic than the stories we hear of a person who had been in an accident and who had the fear of riding in an automobile afterward, the assumption being that the fear grew directly out of the accident experience. By the time a person has already reached the age of seventeen or twenty-seven he has a great many mental qualities with which to evaluate such an experience, and he should have capacities for reasoning, as well as an understandable sense of dread. We are ready to accept and understand that he would not want to run the risk of repeating that painful experience again. But if we understand that, we should also be ready to accept the fact that birth *is* a startling experience with which to begin life. Although the mind of the infant is undeveloped, the painful changes are registered on his brain; they do not pass into thin air.

Impressions of past experience should not be regarded too lightly whether the person was fully aware of the full import of what was happening or not. Some of the wisest and some of the most foolish things we do in our lives we do as the result of impressions rather than carefully thought out planning. One of these impulsive acts is marriage. Many people enter marriage because of certain feelings. They have not given any concrete thought to the matter at all; they have not considered whether the marital partner will be the right one with whom to live day after day. They have not considered their financial ability to take such a step. Yet they have an impression that marriage would be a fine thing and they must make such a move. They are moved by various impressions of a complex emotional nature and are not at all guided by their intellect.

Experience of the Newborn

We must not, therefore, look down on the very young child and the effect of the impressions that come his way. The first days and weeks and months of life are of vital importance not only in the nursing experience itself but in the attitude of the one who is taking care of the child. It may seem we are stressing this idea overmuch but the purpose is to stress what might be passed by as inconsequential, and what our studies of personality indicate are of great consequence. We must take our minds back to childhood and keep them on that age period in order to get used to thinking of the events of this age and of their importance. If we do not think back upon this time, we will have great difficulty in understanding the often erratic behavior of our patients, if we are doctors, and the sensitive emotions in all people we deal with. Moreover, something must be done about this erratic behavior and sensitiveness in people we meet if we are going to be successful doctors in the larger sense. We have not only the responsibility to cure aches and pains but also to be leaders in imparting some information that will help to cure a sick, unhappy, contentious society.

We cannot do all this if we are going to limit our knowledge to anatomy, physiology and pathology and trust to the effects of the pharmacopeia and surgical techniques—no matter how important they may be. All sick people are sensitive and they retrogress to the feelings of childhood. Whether the patient's sickness be of an organic nature or of psychological origin, doctors need to be in tune with the feeling and needs of childhood, since they express themselves at every age period in the life span of an individual.

The satisfaction of the demands of the newborn child through nursing is extremely important to the child, because this act is practically his only source of satisfaction. We should realize that the child's world is small, and that he has no sense of time. He has only rhythms set up by his physiological apparatus. He enjoys the flow of milk into the mouth, down the esophagus, and into the stomach. He enjoys the act of sucking, which incidentally helps the rhythms of breathing and digestion. He enjoys the nearness to the mother and the feel of the nipple in his mouth. We can say he also has a "hunger" for contact with the mother's body—for the security of touch with her or some other human being—

and enjoys the rhythm of being rocked and handled. Babies left too much to themselves do not thrive, as has been noted by many pediatricians long since. As the child grows older other senses come into play and the adult can do many things to gain satisfaction. He can go out of doors, play games, go to the movies and thus gain a variety of pleasant sensations in a very short time, sensations that are satisfying and make the person feel that life is worth living. The infant has largely one satisfaction: being fed and, supplemental to it, being in contact with his mother and having her affection.

Children need to be fed regularly, and they need to be fed in accordance with their own natural rhythm rather than by schedule. If a child is on a two-hour schedule, or a three-hour schedule, and if, before the time of his next feeding, he gets into a state of discomfort, the proper thing would be to feed him and not attempt any discipline at that time. When the child cries and manifests hunger some mothers say to themselves, "Oh, no! I mustn't give in to him. The doctor said he was to eat only every three hours, and I must stick to his schedule." When a doctor, mother or nurse makes too much ritual of the child's schedule and ignores his own rhythm, the child becomes anxious and greatly concerned about whether his fundamental needs are going to be met. Infants allowed to remain too often in such a state of uncertainty tend to develop into the kind of person who later in life is always uncertain about whether specific persons or fate will be kind. They are prone to assume they must be disappointed in plans or aspirations. They doubt their ability to influence the environment by any means whatever because their earliest human environment did not adjust itself to their basic needs. Let us allude again to these basic needs of the human organism.

Hunger-Affection Tensions

It is part of the nature of living human protoplasm to build up tensions as a result of the physiochemical processes of metabolism. These tensions as they increase make themselves felt as a discomfort (pain) and they demand release through some process. Food hunger is an example—the hunger is felt as pain and the taking of food gives the gratification or release of tension. The energy continuously exerted to keep body tensions relieved is termed libidinal energy or *libido*. It is the energy manifested in the activities of the instincts. *Instincts* in turn are psychic representations of somatic processes. Instinct is a term applied to a sensation lying somewhere between cellular metabolism and psychological feeling. For instance, if a person is hungry, exactly where is his hunger? Is the person uncomfortable in his stomach or is he uncomfortable in his mind? The answer is that he is uncomfortable in both places. But if a person were challenged to say exactly where his discomfort lay when he is hungry, he would not find the sensation entirely easy to locate.

Actually mind, stomach and cellular activities do produce local sensations which are promptly carried to the mind, and the feeling of hunger goes with these sensations. The hungry person is indeed hungry all over. Therefore, hunger is one of the tensions demanding satisfaction. This tension builds up in the newborn infant every few hours and food satisfies it. If the tension mounts too high, the infant cries, wiggles and makes known to the persons around that he is hungry. Ordinarily he gets relief. This living energy is referred to as libido, and it is the dynamic force manifested in instinctual drives. The *pleasure principle* is the name given to the tendency in the human being to regulate these tensions so that unpleasant accumulations of energy are discharged at intervals and a state of comfort maintained.

The newborn being who has these tensions soon comes to realize that it is the people around him who can satisfy his needs or reduce his tension and that it is done with varying attitudes. Here we begin to speak about the importance of the attitudes of those who take care of children, our next generation. A child comes to associate the feeding process (nursing) with the attitude the mother takes as she feeds him and we assume, often without justification, that the attitude of the mother toward her child is a loving one. Whatever attitude is shown by the mother in the feeding process (environment) is the attitude the child is likely to associate with food, feeding and the nursing process. Moreover, the child not only associates this environmental attitude with food and the taking of food but psychologically he also gathers much about life in general and makes it important in his mind in connection with food. The newborn child is a newcomer into the world and whatever attitude he meets in his environment he is likely to adopt and to carry throughout his life to a large degree.

The combination of the mental attitude and the feeding process or the psychological process of eating contains many implications. In the first place, when a person is depressed in spirits he cares little about eating. During mourning, after the loss of some loved one or relative, or when a person is under an emotional distress and suffering, his appetite may be very poor. Under better conditions he may eat heartily. Certain restaurants endeavor to intrigue the fancy of the public by advertising the warmth of the atmosphere and the geniality of the personnel, both of which are supposed to put the customer in a special frame of mind so he can enjoy his food the more. In certain homes—the custom differing from place to place—it is unheard of to visit for a few moments and not be served something to eat or at least a glass of something to drink. A person would be considered very impolite to refuse. Anyone desiring to insult another need only walk away from his host's table and refuse to eat with him. Friendship, goodwill, affection and the eating process are connected in many ways.

Feeding and Security

The behavior and the attitude of those taking care of the child can produce important long-run trends. Some of these trends can be illustrated by the following examples. A person can have been fed in such a way or with such an attitude that later he will feel very insecure about his livelihood or his place in the esteem of those around him. He may feel insecure about whether he will have enough to eat, or whether he will be able to survive by holding his job. If in business, he will constantly fear business failure.

Anxiety concerning food has been shown recently in some sections of the country by the way people became anxious because of a dread that there would not be enough to eat; they bought huge stocks and filled their cellars. What is the difference between those who went along and took chances about food and those who felt special anxiety about food? The difference is related to early experiences, going back to the first few days, weeks and months of life. Some children who go hungry, whose needs for food are not taken care of, who have been denied too much because of a feeling that they would be spoiled, have anxiety about food, or just anxiety about attention to themselves. They may react by eating too much daily or by having a pressing, clinging attitude to those around them, demanding attention and reassurance all the time. They are afraid they will not have enough food or enough recognition and love. We claim to understand some of the anxieties that have caused certain men to break down in the army. Some have arisen because they have missed the food at home, because they could not possibly get along on the strange food that the army provided, or because the food was not cooked the way they had been used to it at home. Equally extreme anxiety can be aroused by the type of food given as by not having enough.

Another attitude can be produced by a still different cause. Some mothers put too much emphasis on food. They stuff the child—make him feel that eating is the most important thing in life; food then becomes all important to him, and other things of too little importance. Not only does good food become too important, but the child is also given the feeling that he need never worry, that he will always be taken care of. Those who do take care of him go out of their way to assure him that the good things of life will always come his way without effort. Such an attitude is not made complete in the early years but it is started there. Much, of course, depends upon what responsibilities are given in the child's third and fourth years, upon what he is taught in school, upon how he is encouraged to get a job in adolescence. Nevertheless, the attitude of taking a dependent position toward society is laid down in the oral period. Such a person may say, "I am going to get a job. I am going to do well." However, he always puts it off because he has the feeling he will be taken care of, which is just the opposite from the person who fears he will not be taken care of. The former has had too great assurance that he will never need to take care of himself and may be a baffling social problem during adulthood as a result.

A special disorder which is fairly common and which is becoming more common all the time in every generation is alcoholism. Drinking has more than one cause. One of the reasons people drink is to gratify an oral need. Alcoholics have been known to say that they did not care about the taste of liquor, and they could, with little hardship to themselves, be put on Coca Cola or coffee or tea with very little restraint, and they are just about as content as when drinking alcohol. A second reason for drinking is to gratify a sense of loneliness which seems to defy analysis or gratification and which is a feeling tone in the alcoholic that is very difficult to affect favorably. This sense of loneliness goes back to the sense of loneliness in the early weeks and months of life. Drinking dulls the pain of loneliness and puts the alcoholic in a state where he can fantasy love, at least. This urge to keep up to the early pattern of the first years continues to play a role in people's attitudes for a long time.

Infantile Tensions in Adults

We hope the reader will be able to project himself backward into that early period of childhood and appreciate the situations in it which are being alluded to. Unless there are young children in the home under our very eyes, we pay little attention to them and their behavior, which is perfectly natural because people's interests have been turned in other directions and they have not bothered to look at young children or be interested in them. For instance, in addition to his regular feeding a child will frequently have his thumb in his mouth, or his whole fist, or a piece of bread, possibly a dirty stick from the floor, or anything within reach. Each thing goes to his mouth as if his mouth were the testing apparatus of everything in his environment—clean or dirty. The reason for this is partly because he can use his hands to convey things to the mouth and partly because of a satisfaction in sucking on these things.

That urge to seek gratification by oral means—to allay tension thereby—is seen in later life in alcoholism, in the enjoyment of food, in drinking, in smoking, or in chewing gum. These things are tension reducers. When a person feels a little uneasy or a little depressed, he may go out and buy a good meal or go to a soda fountain for a double-decker. Afterward he feels better. This better feeling is not all due to the sugar he has eaten; it is due to the pleasure he has had in the oral activity. In subtler ways people often show this early infantile trend for gratification. Such a person seems to be of a clinging, beseeching, dependent disposition who frequently makes requests of those he is associated with, or just hangs around and talks as if he needed to be near another person and live a part of his life. His own life is too empty to sustain him so he leans on other people. His attitude is one of seeming to try to eat up the other person. It might appear that he is trying to establish a psychological umbilical cord with words and attach himself thereby to someone else and maintain that attachment through speech.

The presence of such a person is felt and may not be bothersome for a while; but after it goes on for a time the group, or the individual, wishes this person would be more self-sustaining. Often our first impression of certain people is that they are attractive, that they make a pleasing impression, that they are interesting talkers and that they have many winning personality traits, but later their friends say that they do not wear well. There may be many reasons for this, but one may be that the person whose conversations were brilliant and interesting in the beginning never stops, never lets go. He attaches himself too completely to people and the result is that his newly made friends grow "fed up" or tired of him. In many instances such an attitude is very difficult to isolate and describe. However, it is due to the dependent attitude which arises out of the oral phase of development when the needs of the infant child have not been sufficiently gratified, have not been given enough friendly attention by the mother or nurse. The attention he has lacked at this early stage he tries too pressingly to draw from others in adulthood.

These people who attach themselves to others probably have some advantage over the ones who are too anxious even to try to make contact with others or to try to use them for emotional sustenance. In attaching themselves they behave as though they would save their lives by trying to make up to themselves what had been lacking in infancy. While it may be hard on those around them, many neurotic people utilize this behavior as a lifesaving mechanism, not being too sensitive themselves, and get along in society fairly well by frequent changes in friendships. As a mechanism it is satisfactory, provided that in time they are able to do something about it to get themselves built up or "cured" before they have estranged too many people.

Anxiety and Its Consequences

We have used the word anxiety so far without attempting to define clearly what we mean by it. *Anxiety* is an affect. By affect we mean an emotion or feeling tone. Some of the affects are happiness and sadness, elation and depression and euphoria. Anxiety is a special affective state which grows out of the conflict between instinctual needs and a society that is unwilling or unable to gratify the needs. Instincts are energy that is released as a result of the life processes themselves, of the physiochemical processes of the body which release tension right from the onset of the first breath.

The conflicts producing anxiety are intensified by the inevitable helplessness of the young child and the necessity of being at the mercy of other humans if he is to have his tensions gratified. He has a fairly well-developed sensory system making the pain of his instinctual tensions felt but relatively little motor nervous system development with which to effect a relief of tension by himself. Hence, these instincts require an *object* for their gratification and that object is something animate or inanimate in the environment which will reduce the tension. When the

instinctual tension manifests itself in the child and when the environment, in the form of the mother or nurse, meets the demand with indifference, with refusal, with annoyance, with threats, or with punishment,
that painful state has to find some other release than the object. The
child has to find some more direct method of expression or he has to
endure the tension. In other words, the child just may have to suffer
hunger, loneliness, or the discomfort of lying too long in one place. The
necessity of enduring this tension too long by himself creates affects
which, multiplied with the passing of time, result eventually in an
apathy or emotional coldness.

The parental attitude of letting children "cry it out" too often and too
long is bad, and requires the child to have to deal with too much pain
and loneliness by himself and he fails to develop that most necessary
psychic function of being able to relate to and use the warmth and
friendliness of others. These attitudes on the part of the upbringers tend
to give children the impression that they are alone in the world, that
they are likely to be neglected, that their needs will probably not be
met anyway. The baffling lack of emotional response in depression and
schizophrenia is undoubtedly due to this cause. As a result society has
many uninspired persons who do not wish to try to be successful or to
make any imprint on the world around them. Lack of attention in the
early weeks of life is probably one of the greatest stultifiers of ambition.

As the child continues to live, instincts continue to seek gratification.
Some of them are gratified, and those that are not gratified act as a
signal to the child that he has impulses within himself that he would like
to gratify but must not because of loss of love or punishment. To keep
love and avoid punishment the human being erects in his mind *defenses*
against this unpleasant affect of anxiety—worry, fretfulness, apprehension, uneasiness, overconcern about small matters—or certain other defenses. One of these common defenses against anxiety is a *phobia*. For
example, a child may become afraid of an animal, or be afraid to go on
the street alone, or cannot be in a closed room, or cannot go to sleep
without a light. This anxiety is a derivative of instinctual tension or the
result of an instinctual tension within a human being which has not
been mastered in an appropriate way at the appropriate time.

Another big area in which anxiety may find release—rather than in a
direct expression of the instinctual impulses—is in symptom formation.
This area should be of serious concern to medical students and doctors.
The anxiety that has accumulated within a human being brings into

action many symptom pictures with a great amount of psychopathology underlying them. For this reason it is important that we focus our attention upon the very early activities of the human being so we can know just as much as possible about the recognition of anxiety and its many manifestations.

For the purposes of discussion and understanding we can relate anxiety to fear but they are different in certain ways. In the first place we speak of fear in connection with something of which the person is definitely and consciously aware. If a man starts to cross a street and does not see a car that whizzes by and from whose path he must jump out of the way, he probably gets a fright as a result that will make his heart beat faster, bring out perspiration and leave him with a feeling of weakness. In that case he is afraid of something definite and that object has caused specific temporary changes in the body physiology. The effect from anxiety may be the same as that resulting from fear. The difference between fear and anxiety is that the actual cause of neurotic anxiety is not conscious and we usually do not know why we feel the discomfort from it. In every neurosis and in every mental disease anxiety is present. Those who have suffered from mental conditions, such as depression of spirits, or from a compulsion neurosis, say that mental suffering is most intense and that no physical suffering can compare with it. Anxiety is a very distressing state and the suffering from it can be far worse than the suffering from a physical disease because it can last so long and relief be so difficult to obtain.

Anxiety is not confined to the mind. Anxiety is an all-over sensation and is felt in the body as well as in the mind. We shall discuss the various distresses of mind and body resulting from anxiety as we proceed. Having introduced the subject of anxiety, however, and having indicated its importance and some of the ill effects of its presence, we would like to stress that to keep it at a minimum in each individual the infant should have love, affection, interest, attention, and fondling by a close contact with devoted parents. A time for training in conformity to society's expectations comes all too soon. In general we should not fear that the baby will be spoiled by too much love and thus later on not take to socialization. On the contrary the more affection and understanding of his early instinctual needs are given the easier his later socialization will progress.

BIBLIOGRAPHY FOR CHAPTER I

Abraham, Karl, *Selected Papers on Psychoanalysis*, Hogarth Press, 1927.
Bernfeld, Siegfried, *The Psychology of the Infant*, Kegan Paul, 1929.
Freud, Sigmund, *The Problem of Anxiety*, Norton, 1936.
Ribble, Margaret A., *The Rights of Infants*, Columbia University Press, 1943.
Wolfe, Anna W. M., *The Parent's Manual*, Simon and Schuster, 1941.

Chapter II

EMOTIONAL DISTURBANCES THAT OCCUR DURING THE ORAL PERIOD

WE ALL have in our minds a picture of the behavior of an ideal human being. This picture is different for the behavior of an infant, a child, an adolescent, an adult, or an old person. No two persons present exactly the same picture, but in a particular culture these differences are not very great, although they may be so between different cultures. If we observe some person acting too differently from our ideal pattern we feel that he is maladjusted, and according to the particular point of view that we may hold as to the reason for this maladjustment we label him as sick, unhappy or perverse. If we have the task of trying to help him to a better adjustment we do so by dealing with the situation according to our point of view as to its cause; i. e., we look for the cause of his sickness or unhappiness, or we scold or punish him for his perversity.

There are few people today who believe that the maladjusted person is innately bad and perverse, but there are many who feel baffled because they cannot easily determine the cause of the maladjustment. This is because they forget that the individual has basic emotional needs, and that if these needs are not satisfied adequately he suffers pain and discomfort and must try to do something to relieve himself of these unpleasant feelings. In fact we can say that if the behavior of a child deviates too much from the normal pattern one or more of his basic emotional needs are not satisfied; i. e., he is being frustrated. There are two types of frustration—those that are inevitable and those that are unnecessary.

Frustration Associated with Feeding

Every child experiences many inevitable frustrations because he desires what he wants when he wants it. He may desire to be suckled continuously rather than having to learn to eat in other ways. He may want to be carried by his parents rather than learn to walk by himself. He may be hungry at a time when it is impossible to feed him, but he has to endure the pain of hunger because he cannot be fed immediately. He feels disappointed and hurt if these wants are not satisfied. Gradually he learns that he can overcome his feelings of pain and discomfort by adopting new methods of behavior. He can learn to eat a greater variety of food and to use other methods of eating than sucking. He can learn to walk instead of being carried. This is a step forward in his development, and these forward steps eventually bring him more pleasure and enable him to have less pain and discomfort than if he had been able to continue with his old patterns.

Each step in his development is inaugurated by a frustration, which gives him a feeling of discomfort, and this feeling causes him to develop new skills in his ability to live. This is the process we anticipate will happen to every child, but it can occur only if the child first has an optimum period of the method of getting satisfaction for his inner needs, then becomes deprived of this method gradually so that although he experiences discomfort the suffering is mild and causes him to stir himself into activity instead of overwhelming him. The child should experience the necessary and inevitable frustrations in life in small doses and gradually, and should not be exposed to sudden large doses of the necessary frustrations or to unnecessary and unusual ones.

We said earlier that a frustration produces a feeling of pain and discomfort which we have designated as a feeling of anxiety. The child is displeased by this feeling and expresses his displeasure with whatever methods he has at his disposal. If he is a young infant who cannot talk, walk or stand up he lies in his crib and cries, beats with his clenched fists and kicks. He must express his reaction to his feeling of displeasure with the skill he has at his disposal at the time. Basically all his reactions will be of three types or some combination of them: he will fight the cause of the discomfort, he will run away from it, or if he is overwhelmed by it he will remain immobile. These reactions to a feeling of discomfort produce the behavior which we regard as different from the normal and which we designate as problem behavior.

In the last chapter we described the behavior that we expect to find during the oral period of the average child's life. We stated also that he has certain emotional needs that he cannot satisfy himself because of his helplessness and that therefore he has to depend on someone else for his satisfaction. What happens if these needs are frustrated severely or unnecessarily? The child suffers pain and discomfort and may react against the process that produces the pain and suffering, against the person whom he holds responsible for the discomfort, or against both.

If the supply of breast milk is inadequate, if its chemical composition makes for difficulties in assimilation, if the nipples are inverted or are so constituted that sufficient milk is not obtained until the child becomes very fatigued, he experiences a frustration and feels dissatisfied and uncomfortable. Sometimes he reacts by vigorous protest. He cries and squirms. He regurgitates what he has in his stomach as if to say, "If I can't have what I want I don't want anything." He is more liable to do this if the ingested food produces cramps or colic. Sometimes he reacts by turning away and refusing to take the food offered him. Sometimes he reacts by ceasing to suck, and although the process of sucking is a reflex one he seems able to inhibit it so that it requires very strong stimulation to his lips in order to make him suck a few times more. Sometimes he reacts by rather quickly losing all feelings of hunger. When he should be hungry he tends to fall asleep as if he said, "Because my hunger has brought me only pain it is better that I do not feel this painful desire again."

Similar reactions occur if his breast feeding is complemented by new articles of food presented in an improper manner. If the complementary foods are served at too hot a temperature, if their consistency makes digestion difficult, if, as the child gets his teeth, the food given him requires too much chewing so that he becomes fatigued, any of the reactions discussed above can occur, as if the child were saying through these reactions, "I don't want to eat if eating produces discomfort and pain." If the baby is very young he will retain the disorganized, irregular type of breathing, which is normal in the newborn, for a very long time. (This reaction will occur in all very young babies not only in respect to eating difficulties but also as a reaction to the other frustrating experiences mentioned in this section.)

These reactions directly affect the process of eating. If the child, because of the discomfort engendered by this eating situation, blames the mother for his trouble he will begin to turn away from her when she approaches, refuse her breast when it is offered to him, cry in her presence and, as he gets a little older, refuse to do anything she suggests, often doing the opposite instead. This resembles the behavior of an older girl who said that because she became angry with her mother she resolved to go as far away from her as possible and to do everything her mother said was wrong.

The child's desire to suck may also be frustrated. If the mother's breast produces an oversupply of milk the child does not have to suck much on the nipple because the slightest pressure of the lips causes the milk to flow freely down his throat. This may occur also if the child is bottle fed from a nipple whose aperture is very large. In these instances the child does not get enough satisfaction for his need to suck and will have to suck nonnutritive objects—his fingers, his bedclothes, toys, etc., for a much longer period than the two hours daily that he should devote to nonnutritive sucking. His finger sucking also will tend to continue for several months or years past the time when it is usually relinquished (between the second and third year). If he is allowed these extra periods of sucking he does not show any reactions of displeasure. However, if the parents disapprove and try to stop the finger sucking either because it disgusts them or because they have the superstition that it will deform the child's mouth, the child will suffer considerable discomfort and will react with a feeling of displeasure. He may begin to reject the ingestion of food in ways similar to those discussed above. He may act antagonistically to his mother. He may conform to the parent's wishes after a more or less prolonged struggle, and from that point on try to make a virtue of the fact that he does not suck. This means that he makes a virtue out of his ability to suffer the pain of the frustration of an inner desire, and thus becomes able to extract pleasure out of his suffering. If such a mechanism becomes very well developed the child as he grows older may actually seek situations that will cause him pain in order to obtain the pleasure he finds in suffering.

The newborn baby cannot distinguish very well between his own self and his surroundings, but as his sensory organs become better developed he begins to make a distinction between himself and his mother—who to him is the source of all pleasure and comfort—and he yearns for her attentions and presence. If she really loves him and gets pleasure out of doing things for him he senses this in her and he responds to her and tries to please her even if this means occasionally that he has to undergo the discomfort of some frustrations—which in reality will be gentle, slow and careful because the loving mother intuitively understands how the child feels. There are certain mothers, however, who do not love their babies and get no pleasure from caring for them. The baby soon senses this and feels very frustrated. He may express his displeasure by developing reactions against the taking of food—the main activity in which he knows she is interested—or by direct antagonistic reactions to her (instead of trying to please her he does nothing or does the opposite) or by falling into a condition of semistupor where he pays no attention either to food or to her.

Similar reactions may develop if the mother loves the baby but if the circumstances of her life have upset her emotionally. The mother becomes too worried by her own problems to be able to respond fully to her love for the child. In one case of this nature we saw a slightly different reaction. This little girl was referred for compulsive masturbation which occupied most of her waking time. It started shortly after she developed a severe feeding difficulty with colic and vomiting which began rather suddenly following a serious quarrel between the mother and her brother-in-law that severely disturbed the mother emotionally. The child became so ill that she had to be weaned, and only when a formula that agreed with her was found did the gastrointestinal disturbance cease, to be replaced immediately by the compulsive masturbation. It seemed that this child reacted first to the frustration occasioned by the change in the mother's attitude by developing a feeding difficulty, and when this was corrected continued to react by endeavoring to be an older child and to be sufficient unto herself. It was as if she said, "I can get all the gratification I need from my own body. I do not need my mother, because at her hands all I experience is pain and suffering."

Suicidal Defenses

Refusing to eat or vomiting after eating may occur also if the environment in the home is one in which there is too much strife, if there is quarreling between husband and wife, between mother and grandmother, if there is tension between the mother and mother-in-law, too much noise and interference from other children—all of which send a constant bombardment upon the psyche of the newborn child. He may not wish to go on with the life process.

We say "wish" as if the child has the decision, which he does not have, as we think of decision according to our standard. But this small piece of protoplasm, from all we can observe, can seem actually to decide that living under too much frustration and pain is not worth the effort. It has been known that babies who have been very distressed and who have not had life made pleasant for them in the beginning have seemed to turn away from life, from sucking, from eating, from the taking of food. The baby does not do this willfully; he does it instinctively; he does it because he has suffered too much pain. Some adults who have gone through a great number of painful vicissitudes may come to the conclusion that they cannot stand any more, and they jump off a bridge or out of the window of a high building.

The rational mind does not have much to do with the reasoning of people in this state. They feel they have got to get out of a world that has been too painful up to now, and they cannot see any hope that it is going to be less so. Even though an adult person's work and other activities may have brought him to the point of considerable success in spite of obstacles, something else may go wrong. He loses his money, or a member of his family, and he feels he must turn away from the disappointment of life. If an adult with all his past pleasures and advantages can do this it should not be difficult to understand why a child who has had very little pleasure, who has had to live in a cold, frustrating environment, should have sufficient pain of anxiety from what he has suffered to make him stop functioning. The same mechanism is at work in the child who does not want to eat that is at work in the person who commits suicide.

While speaking of these symptoms we are at an opportune point to speak of *incorporation,* which means the psychological process of taking into the body, through the mouth, the objects, human and otherwise, in the environment. For the purpose of study we may have to speak at times of the body and the mind as separate entities but they always function in relation to each other. There are no separate organs for psychological functions such as loving, hating, imitating and rejecting. The brain is the exchange center but the organ and organ systems do the work. Just as in the beginning of life the baby is taking in food, he of necessity takes in the attitudes of the people around him. He takes them in to a large extent by way of the mouth. The mind has to use the body as it struggles to develop itself.

The taking of communion in church is an example from everyday life of the value and importance of incorporation. We are told that in communion we partake of the body of Christ. This is a symbolism which means taking Christ's ideas as well as his body within us, and we are supposed to make new commitments to the religious principles connected with the church. In other words, we have here the process of taking in a person, and the principles and cause that he stood for. In the symbolism of communion the church must long ago have recognized that ideas are taken in along with food by way of the mouth.

Naturally we do not take in everything by way of the mouth; we take in ideas and principles through the eyes and ears for example, but certainly a great deal of what we take in goes in with the taking of food. Every good salesman knows it is a good idea to take his customers to a restaurant and treat them to a good meal at the same time that he is trying to sell them his wares. Whether we are trying to put over our ideas to adults or to children, we must realize that to a great extent much of their enjoyment of the occasion goes with the pleasure they obtain from eating and drinking. Students in private boarding schools or camps may form their opinion of the institution through the quality of the meals served. The reader will doubtless remember that, during his school years, food was a matter of some concern. A person's loyalty to school or camp and what he learned there may have been dependent to a great extent upon the type of food and the way it was served.

At the time when the child has his attention centered on the oral part of the body people are inextricably bound up with oral activity. Therefore, when the people in the environment are unpleasant, irritating, or obnoxious, when they are not kind to the infant, he may eat his meals but he feels he has something inside him that is unpleasant. This unpleasantness is not undigested milk or an unsuitable formula of which he is trying to rid himself. He is trying to rid himself of the unpleasant environment (people) which he has incorporated along with his meals. We have the expression in our language, "I am sick of this job." The expression means that, in the course of time, a number of people have had to become ill and vomit when in a difficult situation in an attempt to rid themselves of obnoxious people or circumstances.

Frustration Associated with Separation

Although the mother may love the child and although she may not be upset emotionally she may go off for a vacation or on business and leave the child to the care of someone else. The absence may be a brief one, of only a week or two, but the child regards the separation as a sign that the mother does not love him. Even though well cared for, he may feel neglected and lonely, with very much the same feeling that the adult has when someone he loves dearly goes away. He reacts to the separation in the ways mentioned above. It is interesting that a similar reaction occurs in the older child if the family moves from one house to another. For some time after such a move the child is unhappy and behaves as if in discomfort. Human beings as a rule are disturbed by being placed in an unfamiliar situation and under these circumstances would like to go back to the familiar situation or action. This is the compulsion to repeat former experiences which was first noted by Freud.

After the immediate reactions to these frustrating experiences have disappeared, the child no longer seems the same. Instead of being relaxed, happy and carefree, he seems tense, anxious and apprehensive. He is obviously apprehensive lest something happen that will cause him to suffer again the discomfort through which he has already lived.

The physician who is consulted about problem behavior in a child in the first year of life should remember that it arises from one of four sources or a combination of these four: (1) the child has undergone a series of painful experiences during his feeding, (2) his need to suck for pleasure and not for nutrition has been frustrated, (3) his certainty that he can depend on his mother for the satisfaction of his needs has been destroyed because of her attitude to him, her behavior to him, or by the circumstances of her life, (4) his emotional comfort has been destroyed by wrangling in his environment. The first and third show the most violent and immediate effects because they are in reality a threat to his life. We do not mean that he can formulate in his mind the clear idea that if his mother leaves him or if he can't eat without hurting himself he will die; we mean rather that he shows a reaction which, if it could be translated into a concept, would have that content. He is able to suppress the desire for nonnutritive sucking more easily because it does not put him in danger of immediate death. His reaction seems less important because it comes more slowly, but it may continue over a long period of time.

The child's symptoms as a result of these frustrations fall into three groups: (1) anxiety symptoms, such as frequent crying, restlessness, insomnia, vomiting, and diarrhea, (2) feeding disorders ranging all the way from simple refusal of food to prolonged vomiting, and (3) negativistic, antagonistic behavior to the parents. Nosologically, therefore, the infant under one year may show an acute or chronic anxiety state, a conversion hysteria, or a chronic aggressive reaction pattern. The state of our knowledge is too meager at this time to allow us to formulate the reason why, as a result of the anxiety engendered by a frustration, one child develops conversion symptoms and another develops chronic aggression.

How is the doctor to proceed in the treatment of these conditions? As always, the best treatment would be to prevent the occurrence of the illness. The mature, loving mother can depend on her own intuitive reactions to prevent the baby's undergoing the unnecessary frustrations we have discussed. However, even though the mother may be mature and loving, fate may step in and she may die. The child realizes to some extent that this suffering came upon him from without. He had nothing to do with its cause. It is as if an adverse fate had fallen upon him. In his apprehension lest he re-experience the discomfort, he dreads lest fate again be unkind to him. This apprehension gives him a sense of impending disaster and he tends to view the future as if a malignant fate were waiting to pounce on him. He begins to behave in ways that will avoid the disaster he anticipates. Since he has reacted in a specific way—by desiring to eat constantly or by clinging to his mother, etc.—to a frustrating experience, that specific way of reacting is more something belonging to him than other methods might be. So in the future he tends to react to frustrations in the same general pattern.

No matter how carefully the child is cared for he has to experience one major frustration in his early life—he has to be weaned from the breast. It is desirable that he be breast fed, even if this has to be complemented, for as many months as possible, and that complete weaning not take place until after the ninth or tenth month. If the weaning is done suddenly the child shows all the reactions already discussed in a rather severe form. It is important therefore that weaning be a gradual process. This can be done if the child receives complementary feedings of semisolids very early in his life.

We have observed very cruel and unnecessary types of weaning which have had disastrous effects on the child's later development. One mother decided she would not spoil her child, so at the age of two months weaned him suddenly from the breast and went on a vacation of several weeks, leaving him to the care of a total stranger. Thus the child was frustrated not only in the feeding process but also in his relation to his mother. Another mother weaned her son by putting him to the breast and then pinching him painfully. In another case the mother became concerned because the child was so anxious and fearful. She had weaned him suddenly at the age of two months. At the age of six months she broke his habit of finger sucking by painful punishment, i. e., the application of mittens that tied his hands to his sides. In the face of these frustrations it was no wonder that the child was anxious and fearful.

Many mothers really love their children but are not aware of the importance of their intuitive reactions to the child, or are afraid to depend on them. This is very evident along two lines, breast feeding and separation. Many mothers actually long to nurse their babies but fear they are doing the wrong thing in insisting upon it, if either the doctor or the nurse tends to disagree, or that their friends or relatives will laugh at them for being too old fashioned. Other mothers are not so aware of their own longing to suckle the infant because they feel there is something too animal about such a desire, and so are very easily persuaded to wean the child.

Similarly although the mother may love the child and be quite heartsick at the thought of leaving her baby when she goes on vacation, she may try to disregard her own feelings because her husband might not have as good a time if the baby were taken along, or because her friends might think her foolish and antiquated to be such a doting mother. She goes on vacation, stifling her own feelings by being sure that the child will get good physical care and by the pleasant feelings engendered by the new surroundings and experiences. In both instances the mother interferes with her own intuitively correct feelings because she dreads some external condemnation and the child suffers as a result.

These types of mothers could be helped greatly to be less sensitive to external disapproval by the support of their doctor or by intellectual knowledge. For such, a course during the period of pregnancy in the essentials of child care and the fundamental emotional needs of the child would be very helpful. This could be given directly by the obstetrician to groups of pregnant women as part of prenatal care, or in clinics as part of the prenatal preparation. We are not of the opinion that intellectual knowledge in itself is a cure-all for these problems. We believe, however, that many women at present show an increasing dread of believing in their own feelings lest they appear foolish in the eyes of their friends or lest the expression of their feelings in some way injure the child. Such women may be more certain of the adequacy of their feelings as guides if they feel the support of outside authority.

Of course we are aware that this fact (that a woman may stifle her own feelings because she dreads outside criticisms) does not account for the majority of mothers who refuse to nurse their children or who go off and leave their young babies in the care of other people. All too often the behavior is the result of a conflict between the feelings of love toward the baby and the selfish desire to do things that give the mother more pleasure, and in the conflict the latter impulse wins, often to the point that the mother is aware only of her desire for pleasure for herself and unaware of her feeling of love for the child. Such women cannot be good mothers regardless of the amount of intellectual education they receive.

Psychotherapy for Frustration

When the illness—i. e., the reaction of the child to the frustrating situation—has started, the procedure of approach is first to ascertain the cause (i. e., the frustrating situation) and the need that is being frustrated. The physician who is called to treat a child with a gastrointestinal disturbance should inquire as fully into the emotional experience of the child as he does into the chemical composition of the food the baby has been receiving.

When the frustrating experience has been ascertained it is important that the mother and physician start handling the child as if he were a little younger than he was when he experienced the pain. If the difficulty was started because a supplemental food was given when it was too hot, it is desirable to take him off all supplemental feedings, and then after a period of time to introduce the supplemental feedings gradually without forcing them on him. It has been demonstrated experimentally that if a baby is forced to put something in his mouth before he is ready to, he reacts by signs of discomfort and by developing colic. If the illness has been caused by the parent's preventing the baby from doing nonnutritive sucking it will be necessary for her not only to allow the sucking to begin again, but also to try to encourage him to start sucking nonnutritive objects. If the frustration has occurred because of the mother's attitude or behavior toward the child this will have to be changed, and the mother for a time will have to go further in the opposite direction than she would usually.

Feeding difficulties in a baby, either vomiting or refusal to eat, may cause serious emergencies in which there is danger of the child's dying. The child will not eat because he feels hostility around him or his needs have not been properly met. In order to get the baby to return to his proper eating habits he needs a warmer environment or a friendlier person to take care of him. As his life may be in danger, it may take too long for safety to change the mother's attitude or the behavior of the adults in the environment. Such a situation requires a change in environment. This may be done by leaving him in his own home but placing him in the complete charge of a more understanding, more loving and more serene person than his mother, or the child must be taken out of his home and put in a warmer, more loving and more affectionate environment than his own home has furnished. During the period of separation, treatment for the home situation should be continued so that the baby will return to a more loving and peaceful environment and be able to remain well.

BIBLIOGRAPHY FOR CHAPTER II

Benedek, Therese, "Adaptation to Reality in Early Infancy," *Psychoanalytic Quarterly*, **7**, 1938, 200.

Winnicott, D. W., "The Observation of Infants in a Set Situation," *International Journal of Psychoanalysis* **22**, 1941, 229.

Chapter III

DEVELOPMENT OF PERSONALITY DURING THE ANAL PERIOD

THE ANAL phase of existence is the next period on which to focus our attention. This term and the period it represents have several implications for psychosexual development which we want to make clear to the reader. The time of the anal period lasts roughly from the end of the first year to the end of the third year and is therefore longer than the oral period. This does not mean that the activities of the oral period cease at the end of the first year; in fact, the activities and the needs of the oral period continue as long as life lasts. The deep implication involved in this period is that attention should be turned to new activities and diverted from those of the oral period in order to keep pace with social demands. As the child nears the end of the first year he has gained a great deal of muscular ability that he did not have at birth. The average child is creeping, actively pulling himself up by holding onto furniture; some children are standing alone, and some are beginning to take steps. Therefore the child's interest is expanding in the world around him and the world around him is likewise beginning to make demands upon him for conformity to certain social requirements.

Toilet Training

Since we are interested in personality formation we should carefully scrutinize the interaction between the child and his upbringers during this period. The most significant manner in which the child has to conform during this period is to go through bowel and bladder training. This is a most important activity because it is a most *personal* phrase of his training and because it pertains to the individual's body and its feelings. Learning to dress himself or put away his toys does not "touch" him nearly so closely in the sense of physiological tension. A second point is that we have to realize that our society has a great many attitudes concerning cleanliness, neatness and the control of eliminations that are in conflict with the child's own instinctual tendencies. As far as the child's personal comfort goes, he would continue to empty his bowels and bladder as tension appeared in these organs; in short, as he became uncomfortable. The world around him does not permit this, however. Therefore, he must begin to accept regulations; he must gain a certain control of himself with the help of others, and he must begin to take certain responsibilities.

A child who is brought up in a family where extreme value is placed on cleanliness will be in the midst of keener conflict than the one in a home where the people are more relaxed about things of that kind. In many homes cleanliness has a moral aspect also. A dirty child is considered a wicked and bad child, so a feeling of guilt can develop in such surroundings. Then, of course, there is just the practical matter of the mother or the nurse having to wash a great many clothes for the child. For this reason a great deal of pressure may be put upon the child to control his excretions as early as possible for the convenience, comfort and esthetic gratification of those around him. This puts a strain upon his psychological apparatus. At best, learning to meet the environment's expectations and demands of cleanliness is actually one of the big problems of human development. Under the most favorable conditions it is not an easy process; under unfavorable conditions it can lead to a great deal of anxiety, hostility and other attitudes that we will take up as we go along.

Let us consider the child who has been the recipient of all bounties of the home for, roughly, a year, and who now confronts a considerable change in his environment. Now, instead of being the receiver, he is asked to begin to be the giver. Now, instead of being contributed to, he is asked to make a contribution. Now, instead of being in the position of irresponsibility, he is asked to assume a responsibility in relation to himself.

The matter of bowel and bladder training is not the only thing of psychological importance that happens in the years between one and three. There are others: getting the idea of keeping the body clean through bathing and hand washing and brushing the teeth; being neat about clothes; avoiding too much contamination with foreign matter in play; keeping the playroom clean and in some order and, perhaps, learning to share toys with other children and paying some polite attention to friends of the family who come into the home. Parents may begin to teach a great many of the social amenities at this time. The child is asked to do what the grownups want—to be a little lady or a little gentleman. However, none of these matters come quite so close to his instinctual needs and none are so personal as the matter of bowel and bladder control.

Whenever instinctual tension exists in the body there is a tendency to seek relief from that tension without regard to environmental standards. The attitude follows the pleasure principle. From the standpoint of the pleasure principle children do not want to bother with the matter of toilet training at all. It is foreign to their wishes, foreign to their comfort; but they have to accept it all the same. In certain homes the child's natural abilities are kept in mind and toilet training is not begun until the end of the first year. At least, it *should* not be begun very much before the end of the year because it has been shown by careful neuropathological study that the tracts of the spinal cord are not completely myelinated until the end of the first year. Therefore, it is rather futile—at least demanding a great deal—to ask the child to exercise a control over his organs for which he does not have the neurological pathways completely laid down.

Nevertheless, toilet training *is* begun somewhat earlier. Most pediatric authorities agree that toilet training should not be begun before the eighth month, better at the tenth month or at the end of a year. It should be done by observing when the child usually has bowel movements, and then placing the child on a comfortable toilet seat around that time and indicating by gestures and tone of voice that he is expected to pass his eliminations in this particular place and at this particular time. This is a difficult matter to grasp because the child's mind is still incompletely formed to comprehend any ideas such as these. He achieves it as a result of repeated attempts, a great deal of patience and a great deal of understanding on the part of those who are doing the training.

Achievement in bowel control in average, healthy, intelligent children will not have taken place until the end of the eighteenth month and possibly not until the end of the second year. Therefore, in the best cases—begun at a year with the expectation of some result at eighteen months —mothers should realize that they have quite a number of days in which to work out the problem with the child. Many undertake the training of a child without knowing much of anything about his physiological makeup and without having even any rough date in view as to when training should be accomplished. Instead of feeling that there is six months or a year in which to accomplish the ability, the mother or nurse acts as if the training should be accomplished in six days or, at most, six weeks, and pressure is put upon the child in terms of demands, scoldings, reproaches, even physical punishments, all of which do a great deal of harm to the child's developing mind.

Personality Consequences of Toilet Training

Universally people have a considerable feeling of shame and disgust surrounding the whole matter of excretions. There is, of course, no need of this. Indeed, such attitudes *should not* exist; yet they do exist. We trust the reader will see that the feeling of shame and disgust that surrounds toilet training is one of those unfortunate social attitudes that in later life causes people to be very ashamed of their body and to be ashamed of sexual functioning especially. In other words, some of the emotion that is engendered at this period over bowel and bladder functioning spreads out and encompasses sexuality, since the organs of sexual functioning and excretion are the same.

In the course of their work, doctors encounter difficulty with certain patients in the wards, in their homes, and in their offices, because these patients are reluctant to undress, reluctant to expose themselves, reluctant to be sensibly examined. They react in a way that is overmodest and inappropriate, and it is often time consuming to get the co-operation necessary to be in a position to give the best advice. This overmodesty is due largely to the way these people have been educated as children, particularly in their toilet habits. Millions of people, we are sure, feel that everyone needs to be ashamed and disgusted about the matter of elimination and that if people do not have shame and disgust, and a great deal of it, they are not nice persons. Some go so far as to feel that people are immoral if they are not ashamed of themselves in relation to the body and its functioning.

We hope the reader realizes that having such a feeling and having it in such intensity is not necessary at all. In the first place, children *do* wish to conform to what is expected of them and will do so in time if they are treated with consideration. *That can be relied upon.* That fact is a very important one for doctors to remember to pass on to their patients, to mothers of children, to nurses, to grandmothers, and to anyone who has charge of a child. Very often these people make the serious error of having no confidence whatever in the child's innate intelligence, in his wish to conform, in his desire to do what is asked of him if he is only allowed a reasonable time for learning. Instead, some believe he will not learn unless treated strictly, harshly, even cruelly. In other words, they ignore that which is positive in the child—his ability and willingness to conform. If they allow time, if they give the child love and affection, if they give him confidence and approval when he meets their expectations, and if they refrain from scolding and browbeating when he does not, the child will eventually master the training in a satisfactory manner.

In the matter of toilet training and, incidentally, in all other little things that the child has to begin to learn in this period, his co-operation is likely to be good somewhat in proportion to the way he was treated during the oral period. In other words, the mother who has been generous, affectionate, interested in her child when he was helpless and at her mercy in the first year of life will be repaid with a much better conformity when the problem of toilet training arises than she whose child has been treated inconsiderately and already has acquired a grudge against those around him. If a child is happy and well adjusted at the end of the first year and the mother indicates what is expected of him in the matter of toilet training—does not hurry him too much, does not become too irritated, does not become unkind on too many days—she will get the desired result.

Children just will not go on soiling themselves or wetting themselves indefinitely if patience and tolerance are used. Probably very few mothers can actually believe this to be true; hence a mother will become rather anxious on certain days and feel that her child is destined to be a nonconformist and that she must put on the pressure or she will have a child who seems to be feeble-minded, or at least behaves in a way that will bring criticism to her as a parent. Too often, intead of realizing some of these aforementioned facts the mother has not related herself to the child and his needs but has fixed her attention on some neighbor down the street who is boasting that her child is clean or dry; then the mother feels she has to become very hard on her own child in order to make him appear as clever, intelligent and capable as the neighbor's child.

Children have their own rhythm about these things just as about eating and sleeping. In the long run what difference will it make whether a child achieves cleanliness at sixteen months or at eighteen months? Actually none at all! But in some homes the perspective is rather short and before sixty days have elapsed the mother is sure she has the most undesirable child that ever existed because he has not become clean or dry.

Dryness is not achieved as early as bowel control and should not be expected so soon. While the average child is very likely to be clean at the end of the second year he may not become dry at night until the end of the third year and, possibly, wet the bed at night even beyond that age. The psychological mechanism by which the bowel and bladder are controlled is partly under voluntary and partly under involuntary control. It is an example of an automatic function that is achieved through the emotional contact of someone in the environment of the child, usually the mother, sometimes a nurse, but it is the *person* of the mother or the nurse that makes the child feel that he can make his body conform to what is expected.

In the course of time the impatient and distrustful mother will make the child impatient and distrustful of himself. The child needs a great deal of attention and confidence from others in order to master this function just as he needs patience and confidence to master the many functions that are concerned with growing up. For example, co-operation is required about going to school. The reader can probably remember something in his own life or in the lives of the children he knows that will make him realize that a child may not want to begin going to school or, if he begins, he may go a few days and because of some incident—known or unknown—wish to remain at home. Then the mother or the father or someone in whom the child has trust must come forward and reiterate the advantages of school. They must point out that it is their desire that the child go to school and ask him if he will do it to please them. That argument is usually won. However, they may have to go with him for a day or two in order to lend the strength of their presence to his weak ability to do the expected thing.

We are speaking now of the average child who has no anxiety problem and who has only a normal amount of reluctance to do the difficult thing. In these cases the parent has to come forward and say, "We want you to do it. It will please us if you do." So the child takes the idea within himself and being aware, consciously or unconsciously, of many nice things his parents have done for him, he goes back to school. The same thing is equally important in bowel training even though the child's vocabulary is limited. Incidentally it is to be noted that the child becomes clean at the end of the second year when he is beginning to get a fair vocabulary and a fair understanding of words.

Difficulties of Toilet Training

We have described roughly how the training should take place in the average case. There are a great many cases that are not average and in which the mother has little feeling and little understanding of how to train a child so that it will be accomplished with a minimum of trauma to him. It is to be remembered that in the matter of bowel training the child is making a sort of present or gift to those who are training him. To him the matter is just a great effort and he does not sense its social implications; he only senses that the parents are asking something of him which is difficult to achieve. Consequently, he feels that the least they could do is to be kind and appreciative of whatever efforts he makes.

There is a delicate balance in this emotional relationship. If the parents are too busy, or personally do not give the child what he feels to be a proper response in gratitude and acceptance of his efforts, he can become rebellious and stubborn, he can become indifferent, and he will not try. Then you have the efforts at training going on for many days and weeks and very little being accomplished because underneath the child is just not responding to what he considers fair treatment. This particular response may easily be misinterpreted, and so more pressure is put upon him to conform, and the situation which was already a little pathological becomes more so. A battle begins. The child refuses to attempt to be clean. If put on the toilet he does not move his bowels, but always moves them in some other circumstance that annoys his mother. She scolds him, reproaches him, whips him, or deprives him in some way, hoping that she will bring home to him the fact that he is displeasing her and that he must mend his ways.

In a great many instances this method does not work. The more the mother complains, scolds and punishes, the more resistance the child has. There is a clash of wills and very often the child comes out the winner. Then the doctor comes on the scene and the mother asks what to do with a child who is not behaving himself properly. The trouble is usually not that the food is disagreeing with the child, or that he is feeble-minded, or that he is particularly bad, or a pathological child. The pathological one is the person who is handling him, who has not started the process off properly, and she is the one who needs to mend her ways.

When doctors step in and attempt to tell the mother she is not handling her child well, they should do this with great tact, of course. The most tactful and easy way is not to tell the mother how wrong she has been but just to give her the explanations of what has been presented so far: the limitations of the child's neurophysiological apparatus, how impressions of what is expected are conveyed to the child's mind; how these two forces work together; how the time element and the value of hope and expectation affect the child's physiological makeup. Thereby the doctor tries to get the mother to see the importance of discarding her hostile and reproachful attitude. By her hostile attitude she has already engendered some of the most unfortunate emotions human beings can develop—hostility, stubbornness and lack of co-operation.

During the course of development in the oral period, the first year of life, many events are encountered that can stir up hostility and start the child feeling unhappy, resentful and rebellious, but generally they are less important when compared to the events that occur in this anal phase of development. The anal phase is the time in which the elicitation of co-operation, goodwill and conformity from the child is brought about. This co-operation, goodwill and conformity are brought about on the first responsibilities, which are in turn connected with the function of the lower part of the gastrointestinal tract. If in teaching control of the bowel and bladder, the mother goes about it with too much harshness, or with too many reproaches, she can get a child who will give vent to his hostility not only in nonconformity in bowel and bladder training but also in other spheres of activity such as temper tantrums, disobedience, cruelty to other children, to animals, destructiveness of toys or property. Over nothing more than the matter of bowel and bladder training a mother can build up a great deal of hostility in the child which finds its way into many diverse channels. Looked at from a different angle, aggression or hostility is built up during the anal period through the frustration of instincts. If the child did what was instinctual and most comfortable for him, he would not bother with this matter of bowel and bladder control at all, but he is able to manage the necessary compromise if he is treated considerately. When he is not treated considerately, and when he has too much frustration of instinctual needs, aggression and hostility are built up.

The Child's Reaction to Toilet Training

What does the child get in compensation for accepting bowel and bladder control, for doing away with the comfort of voiding or soiling at will? The answer is not difficult. He gets approval, he gets the love, or he *should* get the love, of those who are training him. If things go well, we call this process of acceptance of training adaptation to the reality principle as opposed to adherence to the pleasure principle. The reality principle is the ability of a human being to postpone an immediate pleasure for pleasure at some distant period, or to achieve some more distant goal. In other words, the child gives up his desire to relieve the tension of his bowels and bladder at the slightest stimulus and manages the way the adults want him to in return for their immediate approval, or their approval two hours later, or two weeks later, or maybe two months later. He senses that such would be the most sensible result for him in the long run. However, to make it possible for him to grasp such an impression satisfactorily, it is necessary for him to have the love and goodwill and affection of his parents practically *ever present*.

This ability to postpone immediate pleasure for some future gratification is, of course, one of the necessary abilities of adults as opposed to those of the child. In the first place, the child wants an immediate gratification of his needs. His body and mind cannot stand much tension and in the beginning he does not have any realization of why he *should* stand it. He gets a feeling of the importance of this concept gradually during growth, from those around him who make it easy for him to endure more tension as he goes along and make him see good reasons why he should.

Later in our study we will encounter many people whom we will call neurotics, psychopathic personalities and psychotics. One of the chief difficulties of such a person is that he can never seem to postpone gratification. He leaves school because it is monotonous and because he feels he must go out and earn money to buy a new suit or to go dancing more often. Perhaps he has a fine job with a good promise of security but in a short time leaves it because he can get a few cents or a few dollars more at some job that has no promise or is only temporary. In later life people get into many varieties of trouble because they have not become masters of their instinctual tensions, because they have not been able to conform to the reality principle, because they must still act in conformity to the pleasure principle.

As the reader can see, very little is asked from the child in the first year, but a great deal that has to do with human personality development and with the development of the mind and with later conformity adjustment takes place during this so-called anal period.

Whenever material of this kind is being presented the question usually arises as to whether children cannot be spoiled by a training procedure that sounds as lenient in all aspects as this one that has just been discussed. Right away we would like to make the point that there is no such thing as *spoiling* a child *if* the child is expected to do the things required by the average environment and at the appropriate time. It is a matter of careful training on the part of the parents' having some understanding of the child's neurophysiological apparatus—that is, having an understanding of the child's inherent helplessness and limitations and being easy on him in the beginning, then, as time goes on, making social requirements at the appropriate point. With such a procedure there can be no process of spoiling. Spoiling cannot occur, because the balance of what is given the child and what he gives back to the parent is nicely adjusted. If the parent has been wise enough to regulate his interest *in* the child in generous proportion to what the parent is asking *of* the child, then the latter will not be rebellious, heedless, inconsiderate, or un-co-operative.

It is quite true that children are spoiled, but not because of the love and consideration that they have been given. The reason is that, even if the right kind of love and consideration has been given, the parent has never quite had the heart to make the necessary demands upon the child; has not been willing to demand that the child accept responsibilities as they arose. Thus responsibilities are postponed. Parents rationalize their attitude by saying the child is too young. Too often the attitude never changes and when the child is twenty-one he is still considered too young to be considerate of other people and to fulfill any degree of responsibility to his parents and to society. Therefore, if this balance of giving and demanding were better understood, fewer parents would get into a dilemma of wondering whether they were giving their child too much attention and spoiling him and reacting by depriving him of necessary love and pleasure.

In fact, what you give the child in the way of understanding and affection contributes toward making him a more capable, more responsible, more competent and more able individual, provided the proper, usual responsibilities are put upon him. Children who have not been loved, who have not had friendly parents, who have not had a well-rounded education as to how to live life, will be inadequate people because they will be fearful, anxious, hateful or un-co-operative as a result of the emptiness within them. The child who has been treated generously will respect his parents and society as a whole. The parent will get back what he has given if he knows how to ask for it at the right time and in the spirit of fair play and co-operation. Children are fair and co-operative citizens when asked to be so in the right manner.

There is no evidence that children are born rebellious, neurotic or psychopathic. We have only ungenerous and psychopathic parents, and if we did not have parents who were psychopathic in some way themselves, the tremendous problems of psychopathy and neurosis would not be so great as they are at the present time. Someone has said that if a parent wants to have a well-behaved, socially well-adapted child, that parent should figure out what kind of person that implies and be such a person himself, and the chances are pretty good that through association with the parent the child will become much the same kind of person when he is twenty-one or thereabouts.

Conflict in the Child and Parent

This balance between the love and generosity that are given to the young human being and that which he gives in return is bound to bring up certain attitudes in the child. We refer to these attitudes as character traits. One of the attitudes is ambivalence. *Ambivalence* is an emotional state of feeling both love and hate toward a person at the same time. The love or hate, or even both, may be unconscious. Nearly all our attitudes have some degree of ambivalence in them because we rarely completely hate or love a person for long. Yet the concept is a useful one because our reactions may become very confused if we do not understand how we feel toward each other.

Children are often ambivalent in feeling toward their parents, who in turn often are equally ambivalent toward their children. It is not a self-evident fact that children love their parents any more than it is a self-evident fact that parents love their children. Each is necessary to the other. So, if we were honest, we would probably say that in cultivating positive feelings between each other, parents and children were making a virtue of a necessity.

In thinking this matter over, we should realize that a great many adults have children just because it is being done, or because they are ignorant about contraceptives, or because they want to gain some degree of immortality through their children. We should not delude ourselves into thinking that the majority of parents have children because they love them, or that their main goal in life as parents is to help the on-coming generation to adapt to and enrich society generally. We are aim-ing for this goal, but we are farther from it than we realize.

Children impose a great many responsibilities upon parents. They take a great deal of their parents' time, interest, energies and money. Consequently, parents have children with a certain feeling of ambiva-lence about the process. These feelings in the parents are bound to be sensed by the child and the child develops and reflects a corresponding feeling during the change from his tendency to operate by the pleasure principle to adapting to the reality principle of postponing his gratifi-cations to some future time. During his toilet-training period the child does not find it easy to make this change, and he does not accept the training without some degree of resentment against the person who imposes the restrictions. That attitude of resentment can always be mini-mized if the attitude of authority is one of friendliness and understand-ing. Some people in authority can talk in a way that makes people ac-cept restrictions very readily; others in authority make those subject to them want to fight. Thus some parents have the ability to bring chil-dren through the vicissitudes of childhood and get them to accept toilet training and other matters easily. They manage it in an easy, good-natured way and keep the hostility, which is potentially there, at a mini-mum and with the result that the child's feeling of friendliness and goodwill toward the parents always dominates.

Hostilities and Friendliness

An important goal in social relations is to try to increase the amount of positive feeling between people. We once heard a woman make a statement of that kind in relation to her child; she said, "When I take a gay and interested attitude toward my child's behavior, rather than a perplexed and critical one, he is much more relaxed and co-operates much better." This was in relation to an emotional problem of eating in her six-year-old child. Often during treatment for neurosis a parent's *real attitude* toward his children is revealed. We are prone to assume too readily that life goes on smoothly in the home, that the mother and children are living "happily" together. Actually tensions between mother and children can become very high. The mother feels greatly perplexed at times as to how to manage her children, hostilities between them spring up, unfortunate attitudes of thwarting one another go on a long time and hatred develops which will handicap the children for years to come in ways that we will discuss as we proceed.

The drive toward as complete an instinctual gratification as possible leads the child to try to dominate those in the environment and to do as much as he can to gain his ends—even to the point of inflicting pain upon them in the process. The pleasure in inflicting pain is called *sadism*. We see it exhibited socially in some types of "kidding," biting sarcasm, temper tantrums in which those who are loved are nevertheless subjected to these sadistic experiences. The remorse felt after each tirade bears witness to the fact that a large pleasurable element energizes the cruel behavior.

Just as there are those who take pleasure in inflicting pain, so there are those who like to endure pain. They, in contradistinction to the sadist, like to experience pain. It may be harder for the reader to understand why one should wish to endure pain rather than inflict pain, yet who does not know of some person or persons who seem to like to "take a beating" or "get kicked around." The reaction of enduring privation endlessly or repeated misfortune cheerfully, even to taking pleasure in being beaten, pinched or bitten in the act of lovemaking, is called *masochism*.

One of the problems in the inevitable give and take of training children during the anal period is that of keeping hostility at a minimum. This can be done by some real understanding consideration for the child, his ego limitations and the number of responsibilities (relatively) that are being thrust upon him. Since he must control so much of himself at such an early age he feels the least he should get in return is his mother's heartfelt appreciation. Yet some mothers seem to be constantly scheming as to how they can devise some trickery that will get the child to learn what they want him to learn. Such a mother seems to lack any idea of living happily together with the child or doing things together with him —a procedure that should be important to both. Instead, she seems to take the attitude that what the child accomplishes is no concern of hers, provided he makes her as little trouble as possible.

If the mother has been generous in her attitude toward the child during the oral period, and if she is tolerant and understanding with the big problem of toilet training itself, then she will get a child who will always undertake his responsibilities, whatever they may be, with a correspondingly generous spirit. So far as the child's mind is concerned, excretions are gifts which he makes to those around him and which he makes generously if he is asked in the proper way. The whole later-life attitude of generosity gets its start here. Many people have had such a difficult time in the first two or three years of life that they always have difficulty in bringing out their generous impulses. They always have an anxiety about being imposed upon, always fear repetition of the exploitations that occurred in their childhood.

Excreta Substitutions and Self-expression

The child's personal interest in the values of feces and urine in the nursery becomes *displaced* onto money and other things which have a pleasure value if possessed for their own sake or if traded for something else desired. In fact, it must be stressed against the opposition of our sense of esthetic value that the child is naturally quite intrigued by and quite enamored of his own excretions. He finds their proximity to his body when warm quite satisfying. He finds them in no way filthy, disgusting or unpleasant to sight and touch as do we. He would like to touch and play with them in a quite uninhibited manner, and often does so in spite of the careful vigilance of those who supervise him. Many a mother has been surprised and disconcerted to find her child occupying himself with smearing his feces over himself, the bed and oftentimes over the walls of the room.

Any child is prone to do this, and no mother who experiences it should be frightened about her child's nature or worry that he has more primitive or animal heredity in him than the next child. He is merely being an average child and following the dictates of the pleasure principle. He need only be washed and told he can be given something more acceptable to play with instead of the contents of his own body. This promise should be kept by providing plasticine, molding clay, sand and water or finger painting as substitutes for the instinctive tendency to play with material of such consistency. This displacement of interest to something more socially acceptable forms the beginning of *sublimation,* which is defined as the process of helping the instinctual expressions inherent in childhood to find expression on a more socially valuable and accepted level.

All work has to be more or less directly a sublimation, i. e., a refinement of the interests which the child of necessity finds in relation to his own body and its functions. Adults who would reject these humble beginnings of interest in social activity should do a little honest reflecting upon the interests in the human body that persist into adulthood: masturbation, overconcern with aches and pains, fussiness about what they eat and where they sleep, excessive concern with bowel movements (their regularity and consistency), overconcern with the color and amount of the urine passed, etc. This neurotic preoccupation with the body may greatly curtail the efficacy of an individual and make him poor company to those around him. Hence, if the child of two or three is interested in playing with water and dirt even to the extent of an excessive attraction for the toilet bowl, it is but good sense to have a little patience and understanding in helping him to get interested in more socially accepted activities but which do not force him to give up satisfaction to which he will only have to return later on under the guise of illness. (See Chapters XIII and XIV on neuroses.)

A clear picture of the gradual substitutions and new interests which the child adopts in his efforts to sublimate his original interest in feces has been well shown by Ferenczi when he points out that feces are brown, moist, soft, have a bad odor and are worthless. The child turns to mud pies which have all the characteristics of feces minus the odor. He then turns to sand and relinquishes the characteristic of moisture. From there his interest turns to bright stones and trinkets, and he relinquishes softness. Next he adopts stamps, coins and money, gaining more color than the original brown, and at the same time gaining something of social value. The adults in the environment should provide opportunities for these substitutions to take place.

Some people come out of the anal period with a feeling for orderliness, neatness, having things just so, being strictly punctual in every way as their outstanding character traits. Such a person has been made to adopt these ways by his mother so strictly and thoroughly at this time that he is never able to break away from them. He always feels that he must follow this type of behavior, otherwise people will be displeased with him. He cannot believe, for instance, that he will be forgiven if he's a few minutes late, that people will accept him even if things are a little out of order. Everything has to be just so at all times. These character traits have value, but they can be excessive. This type of person can become the kind of character who is so intent on order that he becomes emotionally lost in being orderly, punctual and neat. He is so much that way that he ceases to be a human, warm, friendly person. He lives by the letter of the law and will not tolerate any trace of carelessness in himself or even in others.

A certain amount of this precision makes a careful worker and may make a good person to be in authority provided it is tempered with a little kindness and understanding. However, at a certain point, which is always difficult to define, it can come to be a burden to those associated with him. If he is a parent, he is too strict, and too little fun is allowed in family life. If he is an official or an employer, he is so strict that he makes work disagreeable for everyone. He feels that he has been severely dealt with but that it has given him a sterling character and, hence, that others would profit by the same kind of treatment.

Identification and Personality

A word about the character as it is formed. We started with the instinctual needs of the human being demanding gratification regardless of the environmental forces. For purposes of written and verbal condensation, we call these instinctual forces the *id*. In the beginning, as a matter of fact, the child reacts as if he feels that he is part and parcel of the mother and her body. When he is hungry he cries and she comes to feed him, yet at the same time he seems to conclude the mother is a part of himself. Not until some time after birth—we do not know exactly when—does the child gradually gain the sense that he is a separate entity and that, if he is going to thrive and have his needs gratified, he must begin to conform to those in the environment and their expectations.

As this takes place we have the beginning of the ego formation, the formation of the "I" part of the personality. As time goes on, the child comes to think of himself as a separate individual and during toilet training and during the training in the other habits which must be learned during this period his realization of self is enhanced. When he becomes able to control some of his behavior in conformity with social demands, he begins to have vestiges, at least, of conscience. The conscience is still a part of the ego but a special part of it. This takes place as a result of the child's taking over into himself the wishes and demands of grown-up people and is done through a process called *identification* or *introjection*. First, the child learns to do what is expected of him by reason of his proximity to the parent and being told what is expected of him. He takes in these wishes and ideas, makes them a part of his own mind and begins to be a better and better trained individual. It is this process that is called identification. The child identifies with the mother and what she wants.

We can also use the word introjection, which to some would mean a more thoroughgoing "taking in" or incorporation of the loved object than identification, and which eventually leads to independent thinking and independent functioning. This is a long, tedious, difficult process for both the parent and the child. Parents are always giving advice and admonitions while in their homes and double or treble them if the child goes to visit friends or relatives, or is to stop at a neighbor's, or even later when he goes away from home to school or to work. The parent says, "Don't forget this," or "Don't forget that." This means that the parent fears the child will not remember what the parents have taught him—and not to remember means that the child does not take away *within himself* enough of the parent's thinking, feeling, or point of view. The parent feels that the child has not incorporated within him enough of these good ideas, and so keeps reiterating them.

The phenomenon can degenerate to nagging. The child does his best to swallow the ideas, to digest them and to metabolize and deposit them in his own mind for reference. Sometimes, however, he has to regurgitate these ideas. Sometimes they give him indigestion and may be reflected in the statement, "Pop gives me a pain," or "Mom makes me sick." At any rate, this taking over of social values as correct thinking and behavior for functioning in contemporary society forms a theoretical third part of the personality called the *superego,* to which we shall refer more fully in the next chapter.

Incorporation is a process that is going on continually, and we trust the reader already sees, from the foregoing and before we leave this age period of development, how important a process it is. We want to make clear that before the age of three is reached much has been going on by way of personality development and that the character traits have been in the process of formation in the nursery. Parents are prone to criticize the school system for not making a better child of their offspring. Actually a great many problems which parents blame on the school system are problems that should have been solved before the child was out of the nursery.

BIBLIOGRAPHY FOR CHAPTER III

Abraham, Karl, *Selected Papers on Psychoanalysis,* Hogarth Press, 1927, pp. 370–392.

Ferenczi, Sandor, *Contributions to Psychoanalysis,* Bedger, 1916.

Freud, Sigmund, *Three Contributions to the Theory of Sex,* Nervous and Mental Disease Publishing Co., 1930.

Chapter IV

EMOTIONAL DISTURBANCES THAT OCCUR
DURING THE ANAL PERIOD

We HAVE seen that when, during the oral period, the course of the child's development is disturbed by unnecessary or unusual frustrations he reacts by changes in his behavior. These changes usually will be apparent at the time but they may also show their effects at a considerably later date. This holds true for the child during the anal period. In the previous chapter we described the effects in the personality that appear many years later. Here we will discuss the reactions that may appear during this period itself.

Anxiety Reactions

If the child is forced to become toilet trained too early or too quickly he may develop the symptoms of anxiety either immediately or after an interval. A careful analysis of an acute anxiety situation in a two-year-old child has been reported by Bornstein. This small child developed panic when she was put to bed. She refused to lie down and when she fell asleep it was in a sitting posture. The analysis showed that her acute panic was the result of her fear lest she soil herself when asleep, then her mother would not love her and would go away and leave her. Her toilet training had been very early and strict.

The anxiety does not necessarily appear in acute attacks, but the child may be mildly apprehensive most of the time. He may be jittery during the day and sleep restlessly at night. An acute or chronic anxiety state is the sign that the child has a conflict. At this age period the conflict is usually between the child's desire not to be toilet trained and his fear that if he persists in this desire his mother will not love him and perhaps will leave him.

Direct Functional Disturbances

Instead of showing symptoms of anxiety he may show disturbances of bowel and bladder functioning. If one watches a child during the process of toilet training one can be sure that there are times when the child tries very hard to retain his excretions until he is in the proper place to void them because he wants so much to please his mother and have her love him. At other times he seems either not to care to retain them or seems to get a savage delight in not retaining them. At these times he is angry and displeased with his mother and does not love her because he feels she does not love him. One mother reported that her son of less than two years had been free from the habit of smearing his feces for several weeks. One day she had to leave him alone in the house while she went to bring the maid for the day's work. She put the child in his pen. When she returned, everything in the pen was smeared. She was intuitive enough to understand that the child felt that she did not love him because she had left him alone, and in revenge he did the thing he knew would upset her. Conversely, if a child is angry at his mother he may withhold his movements even for several days, especially if she is anxious to have him produce a good movement. Wetting in the daytime is also an expression of antagonism to the parents. In our opinion all day wetting is based on a conscious or nearly conscious desire to annoy, irritate and defy the parents.

If the child has been too severely toilet trained, or toilet trained too early, he may become afraid of moving his bowels even in the toilet, and so becomes constipated. If a great deal of attention has been paid to his bowels, through the use of a suppository or an enema, he may be loath to relinquish both the sensual and emotional pleasure he receives from this treatment and hold back his own movements to coax his mother to use a suppository or an enema. Constipation in young children is either the result of fear of the mother's displeasure, a desire to take revenge on her, or of a greediness to continue to get sensual pleasure at her hands. Withholding of urine is not as common in children as the withholding of feces. This is probably because an overfull bladder, causing more pain than an overfull bowel, cannot be tolerated so long and because the reverse peristalsis of the large bowel allows the contents to move away from the lower part so that overdistention does not take place, while the bladder has no such capacity to avoid the stretching of overdistention.

Disturbances of Other Functions

Human beings have a tendency to continue an experience with which they are familiar. The experience itself does not necessarily have to be a pleasurable one; it only has to be well known. If a new experience is uncomfortable and we find ourselves unable to derive from it the pleasure we desire, we tend to give it up and hark back to a previous experience with which we are familiar and know by familiarity how to derive pleasure from it. When a child is too severely, too quickly or too early subjected to toilet training he will find himself quite uncomfortable because of feelings of anxiety and may try to return to the pleasures he experienced during the oral stage. He cannot do this completely, since his desire for oral pleasure at this stage cannot be satisfied as a purely pleasurable experience.

Sterba has reported a series of cases in which the child's feeding problem came on shortly after his toilet training began. From certain reactions in the feeding situation Sterba deduced that the feeding problem bore a relation to the toilet training and when the latter was stopped temporarily the feeding difficulty disappeared. In this case it seemed evident that the child, bitterly resentful at being required by the mother to suppress his desires for anal pleasure, protested by refusing to eat because he knew that such behavior would disturb her and make her uncomfortable and worried about his welfare. It had the added motive that the child, feeling under the force of necessity to relinquish his anal pleasure, went back to attempting to obtain his satisfactions in an oral way. This could only be partially successful because he knew that big children must not obtain their entire gratification through the activity of the mouth.

The lower end of the gastrointestinal tract can be used to make noises and smells through the passage of flatus, which may be disgusting to the adult but are enjoyable to the child. If, at his mother's stern insistence, he relinquishes this pleasure before he is ready to do so the enjoyment he experienced at the lower end of the intestinal tract may appear as enjoyment from the productions of the upper end, i. e., through the use of obscene and scatological speech. This is a very common phenomenon among nursery-school children who, from time to time, suffer from epidemics of obscenity in which they delight in shocking the adults through the dirtiness of their language. This is not a regressive but a really progressive process because it is much more acceptable culturally to use obscenity in speech than to express the same feelings by the public passage of flatus.

The obscenity may be obscenity in the adult sense through the use of vulgarisms that the child has overheard from some adult, or may be obscenity in the childish sense through the use of words he knows are forbidden or not usual in his home. Thus if urination is the family word for the passage of urine he will use the word pee; if the word pee is the family word for this activity he will use the word urination as an obscene term, or he may use the simple name of an object, like dish, plate, etc., as an obscene epithet. He may also become apprehensive lest he shout out in some place such as a church where he should be quiet. We know one child who suffered agonies of apprehension lest he yell or scream during the church service. This really was not an apprehension lest he shout out but lest he pass flatus, for which he had been severely reprimanded many times.

If the child relinquishes his anal pleasures because he is too much afraid of offending his mother he may regress to the infantile method of breathing. In this the respirations are not rhythmical, but are very irregular, and catching of the breath is common. When this type of respiration is re-established it produces extreme difficulty in the clear pronunciation of words. Because of the breathing difficulty the enunciation becomes irregular and arrhythmical, and stuttering often results. This stuttering portrays a conflict between the desire to express hostility and defiance toward the parent, by the passage of gas from the body, and the desire to please her by not performing an improper action. The conflict has been displaced from the lower end of the gastrointestinal tract, where the child has really acceded to the parent's prohibitions, to its upper end. At this part of the body the internal gases are used in the function of speech and when the conflict is displaced to it the speech function is involved. Stuttering at this age period usually is started by a sudden shock or fright. This produces a strong startle reflex, which is such a marked part of the reactions of early infancy. The startle reflex is accompanied by a catching of the breath, i. e., a sudden resumption of the infantile breathing arrhythmia. If the child is already in conflict between his defiance of the parent and his desire to please her this startle reflex paves the way for the displacement of the conflict onto the speech function. This is not the only mechanism at work in the stuttering of older children but is of great importance when the stuttering begins at this period of development.

If the child suddenly gives in to the parent's toilet training he may react to her admonitions to be a good boy and grow up quickly and be clean by striving desperately to follow them out. He suddenly appears to become independent, refuses to have anything done for him but demands to be allowed to do everything for himself, even if the activity is manifestly beyond his physical powers. Instead of being interested any longer in his excretory functions he suddenly becomes interested only in masturbation. This masturbation is accompanied by conscious fantasies which are different from the fantasies that appear naturally at the next stage of development. Their content deals entirely with expressions of defiance and hostility toward other people or of other persons toward the child himself. As the child masturbates he is wishing that he were hurting, injuring or defying the parent or that the parent were hurting, injuring or defying him. Consciously he is disgusted with the idea that he would really like to be dirty and do dirty things of which the parent would disapprove. He has repressed such desires completely. The full effect of the toilet training has fallen on the anal pleasures but the sadism and masochism of this stage have been unaffected.

As the child strives to be more grown up he carries this sadism and masochism along and they remain as active as if he were still the cruel little savage that he was during the anal-sadistic stage. We know one boy whose mother made strict demands for cleanliness, and who at the same time encouraged him to be destructive and cruel. She would break up his toys and encourage him to do the same, shouting gleefully when he followed her directions. He responded to her by being overclean and by being destructive and cruel. We might note here that we consider too great independence in a two-year-old, an independence that rejects any attempt to help him, as being as pathological as too great dependence.

Phobias and Compulsions

The child is unable to differentiate between situations that resemble each other too closely. In this respect he behaves like the sheep that has been subjected to certain conditioning experiments. The sheep through repetition is conditioned to anticipate being fed when he sees a circle. After this conditioned reflex has been well established the animal is conditioned to expect a painful electric shock when it is shown an ellipse. And after this conditioned reflex is well established the circle which is shown the animal at feeding time is gradually flattened. A point is reached where the sheep is unable to distinguish between a circle and an ellipse and at this point the animal loses both of his conditioned reflexes and shows a complete change in his daily behavior.

Parents often forget that the child stands midway between the animal and the adult in his powers of discrimination between situations that resemble each other but are not exactly the same. If the child becomes frightened about soiling himself with excreta he may be unable to distinguish between soiling himself with excreta and soiling himself in other socially acceptable ways. A girl of eight was referred by her mother because she seemed to be intellectually retarded although her I.Q. was 108. When her schoolwork was closely examined it was found that her difficulty lay in the fact that she never completed any assignment. She was unable to do so because she spent too much time making each word she wrote on the paper exactly perfect. Her bedroom was always arranged in perfect order. She had a specific location for every object and would become angry if the object was not just where it ought to be. She would become upset if there was one small spot on her dress and would immediately have to change it. She never played with other children because she could not stand getting her hands dirty, and had to run in the house about every ten or fifteen minutes to wash them. She had one game with which she occupied herself endlessly, spending entire Saturdays and Sundays with it. She tore a newspaper into small pieces, placed them in a heap on the floor under a chair, took them out and put them back again. She had little appetite. It can be seen readily from her behavior that she spent her entire time preventing herself from being anything but clean and meticulous. This was more important than having a good time or being successful with her work. Her play was an open representation of moving her bowels in the toilet—"on the chair."

These reactions by this child had started rather suddenly when she was about four years old. Up to that time she had behaved in a fairly normal manner except that she was difficult to toilet train. The reason for her slow response to toilet training was not evident. One may suspect a constitutional predisposition to desire more pleasure from excretory activities than is usual. (There seems little question that there are constitutional predispositions that cause a child to need more of one of the infantile pleasure activities than other children do. There are certain families in which the children tend to suck their fingers longer than usual. In other families all of the children wet the bed for much longer than the customary period. We commonly say that such things run in families, by which we mean there is a constitutional predisposition to need more of the infantile pleasure than ordinarily.) Her mother tried all forms of training. They were not successful. At last in exasperation she seized the child's soiled panties and rubbed them on the child's face. The child never soiled herself again, but within a short time her activities and behavior changed to the way she was when we first saw her. Because she was unable to distinguish clearly between soiling with feces and with other materials, the humiliation of the severe punishment not only forced her to regard soiling with feces as prohibited but also all other types of being soiled. In order to avoid a repetition of the humiliating punishment she avoided indulging in any type of soiling. In short, as a result of her inability to differentiate between soiling with excreta and with other types of dirt the punishment compelled her not only to cease the former, but also to stop the latter sublimatory activities.

Therapeutic Self-expression

Teachers are well aware how often a child on first entering school is unable to use finger paints or other forms of artistic action because he refuses to get his hands dirty. Such children have undergone severe toilet training and have displaced the fear of soiling with excreta onto all types of soiling. It is also remarkable how often after a psychoanalysis an adult begins to be interested in art and how really beautiful his productions are. We believe that there is in general too much emphasis on toilet training in the education of American children and that this overemphasis often interferes sadly with the later capacity of the adult for self-expression. It is interesting that this overemphasis usually produces overconformity. The child is little and helpless; because of his helplessness he has so much need for his parents' assistance and love that he perforce must give in to them in order to get the assistance and love he needs.

Treatment for this overconformity must lie in a retraining of the child. Take the case of the little girl cited above. The child had two emotional problems: (1) she feared any type of soiling so much that she had to live her life in a way that excluded soiling, and (2) she gave in to her mother, not because she desired to maintain a friendly relationship with her, but because she was humiliated and feared the loss of her mother's assistance and kindness. She had felt antagonistic to her mother for asking her to give up a pleasurable activity, but when she relinquished it through fear she was forced to suppress her feelings of antagonism from her conscious mind. Thereafter these feelings appeared only in her behavior which, by the time she came for treatment, was not of a kind to make her mother proud of her. The repression of the two impulses—the desire to soil and the hostility to the mother—

caused them to become combined in the child's mind, and they were kept combined through the fear of a repetition of the humiliating experience. The same fear kept them separated from the child's conscious thinking and feeling.

The aim of treatment will be to remove the fear from the child's mind and to replace it by a desire to be cultured. Such a desire will be sufficient to enable the child to use her desires to soil and her feelings of hostility to her mother in a culturally acceptable manner for her own benefit and the benefit of the society in which she lives. How can this be accomplished? The first prerequisite is that she develop a love relationship with an adult. If the mother can be used in treatment this step is not necessary, for the love relationship already exists. If the mother cannot be used, then the love relationship must be developed with another adult—a teacher, a physician or a psychiatrist.

As soon as the love relationship is established the adult will begin gradually to encourage the child to take part in activities which the child regards as dirty. Mud and water, sand and water, plasticine, finger paints, ordinary painting, drawing with chalk, gardening, are all such activities. No comment is made about the child's desire or attempts to be clean and neat, but the adult will praise all successful attempts at being dirty. Even if soiling recurs the child should be commended for it. This seems like a simple prescription as it is written, but the application of it with the child will take much painstaking, careful labor before she will be able to do the things the adult does with any degree of success or pleasure. If the mother can be persuaded to work in this way with the child the success might be quicker and easier.

During this process the child will begin to express hostility and antagonism to the therapist and also at home to her mother. Again the adult attitude should be to accept without praise or comment all attempts to please or ingratiate herself and to praise the successful expression of hostility. As the child becomes easier with her hostile feelings she will begin to attempt to paint or model better than the adult and any real success along this line should be encouraged. Through such methods the child gives up her idea that the *only* way to get on with the adult is to be clean and conforming and replaces it with the more healthy attitude that not only are her productions and opinions worth while and bring her pleasure, but that she also can produce them and retain her friendly relationship with the adult at the same time. The therapist's approach might begin along a different line. Using dolls, the child would be encouraged to dramatize the feelings a little girl has toward her mother. Again no comment should be made about tendencies to conformity, but the child should be encouraged to express hostile feelings and their successful expression should be praised. During this process the child will become interested in playing with materials which she has formerly regarded as dirty and this interest should be praised.

Both methods are combined in the ordinary psychiatric treatment of children but the therapist does not assume as much direction as has been described here because there are often other problems which are involved in the main one, but which are known only to the child. These must be worked out also. As they are solved the child comes to the solution of the main problem more easily. If they are not worked out they often interfere tremendously with the effect of the management we have described.

As a successful result of such treatment we would expect the child's schoolwork to improve tremendously (for she would be more interested in accomplishing her task instead of putting all her efforts in seeing it was done neatly), her play activities to be as varied as those of other children of her age (for she would have no further interest in the futile paper game and be able to join with other children in their play without regard to whether it got her dirty or not), the state of her room and her clothes more nearly to approximate that of a child of her own age (for she could then wear soiled clothes if desirable and would be able to move her possessions from one position to another), and that her feeding problem would vanish.

It will have been noticed that this child did not react exactly like the sheep—i. e., she did not lose her conditioning; rather it became more pronounced and spread into other areas. Usually, besides losing its conditioned reflexes, the sheep becomes seclusive, stands by itself in the corner of the field, shakes, trembles and shows ticlike movements, eats and sleeps poorly, and although it may have had a very mild disposition before the conditioning experiments, now it will attack any person or animal that approaches it. A similar reaction occurs following another type of conditioning experiment on dogs. A dog is conditioned to anticipate being fed as soon as it hears a bell. When this conditioned reflex is established the time interval between the ringing of the bell and the feeding of the dog is lengthened. When the interval reaches the space of two minutes the dog behaves as the sheep did with the former experiment. The dog cannot stand having to postpone the gratification of a desire (to be fed) too long, so it develops a pathological reaction.

If a young child is toilet trained too vigorously or too early (i. e., before he is ready for it), he may become very antagonistic, negativistic, stubborn, be a prey to fears and develop a great restlessness. In brief, from being a moderately well-behaved child he becomes badly behaved. This reaction usually annoys his parents, who express their annoyance by punishing him for his behavior. The punishment makes him more antagonistic and negativistic; they punish more, he behaves worse, until a vicious circle is rapidly produced. This vicious circle may result in a recurrence of the original soiling. It is as if the child said, "What's the use? I try hard to please my parents but they don't seem to understand that I do so. I don't seem to understand them either because they say one thing at one time and another at another. I might as well give up and return to pleasures I know are certain."

Treatment for this condition will follow the lines laid down for the case already mentioned. It will be more difficult to establish an affectionate relationship with such a child because he has become angry and filled with hate for the adults who trained him. He anticipates that any new relationship with an adult will result in further curtailment of his gratifications and so views the therapist with suspicion and immediate hostility, being ready constantly to defend himself against any demands. He is ready at the least opportunity to take revenge on any adult for the deprivation he has suffered at his parents' hands. Added to this, the conformity of cleanliness has enhanced the sadomasochistic attitude which forms a great deal of the interpersonal relationship of all children of this age. This means that the main ties he has to other people lie in the pleasure he receives from hurting and being hurt. Therefore treatment will consist definitely of two steps. The first is the overcoming of the suspiciousness, defiance and hostility through which the child operates in his relationship to adults. The adult has to refuse to react to this by hostility, which would only increase the child's antagonism, gratify him masochistically and give him a reason to be sadistic. The second step is for the therapist to make every effort to have the child like him. This can be done by being kind and considerate, by doing small favors for him, by helping him in difficulties, and by understanding his point of view. From this point on the treatment, the second step, is the same as described above.

BIBLIOGRAPHY FOR CHAPTER IV

Bornstein, Berta, "A Phobia in a Two-and-a-half-year-old Child," *Psychoanalytic Quarterly* 4, 1935, 93.

Sterba, Editha, "An Important Factor in the Eating Disturbances of Childhood," *Psychoanalytic Quarterly* 10, 1941, 365.

Chapter V

DEVELOPMENT OF PERSONALITY DURING
THE PHALLIC PERIOD

WITH the genital phase of psychosexual development we enter the third phase in personality development. This phase covers roughly the time between the ages of three and six. In every child's life each successive phase has to be lived through, with incidents occurring in each which contribute to the child's attitudes and feelings toward the world around him. As the child enters the third year of life the gratifications in the oral zone have lost their predominance to a considerable degree. Oral pleasures no longer have all the important values they had to the nursing infant. The average child is fairly well through the period of toilet training, the struggles to master and achieve it, and some sublimations of interest in excretions have already begun. Also the child is more aware both of himself and of the outside world and his interests go beyond the gastrointestinal tract and its functions to the workings of the world around him and to the hows and whys of living. The child's curiosity is expanding as he grows older and he asks more and more questions about life. In asking about life he must inevitably touch upon the question of sexuality and reproduction.

Infantile Sexuality

Most readers, we feel, will be willing to agree that active sexual interest appears at this particular age and that, therefore, the term *psychosexual development* seems an applicable one to use for describing the interactions of body, physiology, social attitudes and psyche. For some it is more difficult to see that the sensual pleasures in the oral period (nursing and sucking) and that the pleasures of the child in the bowel and bladder function have a sexual or sensual component. This comes, no doubt, from having been accustomed to confining the thinking about sexual expression too narrowly to the genital region.

It is generally accepted by doctors, social workers, students of social relations or counselors of marital relationships that sexuality has two components: one of procreation, and one of pleasure. Moreover, it is accepted that enjoyment should be derived from the sexual act as a means of enhancing the value of marriage and of life in general, and more and more attention is being paid to this fact. Within the last decade various cities have set up marriage agencies, an important part of whose activities is to help young people, through group or individual discussion, to obtain a more satisfactory knowledge of sexual adjustment in marriage and thus enhance the social value of the sexual act and not confine it completely to procreation.

Therefore, if we emphasize the pleasure element of sexuality, then we ought not to have too much resistance to expanding that component outward from the genital area to include other areas. Moreover, it is generally accepted that there are other zones of the body that are regarded as areas of sexual excitation: witness, for instance, the prejudice some parents have against the petting and lovemaking in which adolescents participate. Thinking honestly through that situation, we realize that the adult fears that the adolescent will be so stimulated by kissing, hugging and close body contact that he will be led into an actual genital relationship. We can say, then, that there are areas of the body that are capable of erotic excitation. They are called the *erogenous zones* which when stimulated are capable of being pleasurably exciting. They are notably the mouth, the anus, the skin and the breasts of the woman. These areas give pleasure when stimulated by touch because of their anatomical structure. They are a constant source of pleasure throughout life and are not magically enervated because a marriage is entered into nor do they cease to be sources of pleasure when a marriage is terminated. Their demand for pleasurable gratification has to be reckoned with at all ages. If this process is "sexual" in the grade- or high-school student, it must be so in the infant child as well. In other words, in order to understand psychosexual development we need only to be logical in our thinking and correlate the growth phenomena of the adult and child together. There is no sudden metamorphosis from the innocence of the child to the sophistication of the adult.

Sex Information for Children

When the child becomes interested in the problems pertaining to sex and birth, his questions should be answered frankly, truthfully and without embarrassment as they come up. That is not so difficult a job as one might think because children need and want very little information at any one time. If children ask where they come from, and they are told that babies grow within the mother's body, that answer will satisfy most children for that particular day and, perhaps, for several weeks or months to come. They just do not get around to asking any more until something in connection with their play with other children or some event in the home life comes up which prompts a question for additional information. Very often parents make a problem for themselves by the feeling that when the child asks the first question about sex, they are obligated to tell him everything that has been written in a twelve-volume treatise on sexuality. Obviously this is neither necessary nor advisable. Any parent who will put himself at ease on the subject of sex, not try to show how much he knows or be afraid of how little he knows, not be flustered with embarrassment but just answer what the child asks, will manage sex education in a very satisfactory manner.

A practical question may arise here in the minds of some readers. What will the child do with the information? Will he take it to the neighbor's children, shock them (or more precisely their parents) and get himself in disrepute? Practically, this rarely causes a problem. When the parents have told a child in a frank, calm, natural way, we have not known of any case where that child has gone out to try to impress the other children with his knowledge and thereby create an emotional disturbance in the neighborhood. The implication here is clear. When a child is answered simply and without embarrassment before his curiosity has grown out of bounds he will take it for granted that he has just learned one more fact and he does not feel the need to go out and display this knowledge. He does not mention it, because it is of no more importance than any other question he has asked that day and he has no special desire to impart this particular piece of information.

The child might handle the matter in another way. Children have a way of disregarding what they do not want to believe and letting it go at that. Sometimes parents are startled when they tell their children the truth about sexuality to find that the children tell them later that they do not believe that babies grow inside the mother but that the stork brings them. They do not choose to believe what they have heard from their parents and may not do so for some time. However, it is a wise idea for parents to have told the truth (when asked), because then the facts are there for the child to use when he is ready.

Moreover, if the child is the kind who is not yet ready to face the truth of sex at three or four years, then that child is not going to be a persistent questioner. Hence parents need not fear being troubled by the child's insatiable curiosity—that it is going to test their knowledge or ability to impart it within a short space of time. Actually parents who fail to accept their responsibility for imparting information to their children about sex and who rationalize their neglect by saying the child is too young are merely being childish themselves and obeying the old dictum of *their* parents, which was, "You must not tell those things," or "You must not talk about that nasty subject." If the child is not anxious and the parents' relationship to him is good, and if he continues as he grows older to ask about the problems of sexuality and where he comes from, then again we really mean that parents can tell the whole truth, calling the body organs by their names and telling the child what takes place. Following the answer, that he has grown inside the mother's body, the child may ask how he got there. Then the mother—for usually the mother and not the father has to answer these questions—has to say, "Well, the seed was put there by daddy."

This answer may suffice for some time, and if so, no more need be said. However, if the child should press for more information and ask, "How did daddy put it there?" it is up to the mother to explain the procedure of sexual intercourse—to say that the man's penis is put into the woman's vagina and that, in the course of that relationship, the sperm, or egg of the man, is deposited into the womb and there is united with the egg of the woman to grow into a new life.

Such a statement is not shocking to the child. Only certain adults have come to feel it is a shocking phenomenon to discuss because they were told and made to feel so. The child is prepared, or is eager and willing, to accept information without anxiety, without shame, without embarrassment, and he will do so if the parents do not convey these unfortunate attitudes along with their discussion of the matter. In other words, if a child of four or five questions the way a baby does grow in the woman's body and how the seed of the male is put in the woman's body, and if the mother tells him, she does not have to respond by thinking later, "Gracious! What have I said?" She has merely told a truth which will *not* shatter her child's mind. He will simply store up the knowledge as he does other facts, and they will be in his mind for his use always. He is left free to go about his play or work without all the ruminations and preoccupations with sex which the children who do not get the facts from their parents have to struggle with. Often these children never have their curiosity satisfied no matter how much they read or how much experience they have. They are always seeking the truth about sex which they feel was withheld by the parents and spend a great deal of time in fantasies, and a great deal of emotion and energy in thought, trying to find the answer.

Sources of Sex Information

Children find it difficult to believe the stories they hear from other children. The stories are varying in many aspects, and even if they hear the true facts from other children, they would prefer to have them confirmed by the parents. All too often they have already been treated by the parents in such a manner that they dare not ask the questions that are going around in their minds. They feel the questions are bad, and that even if they are not reproached openly, they will have burdened the parent with an unwelcome subject. Consequently, they continue to struggle with piecing together what information they can from extra-parental channels, and they may never feel at ease with the truth about sexuality, even when they become adults. A great many of the problems that beset adolescents arise because they are using up too much energy, too much thought, too many fantasies and preoccupations with the question of sexuality which has never been properly handled at the right period; namely, the period we are discussing right now—the phallic period.

It seems clear from numerous case studies that many of the sex problems in adolescence are not due to the desire for sexual intercourse, nor to a great sexual hunger, but to a great unsatisfied sexual curiosity which could have been alleviated if the subject had been treated frankly and straightforwardly in childhood.

In some families the mother and father deal poorly with the child's curiosity—every phase of curiosity. Other families are willing to answer questions on every subject but specifically forbid those having to do with sexuality. For the sake of a more adequate personality and a better social adjustment and as a help in the prevention of neurosis, psychosis and psychopathic personalities, the subject of sex should be dealt with frankly by the parent.

Obviously, from what has been said, the idea of leaving a child ignorant of the subject until puberty and then taking him to the doctor to have a "good talk" is bad practice, is evading the issue, and is practically valueless, because when a child is forbidden to deal with the sex question up to twelve years and is then brought to the office of a relative stranger, he is not likely to talk about what he knows or what he wants to know or to ask or answer questions very intelligently. If the doctor rushes in and tries to "tell him all," the boy is not likely to be comfortable enough to take in and organize much of what is said. The whole setting is unnatural. The way for sexual information to be given is through as sincere and frank treatment of the subject *by the parents* as any other matter that arouses his curiosity during his growth and development. Moreover, when the sex question is dealt with in this way by the parents, it denotes to the child an acceptance of himself, an acceptance of his body and of the impulses of his body.

This is in line with what we said in the previous chapter about talking to the child about toilet training. We cannot in good sense and fairness disapprove of the child because he must excrete. We merely disapprove if he does not learn properly to control his excretions. So in the matter of sex we do not disapprove of the child because he has sex impulses. We merely ask him to accept a code of reasonable control of his impulses. Such a frank treatment of the subject tends to reduce the anxiety that people acquire about their body functions, particularly about sex and even about other body functions that have their sexual component.

Case histories indicate that information that is given to children about sexual matters and that is given early will not cause them to misuse the information or become sexually delinquent during grade-school years or during adolescence. Children do not misbehave by utilizing what they know nearly so often as they misbehave because of what they do not know. It is the unsatisfied curiosity to which we referred that causes so much of the sexual experimentations that go on during adolescence or that exerts its pull upon adolescents and makes parents suspicious that they are too interested in the subject.

Children are much calmer and more willing and able to accept a fair code of sexual behavior when they know the facts and when they get them from their parents at an early age. Out of gratitude for the information and out of the close relationship with the parents which is bound to occur when the young person is dealt with thus frankly, he as an adolescent is more likely to accept the values in behavior that the parent would like him to accept. It is not sexual information that leads to promiscuity or to the danger of illegitimate pregnancy or venereal disease. It is often, rather, the lack of proper information or of an altruistic code of behavior taught by friendly parents that leads to these results.

The Family Romance

It has been observed at this age period between three and six that children tend to be drawn emotionally toward the parent of the opposite sex and in a way that is erotically tinged. This is called the *Oedipus complex*—that much discussed concept of Freudian psychology. As a result of careful studies over a long period of time there is assembled ample proof that about the time the child is leaving the home and entering school he goes through the struggle of a minor love affair—with the mother if the child is a boy and with the father if the child is a girl. Some suggest that this is due to a sexual glandular activity in children. Others tend to discount this possibility and say that sexual glandular activity does not start until puberty. However, something is present within each sex which we have to call, for the time being, biological, and which draws the sexes toward each other.

Manifestations of this phenomenon can and do take place as early as the genital period which we are discussing. The boy talks about being in love with his mother, about wanting to marry his mother and, because of his feeling for her, wanting her attention to the exclusion of other members of the family. He is acting like an adult lover and has a corresponding ambivalence toward his father, partly because of this interest and feeling for his mother, and partly because his father is standing in his way and being, at the same time, a disciplinarian. In the same way the girl is drawn toward her father, courts his interest and seems to seek to be his favorite. Also, in a corresponding way, she resents the mother and feels a hostility toward her for being in the way of her complete possession of the father.

When the reader accepts such a situation, he can see that it needs to be understood and handled carefully by the parents, since there is a tendency for some persons to remain in love with their parents indefinitely, and thus never quite to be able to free themselves, or to become interested in a person of the opposite sex, or to get any idea of marriage and home formation of their own. Almost everyone knows of a woman who lives at home with her father—either with the mother being on the scene or not—who keeps house for him and has never taken any interest in another man and who continues to be emotionally incapable of marriage because her emotional ties to her father are so strong she may quite consciously say that she never found anyone else good enough. In such a case, incidentally, the father may have helped her in this belief. He may have been intrigued by the interest and affection of his daughter and have sought to keep his hold on her. He may have found it convenient to have her devotion and attention and never to have tried to direct her desires toward a home of her own; he may have encouraged this emotional relationship which we call the Oedipus complex.

We all know men, too, who are caught in the same dilemma, who have emotional ties to their mothers which they cannot break or relinquish. They do not marry, or if they do, they have an unsatisfactory marriage because they are trying to be a lover to two women—the wife and the mother. The result usually is that such a man satisfies neither woman and is himself in great conflict.

This emotional bond between the parent of the opposite sex and the child has its first manifestation around this genital period. It has a sexual erotic basis and many ramifications, which we will see as we go along and which make it a most important phase of human development, warranting our close study and thought. It derives its name from a Greek myth concerning Oedipus, the son of Laius, king of Thebes. It was prophesied that the boy would grow up to kill his father, whereupon, to avert the tragedy, he was given by his father to a shepherd with instructions that he was to leave the boy on the mountain to die. The shepherd, instead, gave the child to the king of another realm where he grew to manhood and eventually met his real father and, being unaware of his identity, slew him in a quarrel. Oedipus eventually returned to the land of his birth and, in return for solving a riddle, was given the queen, his mother, to wife. Still unaware of the identity of his real parents, he lived with his mother for a time as man and wife. When he finally learned the truth, in his guilt he put out his eyes, and his mother hanged herself. He later was destroyed by the avenging deities. The theme of guilt and tragedy associated with incest has carried the name of Oedipus and is applied to the ubiquitous presence of the emotions surrounding the family romance.

In this family romance the boy with his instinctual drive and his conformity with the social pattern talks and thinks in terms of marrying his mother and of excluding his father. In the same way, the girl talks and thinks in terms of marrying her father, or being his wife and having a baby by him. Are there many readers who have never heard small children make statements such as this? If they have not, the facts can easily be verified by listening a little more closely to the conversation of small children for a while. A boy of five recently came downstairs in the morning after his father had been away on a two-day trip. He was hurt and annoyed to find the father there, and he started to cry, saying, "You aren't supposed to be eating with my mummy. She is just for me. You go away again." It took considerable reassurance on the part of the mother to quiet him and to get him to accept the fact that she could love them both enough for his happiness.

Another child of four and a half years we know insisted one night that he sleep in his father's bed in the same room with the mother while the father sleep elsewhere in the house. Some fathers find it difficult to acquiesce to such a high-handed attack upon their importance and authority; but on the occasional times that the boy or girl does show intense feeling of this kind over the family romance, it is well for them to forget their dignity and concentrate on the fact that the child is going through a critical and emotional conflict that needs help. To give in to these momentary needs of the child is to promote an understanding that will bring about the best kind of co-operation later, while to discipline or reprove the child at the time he is suffering jealousy can bring about an obedience only at the price of sullenness and resentment. The parent who realizes that these ideas and thoughts are going on in the child's mind is in a better position to help the child to a solution of the problems they create than if he were not aware of them. The solution of these ideas has to be reached in one of two ways, either by repression or by redirection.

Repression is the ejection out of consciousness into a hypothetical area or realm of the mind of those ideas and feelings that are not acceptable to the conscious ego. The most frequent way in which a great number of the problems of childhood are settled is by repression, by this forcible ejection into the unconscious.

Another and better way, of course, is by what is called a "working through." This can be defined as a rearranging and reassembling of ideas and emotions so that they become acceptable to the ego or become redirected away from the parent to other persons and other activities in the environment.

We want the reader to understand as clearly as possible the difficult problem that both the girl and boy encounter in the Oedipus complex and its eventual solution. To a varying degree the boy naturally fears his father's disapproval, anger and, possibly, punishment because of his ideas and feelings toward his mother. In the average family setting the mother is usually generous and giving, while the father is more the disciplinarian. This love relation between the boy and his mother gradually comes to be broken up by the presence of the father and by the fear of his disapproval, anger or punishment. Among the punishments that are feared by the child for manifesting the ideas inherent in the Oedipus complex is the threat of harm to the genitals specifically. Thus the boy finally renounces his mother as a love object; he gives up the idea of supplanting his father in her affections and redirects his energy toward those persons in the environment who are available. The child is usually in school at this age period. There he enters into play with his chums and at home with his brothers and sisters, if he has any, and contents himself with their companionship, giving up the hope of being the mother's lover.

At this point, the boy's feelings toward his father are mixed. He is, of course, ambivalent toward him. He does not want to give up the feeling he has for his mother but if the father is a reasonably kind man and a reasonably desirable character, the boy decides, in the solution of the Oedipus complex, that since he cannot depose his father, he will imitate him, he will be like him, with the hope, thereby, that some day he will be able to marry like his father and enjoy the many privileges he enjoys. The kinder the parents are, and the more aware they are of this family romance, the easier it is for children to solve the Oedipus conflict without too many difficulties.

Masturbation and Psychosexual Development

Masturbation is another phenomenon that occurs during the genital period. Masturbation is simply the act of manipulating the genital organs in order to produce pleasure. *It is a universal and normal phenomenon to human growth and development.* We want to stress the universal and normal aspect of this phenomenon because a great many people feel that there must be some harm in any kind or degree of masturbation at any age. The very word masturbation frightens, disgusts or disturbs many people. Yet psychiatrists, psychologists, teachers and educators who have made a serious study of personality development agree that masturbation is merely a normal and universal phenomenon of human development; in fact, they agree further that it is a necessary phenomenon to a satisfactory psychosexual development. Before the end of the first year, children discover that the genital area is sensitive to touch and capable of pleasurable responses. For this reason the child will play with himself in that zone at various times.

Masturbation tends to increase in intensity during two periods of the child's life: the first is during the genital period and the second is at puberty when the sexual glands become active and endocrine secretion of the sexual glands gives an added impetus to the sexual part of the personality. A mother may say that her child never masturbated. This cannot be true. The statement appears authentic to this mother because she was so disturbed and frightened and unhappy over the idea of masturbation that when her child was very young and attempted manipulation of his genitals, for the first few times she may have frightened him so severely as to have killed any further attempt at masturbation, or at least prevented his doing it again *in her presence*. Therefore, she can honestly say from what she has seen of her child's behavior that he has never played with himself. However, when we question mothers who are able to answer honestly because they are not afraid to face the fact of masturbation, we find that it is a universal practice for children of both sexes to play with themselves genitally and that they will do so more or less and from time to time. In various degrees masturbation is a normal phenomenon from the first year of life up to the time a marital relation is established.

Let us speak a little about the meaning of masturbation and what our attitude can be toward it. What should be done to control it, or direct it, or have it fit in with the personality in order that it does not become either a personal or a social problem? The problem of masturbation can be compared to the problem of drinking. For some people drinking is never a problem. They drink with dignity and restraint. In the same way, for a great many people masturbation is not a problem. They indulge in it occasionally, but they never worry about it; they have no excessive mental conflict about it; it does them no physical harm, and as a piece of behavior it fits satisfactorily into their whole personality structure. However, masturbation can become excessive and can become a pathological manifestation of an underlying personality difficulty.

We feel that the attitude toward masturbation should be one of considering that the child is a pleasure-seeking animal who seeks pleasure from various sources and who, finding it in masturbation, may pursue it to too great a degree if he is not receiving sufficient affection from the people in the environment and if his energies are not being directed into other channels. If those in the environment make the child feel happy and contented, if they see that he has companions and toys to play with, he will not gravitate toward any excessive degree of masturbation.

He will curtail his indulgence for much the same reason that he learns to control his bowels and bladder, for the same reason that he eventually learns to eat three meals a day instead of demanding to eat at any time or at all times. He learns that his parents do not approve of masturbation being indulged in too frequently or too indiscriminately and so he follows the pattern of behavior of which they approve. He is helped to put his interest in other things and to find pleasure and approval in them and hence he has relatively little urge to seek a pleasure in and on himself, a pleasure that does not have parental approval.

If a parent sees a child of two or three masturbating he should consider the child's behavior a signal of inner tension and a need for affection and for someone to draw his interests into wholesome activity which will give libidinal gratification. Therefore, it would be an indication for the parent to show an interest in him and direct his activity into some other channel and to do this without scolding, without reproof. It is enough for the parent merely to indicate that he does not entirely approve of what the child is doing and that he would approve more of his doing something else. By using a calm, friendly manner in directing the child's mind away from masturbation the parent will succeed in preventing a fixation of interest in this particular activity.

The child will still masturbate enough to further his psychosexual development. During the genital period the child's romantic interest in the parent of the opposite sex acts as an extra stimulus to excite him, or her, sexually. For this reason masturbation is more frequent at this time, and the mother needs to have an unusual amount of patience and tolerance. Also, she has to realize that the child is going through a special phase of excitation and she has to help him put a great deal of interest in his recreation and she may, at times, even have actively to discourage him from the habit of playing with himself and say, "Everyone will not understand your doing that as we do. Even though it won't hurt you it doesn't look well and you may be criticized."

If the relationship between the mother and child has been good up to this time, and if the mother realizes that this is just a phase he is going through, then the child will come through the genital period without becoming a frequent or "chronic" masturbator. When the psychic energy remains attached to a phenomenon of psychosexual development instead of passing on to a more mature and socially accepted expression, we term such a condition a *fixation*. Individuals may remain fixated at the autoerotic stage of psychosexual development and remain self-centered, seeking pleasure in their own activity or in fantasy rather than in a warm emotional relationship with others. Persistent and excessive masturbation can be a phenomenon of this process if parents foster such fixation by condemning the habit of masturbation rather than by lovingly helping him to go through the difficult period of socialization. Parents who are very much distressed about masturbation may tell the child that he is wicked, that he is doing something dirty and shameful, that he will ruin his health, that he will make himself feeble-minded, that the practice will harm his heart, that it will give him tuberculosis. They may threaten to mutilate the child's organ, a threat more frequently made against the boy than the girl. Such parents often say and do a great deal to scare the child out of what they consider a nasty habit and not a normal phenomenon of development.

We must remind the reader again that the world of the child is still very small at this age and that what the father and mother say is law. When the mother, father and other grown-up persons in the household tell a child over and over that the thing he is doing is wicked, shameful, dirty or will harm his health indefinitely, they put an idea into his mind that may be a most painful burden for him to carry all his life. The number of mentally sick people in the hospitals of the United States always outnumbers that of any other disease. When we talk with mentally sick people whose minds have grown troubled, we find frequently that one of their most common, torturing beliefs is that they have committed unpardonable sins or that they have injured their health irreparably through self-abuse.

We need not consult such troubled people but merely question a cross section of the student body of any college to learn that fears of the harm of masturbation linger all too long. Often unconsciously and in an honest and well-meaning attempt to curb or cure what they felt to be an innate weakness and "dirtiness" in the child, parents put lifelong ideas of inferiority and unworthiness into the minds of people when they were children going through the genital period. That kind of education is wrong during this age period; it is almost always harmful and should not be carried out.

Masturbation does not produce nervous trouble, does not weaken the mind, does not weaken the body organs. In fact, we know of no harmful effects of masturbation other than the mental conflict engendered. In an average home where the parents and the child have a good understanding, the matter of masturbation can be accepted along with accepting the child's need to nurse, to suck, to evacuate, to eat, to ask questions, and that far from being any special problem it is one that responds as well as the others to the intelligent combination of gratification and direction. The adult who indulges in excessive masturbation has a neurotic problem and may be a little sick emotionally, but he is not harming himself by the act itself. The question that should concern the doctor in any case of excessive masturbation is: why does the patient need to carry on this compulsive drive for pleasure in and on himself, why is his social adjustment not sufficiently satisfactory to give him enough pleasure without resorting to this particular practice?

If a parent is resourceful and can interest the child in many kinds of games and in playing with a number of other children, he will divert the child's attention from masturbation and make the problem much easier for him than if the problem is allowed to continue until the child becomes adolescent. The boy or girl in adolescence who is masturbating to excess is failing socially. He or she is unable to gain enough recognition in the classroom or to secure sufficient popularity in the dance hall or drawing room or wherever to achieve adequate prestige. Such a young person is lonely and unhappy. Life is not satisfying him; he is not getting sufficient pleasure in the outside world. Instead, he is falling back upon a pleasure in and on himself, and this is his personality problem. This person needs treatment for his social difficulty. Merely to say that he is doing himself harm is too limited a way of looking at his problem, and the statement is useless or even harmful to him.

Masturbation has at least two important aspects. In order to function sexually men and women need to have some feeling developed in the genital area. Masturbation is an aid in bringing feeling to that area and centering it in the sexual organs. Children who have been made to feel ashamed of the sexual desire that leads to masturbation and who have been made afraid of sexual feeling by having been threatened about injury will as a result repress and dam back upon themselves this feeling. By punishment and threat of injury for the practice of masturbation, the parent runs the risk that the grown woman will be frigid and the grown man impotent. The anxiety engendered in these frightened people becomes a barrier to the process of psychosexual development and hinders the process of the libido's becoming genitalized.

Furthermore, impotent men are a threat to the whole race, for if enough men became impotent, the race could not be carried on. Frigid women can, of course, have sexual relations and become pregnant, yet it is important for the race that they not be frigid. When women become frigid and do not allow themselves to have sexual feeling, there is a danger that they will be unhappy in marriage, or fail to have warm feelings toward their children, or both. They are also more prone to develop neurosis and psychosis; they have less to contribute emotionally to the marriage and their whole joy in living is reduced.

So if the sexual feeling that is struggling to express itself through the child's masturbation is dammed back and the development inhibited, that child will grow into a person with little interest in marriage, or one who, marrying reluctantly, will have a rather lukewarm interest in marriage and get an early divorce, or drift on through an unhappy married life, or suffer, after marriage, from frigidity or impotence. Thus serious problems arise from a too thorough and unrestrained condemnation of sexual feeling in the child. It is important that this restraining process not be started in childhood and that children not be frightened into a state of stagnation in their sexual development. Such treatment will inhibit not only their ability to procreate children but also, to a varying degree, their buoyancy and enthusiasm for life in every sphere; it will suppress that part of their personality which would lead to a happy home and family.

Many people by the time they reach thirty or thirty-five become discouraged and fed up with living; they wonder what they are living for and find little joy in any activity. They are not working for any person of the opposite sex, and their interest in life and persons generally is greatly diminished through having been inhibited so thoroughly in their sexual development. This can come about *partly* at least by the wrong treatment of masturbation either before the genital period or during it. No modern psychiatrist would say that masturbation causes frigidity in women or impotence in men. The difficulty has arisen over too much attention having been directed toward the supposed evils of masturbation and at the same time disregarding the evils of the social maladjustment which was setting in when the excessive masturbation arose. Excessive masturbation in a child or an adult always arises in a somewhat pathological setting. What we want the reader to see in these cases is the pathological setting and not exclusively, in a too shortsighted way, a pathology in masturbation itself.

Anxieties Associated with Masturbation

Threats that are given to children concerning masturbation may give rise to an emotional attitude described as the *castration complex*. A *complex* is an emotionally toned group of ideas. The castration complex merely means that there has been implanted in the child a fear that something may happen to his genital organ, a fear that has important results for the male. The female, too, has a castration complex, though its results for her are somewhat different. The female's distress is over the feeling that since she has no penis she has already been castrated. She may feel that her mother cheated her out of the penis at birth or that she once possessed it and lost it through some act of "naughtiness."

It should be quite easy to see why a child who is threatened horribly about injury to his genitals should have a castration complex. Anyone who gives much thought to the worries of the small child can imagine the pain of the female child struggling alone with the fact of her anatomical defect. Physicians do not need to be in medical practice long to encounter men who can remember that their parents threatened to cut off the penis or to do it some harm, or women who feel bitterly that "men have all the advantages." The idea that the penis might be lost through some measure taken by the outside world is reinforced in the male child when he sees the female child and realizes that she does not have this organ. Then he thinks the same thing may happen to him.

We may have to ask the reader's tolerance in discussing these things and putting forth these ideas. We realize that many people are skeptical about such ideas going through a child's mind. Children are naïvely regarded as being always gay, happy, innocent little things who play with their toys and dolls. They are not regarded as being concerned with the problems of sex, with worrying about these anatomical differences, or with being envious of each other. Actually they are. Children do a great deal of talking about these matters and actually get little help from grownups, but the sexual problems of the child are very important to him.

It is an interesting fact that while the tolerant and enlightened mother sees outward manifestations of the ideas that are going on in the child's mind, the intolerant and unenlightened mother does not notice them. The frightened mother senses something of her child's questioning attitude, but she tries hard to silence him in an effort to dislodge the ideas and get them out of his mind, as she thinks; at any rate she believes she can make a better person of him if she can prevent him from putting the inquiries into words. In sum such a mother thinks she has settled the matter by ignoring it, but instead, she has merely left the child to ruminate by himself, to settle all these questions by himself or with the aid of the misinformations of other children. Some mothers refuse to see and help their children with these problems; others accept the problems and hear them but do not know how to help; still a smaller group *do* see and *do* try to help the children.

Sex Problems of Girls

The problem of castration fear is very real and comes in some way or other into the life of every child, male or female. To some it comes very strongly; to others less so. Little may be said in the home about the danger of castration, yet there are very few male children who grow up never having heard stories or ideas passed around by some other boys. The female tends to be quite concerned about the fact that she does not have a genital organ like the male, her feeling about it arousing a state called *penis envy*. On seeing boys, little girls feel jealous of the fact that they have this "extra" tissue in the form of the phallus. More than that, the girls are jealous of the extra prerogatives which being male gives to the boys. There is no question but that having a penis gives the man certain privileges in our society. We do not know many women who do not resent this fact in one way or another, for which they can hardly be blamed.

We want to stress the point that the child does go through certain anxieties, doubts and questions concerning these differences in anatomy and that they are the source of considerable anxiety to him. They stimulate questions in his mind that should be answered by the intelligent parent. Obviously, for the girl who feels that the boy has more privileges than she the obvious procedure is to state the truth to her in no uncertain terms. She should be told that she has sexual organs as good as those of the male, but that they are of a different kind; she should be told that she can have as much pleasure out of life as the boy, despite external differences; that she can grow up and play the role of being a mother, that she can produce a child, which he cannot, which is one of the compensations for being a woman.

Up to the present time female children have had far too little help with their emotional problems, especially those beginning at this age. With the boy it would be enough to refrain from frightening him because he is usually proud enough of himself and already getting enough out of life. However, in order to make the female satisfied with herself a definite explanation about the reasons for anatomical differences in the sexes should be made, and as early as she shows concern about them. This will be during the genital or phallic phase of development, if not before. Surely it will not be later to the mother who intelligently observes her children.

BIBLIOGRAPHY FOR CHAPTER V

Freud, Sigmund, *Three Contributions to the Theory of Sex*, Nervous and Mental Disease Publishing Co., 1930.

Chapter VI

EMOTIONAL DISTURBANCES THAT OCCUR DURING THE PHALLIC PERIOD

THE PSYCHOLOGICAL illnesses of childhood fall into two groups—fancied illnesses and real illnesses. This distinction is not made on the basis of the child's condition, but on the parent's reaction to it. This is true of all age levels, but particularly true of the child in the phallic period. As has been mentioned in the last chapter, a child's behavior during the phallic period and particularly during the struggle with his feelings to his parents is not very conforming, and is often very annoying to them. He is frequently negativistic, obstinate, stubborn, disobedient and antagonistic. He has temper tantrums and nightmares. The adult who has lived with a child through this period will remember that neither his life nor the life of the child was entirely happy.

Some parents, particularly those who want a good, conforming child who will be a credit to them, regard these manifestations of the child's normal development as abnormal and consult the physician or psychiatrist about them. The only therapy desirable is to review the whole family constellation, including the child's behavior, and if everything seems to be normal to inform the parents of this and to instruct them in the kind of behavior which they may anticipate during these years.

In order to understand the real emotional illnesses of the phallic period and of the period of latency it is necessary to discuss what causes psychological illness in children. The child has certain needs, which may be summarized as follows:

1. He needs the security and backing of two present parents.

2. He needs their love and understanding.

3. He needs an optimum period of gratification for his infantile sensual desires. (This is an optimum period. It should not be too curtailed nor should it be allowed to continue too long. If it is too brief he suffers too much painful anxiety when it comes to an end. If it is too prolonged he does not learn how to tolerate anxiety, and when the gratification necessarily has to end, the amount of anxiety experienced is too great. A

child has to learn how to tolerate anxiety but he has to learn this through minute doses.)

4. He needs to have opportunities to express his hostilities, antagonisms and aggressiveness in order that he learn what these feelings are like and how to deal with them efficiently. All children during the period of infancy develop three fears—fear of being deserted, of not being loved and of being punished by horrible mutilations. If the reader doubts the presence of these fears as part of childhood he should try to explain why most little children cry when their parents go out for the evening, why a child has a panic when he is lost and why he has a panic when he is about to be punished by whipping. (In regard to the last mentioned fear the reader must realize that the average child is not really very cowardly, that he has been spanked before, and that in the majority of instances the previous spanking did not really hurt and that therefore he knows it will not be worse this time.)

Anything that occurs that prevents the effective satisfaction of needs or that increases the fears mentioned above will have a deleterious effect on the development of the child's personality and is likely to produce an illness. Such occurrences are known technically as traumatic events, i. e., events that are injurious. They can be grouped into three classes: (1) acts of fate, (2) adverse parental attitudes, and (3) exposure to premature and excessive sexual stimulation.

ACTS OF FATE

We have discussed in the previous chapter why the child needs the security and backing of the visible presence of two parents—a father and a mother—in order to solve the problem of his conflicting feelings toward them. What happens to the child if one parent is absent because of death, marital separation, or separation through the necessity of patriotism or business? Since there are two parents and since their sex and the sex of the child all affect the result, it seems desirable to consider five forms of the problem:

1. The effect on the boy of the absence of the father.
2. The effect on the boy of the absence of the mother.
3. The effect on the girl of the absence of the mother.
4. The effect on the girl of the absence of the father.
5. The effect on either boy or girl of separation from both parents.

The Effect on the Boy of the Absence of the Father

The small boy needs the visible presence of his father for two reasons: he needs a male person to imitate and he needs a masculine foil with whom he can learn how to temper and exercise his feelings of aggression and love, for the adult male's main difficulties of adjustment lie in his relationships with other persons of the same sex. The presence of a visible father is most necessary during the period from birth to the age of six or seven, is less necessary but still very important during the latent period, and is much less important though still desirable during adolescence. In adult life the man derives pleasure from the fact that he has a father, though there is no imperative need for his existence.

If a boy is brought up in a fatherless home he suffers from the fact that he has no father to imitate. The word imitation is used here loosely to express a phenomenon more properly designated as *identification*. The small boy loves his father and because of this love he desires to be exactly like him, i. e., to do, think and feel exactly as the father does. In his daily life he automatically observes his father very closely. He is not really aware that this observation is going on, but he soon finds himself behaving or attempting to behave exactly like the father. This reaction is so automatic that the child is unaware that it takes place and when confronted with the fact will often be quite surprised. (The automaticity of the process is one of the reasons for the prevalent belief that the child behaves like the father because he has inherited his traits.) If there is no father present with whom the boy can identify, this process does not take place and the boy is deprived of the advantage of having at his disposal the useful reaction patterns which the father has developed from his life experiences for solving his conflicts, and which have contributed to his success.

This is a complicated way of stating a simple and well-known fact: that the boy who is brought up in a fatherless home is deprived of the benefit of his father's knowledge of the world and of life. He can identify with his mother but this identification is not very helpful to the *boy*. His mother has learned about life and the world only from the point of view of a female and because of her feminine needs and desires. Such a viewpoint is of little benefit to the male person, for masculine ways of thinking and feeling are different from feminine ones and vice versa. Therefore the boy who has been deprived of the visible presence of his father has to meet life with little real knowledge of how other men think and feel and so is at a constant disadvantage. Though he has not been deprived of the greater part of his ability to think and feel in a masculine fashion, since this ability rests on an instinctual basis, he is deprived of the cultural accentuation that produces its precision and definiteness.

The lack of a father with whom to identify works a deeper psychological harm on the boy than the difficulty in thinking and feeling definitely in a masculine way. The boy identifies with the father because he loves him. He would like to be his father. In order to accomplish this he will have to get rid of the father. But his love protests against this solution and impels him to a better one. He must not *be* his father and have and do *exactly* as his father does but he can become *like* his father and have and do things the way his father does, but in other situations and with other persons. By the identification with his father he learns to renounce through love for another person the uncultured methods of gratification for his needs and desires, realizing that such renunciation still permits him their gratification and does not expose him to the anxiety that would be his lot if they could not be gratified. This is important because the whole structure of civilized society is built on this renunciation, because of love for other persons, of a method of obtaining gratification, not of the gratification itself.

When a boy is brought up in a fatherless home there is no possibility of this renunciation through identification taking place nor is there any need for it, because there is no father to love. The boy feels he possesses his mother. He feels that she will gratify him completely and therefore feels no need to look for his gratification elsewhere. Even if she will not gratify him completely now he believes that if he waits long enough she will. Gratification, therefore, is his by right and he does not need to procure it through his own efforts. There is no day-by-day struggle between his jealousy, love and fear of his father through which he learns gradually and somewhat painfully how to compete successfully. When he reaches the age when the social situation and reality demand that he compete, if he wishes to continue to live successfully, he is baffled and helpless because he has never learned how to do so. There is no possibility of real gratification for him and so he is overwhelmed with anxiety. If he attempts to abolish the anxiety he acts in a fumbling, ineffectual, unsocial manner which gets him into trouble, and now this further pain is added to his suffering of anxiety.

Often the mother contributes to the boy's difficulty. She is deprived of a husband and she may try to make up to herself for her own deprivation by trying to obtain her gratification from her son. The reader will be able to supply from his observations many examples of such doting mothers and spoiled sons.

A result as serious, if not more so, follows when the father dies during the height of the boy's Oedipus conflict. The boy is jealous of his loved father, hates and fears him and wishes he would die. He believes that his wishes are magical and will avail where his actions would fail. If his wishes were effective, he thinks, then life would be paradise. His father dies at the height of these feelings. He finds that the result is the opposite of what he expected. During the period of the funeral the dead father is more the center of attention than he was before. No one pays much attention to the little boy. The mother is consumed with her own grief and has little real time for the child. If he has a wish or discomfort that he feels needs attention she will attend to it but perfunctorily.

After the funeral the mother is still unhappy and concerned with her loss and does not give him all the happiness he anticipated. He often finds that he does not have as many material benefits as before because there has been a change in the financial situation. Formerly when the mother was busy or withdrawn for any reason, he could turn to his father for pleasurable activities. Now there is no father to play with, to tell him stories, or to bring him gifts. He comes quickly to realize that this event has brought him pain rather than pleasure. He remembers that he wished it to take place and that at the time he was irritated that his wishes did not act magically quickly enough. These aggressive wishes were the cause of his father's death but instead of bringing him pleasure and gratification they brought exactly the opposite. Therefore aggressive wishes are very powerful and result in suffering. Henceforth he must never permit aggressive wishes of any sort. Every time he has an aggressive impulse, which would appear in his consciousness as an aggressive wish, he must put it out of his mind. In fact it would be better if it never appeared there at all.

How can he keep such wishes away? If his father had punished him for the wish as soon as it appeared the magical wish would not have caused the catastrophe, his father would still be alive and he would be happier. Perhaps he can learn to punish himself for such wishes, or better still perhaps he can learn to experience a small amount of suffering to warn him that an aggressive wish is about to appear, and thus be able to kill it in the bud. He develops an immense feeling of guilt about any aggressive feeling or impulse; and because success in life (whether in the realm of sexuality or ambition) depends on the proper and adequate exercise of aggression, he later on finds himself failing constantly.

These disturbances of development follow the death of the father. As death to the young child is only a prolonged separation, the disturbances also follow the permanent absence of the father due to marital separation. Even when the separation is not permanent but long continued (i. e., when the father is away from home for long periods due to business, or during time of war due to patriotism), the effect on the boy is the same although perhaps not so marked. It is less marked, although still present, when the father is often away from home for periods of several days at a time.

It can be seen that separation from the father constitutes a definitely injurious situation in the boy's development. We wish to point out that these reactions of the child may continue into adult life if nothing is done about the situation. If, however, other events occur in his life which make up for his deprivation or if circumstances provide a substitute father the effect of the trauma is not so long lived.

The Effect on the Boy of the Absence of the Mother

From a practical point of view the absence of the mother is not so serious an injury to the small boy as the absence of the father. We have never seen a boy who was brought up in a completely motherless home, although we have seen many cases where the home had no father. Some mother substitute—a housekeeper, an aunt, or an older sister—is always present, so the boy is exposed to intimate personal relationships with some woman. Arguing from what happens when a girl is brought up in a completely fatherless home we suppose that if the boy were raised completely isolated from women there is a probability that he would develop into an adult homosexual. Any long-continued separation from the mother has a definite effect on the small boy. Since his relationship with the mother is different from that with the father, the effect is bound to be different. The mother is the main love object of the small boy and so separation from her will affect his erotic relationships more than his aggressive, ambitious ones.

This will show itself in two directions. The very small child, whether girl or boy, slowly gives up his infantile methods of obtaining gratification and proceeds forward in his development because he feels certain of his mother's love. If she leaves him he regards her leaving not from the point of view of the real cause (which usually has nothing to do with him at all) but as an indication that she does not love him. When this realization strikes home his development immediately ceases. Instead of being willing to do for others he begins to demand that everything be done for him. Instead of being as free from fears as it is possible for a small child to be, he becomes increasingly fearful. Instead of wanting to dress, feed and bathe himself he acts as if he were unable to perform these routines and must have them done for him. He seems unable to walk as well as he had and makes demands to be carried. His speech becomes more babyish. If he had ceased to suck his fingers, the habit starts again. If he had been toilet trained he may begin to wet or soil himself either during the day or at night. He has temper tantrums more frequently. He develops a feeding difficulty. He whines and cries a great deal, seems unhappy and constantly demands the attention of adults. In all of this behavior he is using every possible action to express a very simple feeling. He says in effect, "Dear mother, see I am only a very little baby. Please love me and stay with me."

This regressive demand for the mother's love is often seen in children. It is noticed in the older child when a new child is born in the family. It occurs when the mother dies, when she leaves the family because of marital disagreements, when she goes on a long trip, when she goes to work, or when the child is placed in a nursery school or in a camp. It lasts until the child makes a love relationship with another woman, i. e., until he finds a satisfactory mother substitute. When this occurs his development starts again.

Although from this point on the development may seem to proceed satisfactorily and even the memory of the separation from the mother seems to be forgotten, the memory of the pain of the interlude has only been repressed and, being repressed from consciousness, tends to become a governing factor in the child's future life. As he grows up he may tend to avoid having any close relationship with a woman. He has been hurt by the prototype of all women, therefore all women have a tendency to hurt men. Why should he put himself in a position where a woman can hurt him? (Witness the well-known reaction of the burnt child who dreads the fire. Technically the psychological mechanism underlying the behavior is known as *inhibition*.)

He falls in love with a woman and as soon as he is sure she loves him he deserts her or acts in such a way as to break her heart. Since he had been hurt by a woman he will now take revenge on this one. Sometimes after marrying a woman and treating her badly and then leaving her he marries again quite satisfactorily. It is as if having taken revenge on one woman he now can have a decent relationship with the sex. There are two psychological mechanisms underlying this behavior. The first is known technically as *displacement:* the individual having certain emotional reactions expresses them toward a person other than the real object. The second is known as *changing an instinctual drive into its opposite.* In the instance cited above, the child had to be passive in a very painful situation. He could overcome this pain by becoming active and inflicting the pain on another person; i. e., he changes passivity (one instinctual drive) into activity (its opposite). This mechanism forms one of the important reasons for children's play. A small child is taken to the dentist. He is frightened and perhaps hurt. He is compelled to sit quietly in the dentist's chair and has to force himself not to express any of his fear, resentment, or anger. When he comes home he will invariably take his younger brother, sit him in a chair and play that he is a dentist and the younger child the patient. In his activity he reacts off the emotional reactions engendered in the passive situation.

To continue, he may fall in love *only* with a woman who he is certain will desert him, who in the pursuance of her interests will be away from him a great deal, who is an invalid, or who has a serious physical condition from which he knows she will die shortly. It is as if he said, "In my first relationship with a woman I suffered much at her hands. Because I was little I was unable to react completely emotionally to the situation. If I can reconstruct a similar painful situation I will be able to react more fully and so feel less tense inside." This is the psychological mechanism of the *repetition compulsion,* which we see around us all the time disguised under the concept of fate. As one watches human beings one observes certain of them acting as if they were pursued by a malignant fate. Often the individual himself feels that fate is against him. This fate arises from an unconscious need to repeat an earlier painful situation in order to react fully to it. Its manifestations can be studied most clearly in the nightmares of a patient suffering from a traumatic neurosis.

The Effect on the Girl of the Absence of the Mother

Just as the boy's relationship with the father is the most important factor in his development during the Oedipus period, so is the girl's relationship with the mother her greatest problem. She will react to the mother's absence in somewhat the same way the boy does to the father's. Also because, as is the case with the boy, up to the beginning of the Oedipus situation the mother is the important parent, so will her reactions to the loss of the mother be to some extent similar to those of the boy when he loses the mother.

The Effect on the Girl of the Absence of the Father

When the small girl loses her father she may show the same types of reactions as were described for the boy who has lost his mother. She may tend to become too strongly attached emotionally to her mother because of the strength of the very early emotional relationship. This helps her to have few emotional reactions at the time of her separation from the father, and therefore regressive behavior is not so common as when the boy is separated from his mother. The effect of the separation is more likely to show itself later in life. She may become homosexual, as we stated might happen to the boy if he lost his mother and was brought up in a completely male environment.

The Effect on Either Boy or Girl of Separation from Both Parents

This will be a combination of all the reactions discussed above. The war has brought forcibly to our attention that separation from parents is an exceedingly traumatic experience for any child. It was learned in England that the child suffered more from being separated from his parents through the evacuation scheme than he did when he remained with them and underwent the experiences of the blitz. It seems that separation from the mother is more traumatic for small children than separation from the father. This, however, we believe to be only an immediate finding. The small child reacts immediately to separation from the mother. His reactions to separation from the father tend to go on under the surface and not to become evident for several years. We feel that in the near future we will be observing as many adverse reactions as a result of separation from the father (due to his military service) as we now observe as a result of separation from the mother. We must reiterate the fact that the child is not consciously aware of all his feelings in these situations nor of the relation between his feelings and his behavior. Neither does the adult in the reactions described above say to himself, "My mother deserted me, therefore I will take revenge by deserting another woman." The connections and motivations are unconscious and the individual is genuinely surprised when he finds out what is occurring beneath the surface of his conscious mind.

Since these effects are so deleterious on the child's psychological development, can anything be done to ameliorate them? We cannot prevent these situations from occurring because we never can hope to abolish death or marital disagreements. In fact, it seems to us to be the best of two bad choices, from the standpoint of the child, for the marital partners in an unhappy marriage to separate rather than to remain together for his sake. If they do the latter they are almost certain to come to regard the child as responsible for their unhappiness in the marriage and to take revenge upon him for it. The effect on the child will be better understood after we have discussed the effect on the child's development of adverse parental attitudes. We feel that when a child has been separated from one or both parents there will always remain a psychic scar which will affect his relationships, happiness and success to a greater or less extent. However the injuriousness of the effect can be ameliorated.

When the child is separated from a parent he passes through a period of mourning. We are not going to discuss the mechanisms and purposes of mourning here, but will do so later, in connection with adult mourning. The child's mourning has the same mechanisms and purposes as that of the adult but is often expressed differently. Children are less verbal and tend to use their vegetative and sensorimotor nervous systems rather than their psychological systems to express their emotions. A small child, if frightened, will soil himself, while the adult tends to feel frightened and to talk about his fear. Children often react to a mourning situation by regressive behavior, by disturbances of the gastrointestinal tract—vomiting, diarrhea, constipation, etc.—or by naughty behavior. These reactions may continue for several months or for the duration of the period of mourning. (In the adult it usually lasts about a year.)

The adult should abstain from scolding, punishing, or criticizing the child for these reactions. They are to be expected and should be accepted with kindness. Every attempt should be made to encourage the child to talk about the absent person, express all his feelings verbally, whether these feelings be love, resentment, or hatred. We know that this may put a great strain on the adult. The mother whose beloved husband has died may not like to hear her son express resentment of his father. The wife whose husband has deserted her may not like to hear her daughter eulogize her father. From the point of view of the development of the child, however, as much verbal expression as possible of the relationship with the absent parent will be helpful. A parent substitute should be provided as soon as possible. It is not as difficult to provide a father substitute if the father has died or deserted as it is when he is absent on a prolonged business trip or in military service. Such a parent substitute is imperative. The parent substitute must realize that it may take the child some time really to accept him and he must make every effort to win the child's love and confidence. The remaining parent must try not to make the child a substitute wife or husband.

These measures and the passage of time will be helpful for the child, but just as an exposure to tubercular infection renders a child potentially suspect for tuberculosis for some time, so does such a traumatic experience render the child potentially suspect for a neurosis. He should remain under skilled observation for many years. Careful observations should be recorded by his teachers particularly as to his reactions during the change from grammar school to junior high school and from junior to senior high school. If at any time he shows any evidence of neurotic symptoms, either overt or in his character reactions, he should be studied by a child psychiatrist, and, if deemed advisable by him, placed under treatment.

The Effect on the Child of Prolonged, Painful or Crippling Illness

Another act of fate that may seriously interfere with the child's development is the occurrence of frequent, prolonged, painful or crippling illnesses. In an unpublished study of restlessness in children, one of us found that in a great percentage of cases the beginning of neurosis in a child follows immediately after a prolonged illness or a succession of illnesses within a short period of time. When a child is stricken with a serious illness the parents become much disturbed by the fear that he will die or become permanently disabled. This fear results in an over-solicitous attitude. They come to the child if he makes the slightest complaint and tend to do for him anything he wants. As the child becomes convalescent he begins to recognize this solicitude and to exploit it. When he wants something he wants it right away and if his parents do not do it for him he will complain of feeling ill. His illness has given him the right to make demands and have them satisfied even when they are unreasonable. He resents any attempt to bring this situation of constant gratification to an end and feels that he is not loved if it does not continue. Eventually he may accept the reality of the situation and continue with his development, but a certain reaction pattern has been laid down.

Similarly the parents have developed a new reaction pattern. Their solicitude tends to continue even after the child is well and they become alarmed when he shows any slight symptom of illness. This reinforces the child's pattern. Often adults who have suffered a serious prolonged illness in childhood continue to show this pattern. If they meet a disappointment they react by becoming ill, often with much the same symptoms they had when they were ill in childhood. Illnesses that involve the lower gastrointestinal tract have a marked effect in this pattern on the small child. They are often accompanied by loss of sphincter control which has to be re-established after he recovers. This second period of toilet training makes the future development of the child difficult because he prefers to remain untrained, even at the expense of being sick.

Within the first year or two after the child enters school the American parent can count on his contracting a succession of infectious illnesses, ranging all the way from a series of colds (which all too frequently develop the sequelae of otitis media and mastoiditis) through mild attacks of measles, mumps, chickenpox, whooping cough, to more severe attacks of these same diseases and to scarlet fever (perhaps with the sequela of acute rheumatic fever), anterior poliomyelitis or encephalitis. Diphtheria should be a thing of the past owing to the efficacy of preventive inoculations.

Often the child will have three or four different illnesses in rapid succession, which will mean a period of several months when he is ill or convalescent and when his ordinary routine and that of the home are seriously interrupted. Such periods can result in the disturbances of emotional adjustment we have just mentioned. It would be most desirable if there were some way to prevent the occurrence of these illnesses, but up to the present, preventive medicine has not made the necessary discoveries. Theoretically their occurrence could be prevented by the maintenance of absolute isolation of the child from other children, and some overprotective parents attempt to do this, but the results to the child's emotional, intellectual and social development would be disastrous. For the present we have to depend on other measures to ameliorate the effects of school-bred cross infections.

Can this reaction be ameliorated? It seems to us that an essential part of the treatment of a child for a serious illness should lie in the management of his convalescence. Kindly, consistently and firmly he should be encouraged to derive pleasure from the things he can do for himself as he gets better, and the gratifications he obtains from being ill should be reduced to the absolute minimum. It seems better to err a little on the side of encouraging the child to do more than he is able.

A child who has suffered a painful illness in childhood may show a peculiar reaction later. He may act as if he were not subject to ordinary social customs and manners and may, without any feeling of guilt, do things which if done by the average person would overwhelm him with guilty feelings. This absence of guilt feeling comes about in the following way. The child has suffered great pain through no fault of his own. He has been punished without having committed any crime. Therefore he should have license to commit crimes without any punishment. It is as if he lived in the Middle Ages when through the expenditure of a certain sum of money (in the child we are discussing, through the submission to a certain amount of suffering) the individual could buy absolution for all sins he might commit in the next year or two. It would seem to us to be desirable to have a child see a psychiatrist after he recovers from a very painful illness in order to prevent the development of such difficult character reactions.

The child who suffers from an illness such as valvular disease of the heart, poliomyelitis, etc., which leaves him with a permanent defect is faced with a problem of reality in his adjustment. From that time on he no longer is like other children. He cannot do the things they do and therefore is really inferior to them. He is forced to compensate for this inferiority by developing other modes of obtaining success in life. Sometimes these compensations are socially acceptable, as when a child compensates for extremely defective vision by developing an acute sense of hearing. Sometimes they are not so desirable, as when a child compensates for a weak leg by making himself the leader of a delinquent gang or by giving up all physical and social activity and spending all his time reading and studying.

The degree of need to compensate, i. e., the amount of the feeling of inferiority, seems to depend more on the extent to which the defect wounds the pride than it does on the actual extent to which the defect interferes with the child's life. For example, a child reacts more strongly to a cosmetic defect, and to the parents' attitude toward the defect, if the parents baby the child because of the defect. From the time the parents are informed that the child's illness will result in a permanent disability they should begin to help him lead a life as close to normal as possible. The physician should carefully evaluate the child's capabilities and should inform the parents in detail what the child should be encouraged and permitted to do. Here again it is better to err on the side of allowing him to be a little too active than too inactive. The emphasis should be placed on what he can do rather than on what he cannot. Commiseration and maudlin sympathy are not only not helpful but are injurious. The child has the defect. He has to learn how to live with it and the physician, nurse and parent should do everything possible to attain that end.

Some time ago one of us reported a study of the effect of operations on the child's development. Limitations of space prevent a full discussion of this subject here, but we feel it important to quote our conclusions:

Surgeons are well aware that operative procedures are associated with surgical shock, which is at times of serious import and which is more common after some operations than others. The cases I have presented illustrate that operative procedures are associated also with psychic shock in all children. This psychic shock stimulates the child's imagination, and the imaginative concepts increase the degree of the shock. To this shock the child reacts by attempting to rid himself of his fear, either by attacking its cause or by running away. Since neither reaction in childhood can furnish an adequate motor response to the sensory stimuli, the child is forced to deal with the shock by repression which results in changes in his behavior and in his personality reactions.

Verbalization by the child of his ideas and feelings about the operation helps the motor response to be more adequate, but its inadequacy is increased if the child is not told that the operative procedure will be carried out, if he is not informed of its real nature or if he does not have the opportunity to discuss the products of his imagination about the operation and have them corrected by someone whom he trusts. If an outlet is denied, the operative shock affects his behavior and his reaction patterns in the future, although after a while it may be difficult to recognize the connection between the child's behavior and character and the operation.

Physical shock shows its effects immediately. Emotional shock may not express itself openly for some time. Therefore it is highly important that the physician and the parents of a child who is scheduled to undergo an operation inform him accurately concerning what is going to happen and what he will feel. After the operation the child should be helped to verbalize to the fullest extent his ideas about and his emotional reactions to the operation. *Such complete verbalization is the crucial procedure which pre-*

vents the development of excessive emotional reactions. His ideas should be listened to carefully, and only after he has expressed them completely and in detail should any attempt be made to correct the errors of his imagination. His ideas should not be spurned, scorned or ridiculed.

Even before an emergency operation, some attempt is made to determine the physical ability of a child to survive the shock of the operative procedure. Such an evaluation is always made before an operation which is not done as an emergency, and in many cases if the child's ability to tolerate the procedure is not satisfactory the operation is postponed until his resistance has been raised. If the value of the operative procedure is dubious, it usually will not be attempted at all if the child's condition is unfavorable. Just as physical shock may result in death, so emotional shock may result in a lifetime of unhappiness; consequently, it seems valid to apply the same rules to determining the ability of the child to adjust to the emotional shock of the operation as are employed in evaluating his capacity to stand the physical shock.

If the operation is demanded by an emergency, to save the child's life, it must be performed, regardless of the emotional shock it may entail. However, such an emergency will seldom prevent one's telling the child that the operation is going to be performed and giving him an opportunity to verbalize his reactions after it takes place. If the history shows that the child has little capacity to tolerate anxiety, that is, that he has had unreasonable fears or other neurotic symptoms, then the operation should be followed by psychiatric treatment. If the operation is necessary but can be postponed for a little while without too great danger to the physical health and if a careful history reveals that the child already shows symptoms of neurosis or has suffered unusual traumatic experiences, such as deaths in the family, separations from his parents or exposure to adverse parental attitudes, treatment for the neurosis or study as to whether the child is reacting inadequately to the traumatic situations should be carried out before the operation. The introduction to the operation and the management during convalescence need more careful handling in the case of such a child than in that of a nonneurotic child.

If the history indicates that the child has undergone emotional trauma or that he at present is suffering from a neurosis, operations the value of which may be dubious should not be advised. There are many such operations, for example, circumcision because of masturbation, cytoscopic examination because of bed wetting at night without any other signs of disease of the urinary tract, tonsillectomy for enuresis, circumcision or tonsillectomy because of nervousness or fears, administration of drugs by injection (which could just as well be given orally) because of nervousness or fears in a child who shows some slight deviation from normal in laboratory tests. For such a child treatment of the neurosis is the necessary procedure, and although the symptoms may cease as a result of such operation, their use may be followed eventually by a more serious neurotic condition which may be reflected in malformation and defects of character.

We conclude therefore that:

operations on children produce emotional shocks and therefore should be performed only if absolutely necessary.

The degree of the shock to the nonneurotic child may be lessened by explaining in detail before the operation what will be done and how he will feel as a result, by giving him an opportunity to express his emotional reactions to the operation and by allowing him to verbalize his ideas concerning the operation after it has taken place.

If the child already suffers from a neurosis or has been exposed to situations which would increase anxiety, he should not be operated on without treatment for his neurosis except as an emergency. Such a child should never be subjected to operative procedures for the relief of neurotic symptoms, for the value of such treatment is extremely dubious.

The whole subject of the effect of physical illnesses on the emotional life of the child and his future development is one that has not been investigated fully or carefully enough to date. As a result of such investigations we hope for the day when the physician will be as aware of the necessity for dealing with the psychic life of the child during his illness as he is of the need to deal with his physical condition.

The Effect on the Child of the Birth of a Sibling

Any change in a child's circumstances tends to have a traumatic effect on his development. It is interesting to observe that the child reacts adversely even to a change of residence. We once saw a child of less than a year whose digestion was greatly upset for nearly a week because the family had moved to a new house. A boy of seven immediately after the move to a new neighborhood had nocturnal enuresis for two nights. We believe that the traumatic effects of these moves are reduced greatly when the whole question of the move is discussed openly before the child, when he knows precisely what is going on and is allowed to participate in and express his opinion about the move. We believe also that the traumatic effects of all changes in the child's life—separation from parents, deaths, illnesses, the birth of new brothers and sisters—would be reduced if there were a similar full and free discussion of them before and with the child.

It is the traumatic effect of the birth of a new sibling in the family that we wish to discuss now. The child resists change; i. e., he is disturbed by anything that will deprive him of his accustomed modes of gratification or by anything he thinks will deprive him of them. He reacts to this inner feeling of discomfort by feeling antagonistic and annoyed with the source of his deprivation. When a new baby is born in a family the older child in reality is deprived of a certain amount of the parents' time and attention. So much is being done for the new baby that the older child, contrasting the much smaller amount now being done for him, feels he is being deprived more than he really is. There is no question, however, that in many instances the parents are really more interested in the new baby and tend by their every action to demonstrate this to the older child. The older child reacts to this feeling of deprivation by strong feelings of jealousy.

If he is very young he may show his jealousy to the new baby by actually attacking him or trying to injure him. He may do the same if he is older, but is more likely to make derogatory remarks about him or to express wishes that he be sent away. If his parents object too much to his behavior or if he seems to feel guilty about his jealous feelings he may still express them but in a disguised form: the baby is bad, or he cries a lot and therefore should be punished, or the baby had his toys and therefore he has to hit him. (This is the psychological mechanism known technically as *defense through rationalization*.)

If the feeling of guilt is great he may seem to have no jealousy at all. He may appear to have no feeling for the baby except one of love and adoration. He wants to participate in all phases of the baby's care, but if he is allowed to do so it is almost certain that some accident will happen to the baby through his clumsiness. He thus can exercise his desire to hurt the baby (of which he may be unconscious) by denying it and feeling that he is too inept to do things properly. If his fear and guilt about his hostility are great he may deal gently, lovingly and carefully with the baby, but become a bully toward smaller children at school or in the neighborhood. (He displaces his hostility onto a different object.)

In all of these instances he is expressing his hostility to the baby. At the same time he may feel annoyed at his mother for daring to have another child. He may attack her physically or verbally, or he may refuse to give her any demonstration of affection; e. g., he may refuse even to kiss her again, as did one girl who from the birth of her brother when she was three years old never kissed her mother until she was twenty-four. He may pointedly be affectionate to other adults in her presence, often those whom he knows his mother dislikes. In this he says, "I won't love you, I will love people whom I know you dislike, because you don't love me any more." If he is too afraid or guilty about expressing this antagonism openly he may suddenly become naughty in his behavior toward his women teachers or other women who are in authority over him. (This again is a displacement.)

Instead of openly expressing his jealousy he may become demanding of his mother's love and attention—the attention she seems to be giving the new baby. He may develop a feeding difficulty. He may suddenly become timid and fearful. He may resort to childish speech. He may start to wet or soil himself again. He may recommence finger sucking. He may have frequent attacks of minor illnesses about which he makes great complaints. There will usually be a combination of these reactions which will last for a varying period of time until he has learned to adjust himself to the new situation. There is often the possibility that he will make his adjustment simply by repressing his reactions without solving his problems, and that these repressed reactions will continue to interfere with his ability to adjust to the numerous jealousy situations he will meet later.

How early does the jealousy reaction appear? We feel from numerous observations that it begins as soon as the child learns that his mother is pregnant. This is often as early as the second or third month. Little pitchers have big ears, it is said; children do overhear conversations about the coming baby when the parents are unaware that they are listening.

It is reasonable, therefore, to expect that children will naturally feel jealous of a newcomer. The amount of the jealousy reaction can be increased or decreased by the parents' handling of the child during this period. In our experience the child who already is really certain of his parents' love does not have so much difficulty in making an adjustment. The parents who really love their child will recognize that jealousy is a normal reaction and will not punish him for expressing it. Instead they will protect the baby from harm by not leaving the two children alone together. As soon as the mother learns she is pregnant she will begin to take the older child—even one of two or three years—into her confidence and explain to him what is about to happen. She will realize that the child is going to feel deprived and she will know that one way for a human being to overcome a feeling that he is not loved is to love someone else. She will see to it, therefore, that the child has a pet that will be his own, that he can play with and do things for, although he need not be required to look after it every day. She will encourage him in every way possible to try to be more grown up and to attempt more grown-up pursuits; in short, to be more like the adult parent who can do and give, rather than like the baby who must receive and have things done for him. He will undoubtedly ask many questions about sexual matters. These should be answered realistically for two reasons: the questions should be answered anyway for he needs the knowledge; the discussion of sexual matters and the parents' answering of his questions make him feel more mature and more certain of his relationship with his parents.

After the new baby is born the parents will expect the older child to be jealous and will protect the baby from injury by him. They will explain to him the reason for the difference in the type of attention they pay to the baby and to him, stressing the fact that the older child is older and more like his parents. They will praise every new accomplishment by which he attempts more mature activity—and will abstain from criticizing the slips backward he makes. They will see that he has the prerogatives of an older child and will see also that there is a special time set apart for him in which he has his parents' whole attention. This will be gradually shortened as he gets older and becomes more accustomed to the new situation. If he is old enough to look after the baby they will not request him to do so, as is so often done when the care of the baby really interferes with the child's life. If the parents follow these directions (which in most instances will occur to them from their own intuition) the traumatic effect of the birth of the new baby will be materially lessened, and the older child's adjustment will be made more satisfactory.

THE EFFECTS OF ADVERSE PARENTAL ATTITUDES

If the reader has been an observer of human beings he will recognize that all parents are not wise in the handling of their children. Also he will recognize that all parents do not feel the same way toward their children and that a parent does not feel the same way toward each of his children. Consequently he will be able to see that the concept that parents universally love their children is a fiction—a theory really unsubstantiated by fact. The feelings of parents toward their children form a graduated continuous scale starting from the parent who *really* loves his child and ending with the parent who *really only* hates his child. Since parental love is so necessary for the child and since the reasons why this is so have been discussed already, we intend here to consider only the effects of adverse parental attitudes, i. e., those in which some serious degree of hate is present. Realizing that there is a graduated continuous scale, it seems necessary for purposes of presentation to classify parental attitudes into three groups:

1. Rejection of the child.
2. Overprotection of the child.
3. Indulgence.

Similarly we classify parents who have adverse attitudes to their children into three types: (*a*) overstrict parents, (*b*) overstrict parents who feel guilty about their dislike of the child, and (*c*) weak parents.

Parental Rejection

Overstrict parents whose attitude to the child is one of rejection actually hate the child more than they love him. We wonder if the reader has ever considered the daily life of a child whose parents hate him. From the time he awakens in the morning until he goes to bed at night he is nagged, scolded, and frequently slapped. His attempts at conversation are received with curt, cold silence or he is told to be quiet. If he attempts to show any demonstration of affection he is pushed away and told not to bother his parents. He receives no praise for anything he does no matter how well he has done it. If he walks with his parents and lags a little his arm is seized and he is yanked forward. If he falls he is yanked to his feet. He is supposed to be seen and not heard. At mealtime he is either ignored or his table manners and inconsequential food fads are criticized severely. He is made to finish whatever is on his plate. (This is frequently done and we think quite unnecessarily by parents who really love their children, but they do it in a different manner than the parents who dislike their children. The latter insist not to help the child but actually to express their irritation with him.)

This same feeling underlies the application of all the routines of the child's life. It can be seen best in such a parent's handling of the small baby. Bathing, dressing, undressing, diapering, feeding—all are done in a rough, nontender manner. The child soon realizes that he can expect nothing but a hurt body or hurt feelings from his parents. He tries to avoid them as much as possible, and instead of wanting to see them and be with them, i. e., instead of feeling love for them, he feels fear, loathing and hatred. As a baby he cries when they go toward him; as an older child he often tries to run away but of course he is brought back and punished for running away.

At first he tries to stand his own ground, but as this brings him discomfort he begins to try to avoid doing anything that brings punishment. This means that he has to abstain from the majority of activities, for there is practically nothing that he does that is not punished. His thoughts are rebellious and antagonistic; he fears that his parents may be able to read his mind and he knows if they do his punishment will be even more severe. He tries to stop himself thinking these hostile thoughts. When the repression is successful it is accompanied by a repression of all initiative and individuality. The sad part is that the child—every child—believes that all adults are like his parents. So to other adults and to society in general he behaves rebelliously and antagonistically or with complete acts of submission.

If the father dislikes the boy the mutual antagonism is greater during the Oedipus situation, but the father is so much stronger and can enforce his hatred so much more painfully that the boy continually gives in. All his initiative and individuality disappear, and he learns that he can gain the most comfort by fawning on his father. He finds that this fawning attitude gets him some attention or at least avoids the pain of disagreement. He gets pleasure from it, and comes to desire the pleasure still more. He begins to find pleasure in being submissive, and even if the submission brings a certain amount of pain he puts up with it. The passive, submissive, fawning attitude from which he obtains pleasure gradually produces a feminine orientation to his father, i. e., this feminine orientation, instead of leading the boy to identify with the father's masculine traits, and so growing into a man, produces just the opposite effect. If the submission does not bring sufficient pleasure to make it profitable the boy may outwardly submit and store in his mind ideas of revenge. It is as if to say, "Now I am small and you are big and you can make me do things I don't want. Some day when I am grown up I'll be big and you'll be small and then I'll enjoy making you do things you don't want to do." Gradually as the years pass this fantasy of revenge becomes unconscious, but when the boy has a son of his own he may tend to treat him in just the same way as the father treated him when he was a boy.

The effect of rejection by the father falls on the boy's masculine activity, which it injures seriously. When the mother rejects her son it affects his relationship with the opposite sex. The boy wants his mother to love him and tries hard to please her. Still she rejects him. He then tries further to please her or becomes hostile and antagonistic and rejects her in turn. This may cause him to turn his love to his father and assume a feminine attitude to him. It may cause him to reject all women and be homosexual, or it may cause him to be too concerned in pleasing the woman with whom he falls in love.

If the mother rejects the daughter the effect on the latter is the same as when the father rejects the son. If the father rejects the daughter the effect is the same as when the mother rejects the son.

Rejective parents are usually harsh, domineering and strict. If a parent does not reject the child but is a harsh, domineering person the effect on the child will be similar to that of rejection. The parent who rejects his child may be conscious of his feeling of hatred to the child and also conscious that his behavior to him is the result of the feeling of hatred. He may be conscious of his dislike of the child and at the same time feel that this feeling is inadvisable and may consciously attempt to act toward the child as if he did not hate him. However the attempt is usually unsuccessful because the force of the hatred will overcome the conscious attempt at action and because the child can sense the underlying hatred, for children are very intuitive—intuitive enough to sense the real attitude of adults. Then again the parent may be unconscious of his feeling of hatred and attempt to excuse his harshness with the alibi that children profit by a strict upbringing. If this excuse allows him to express his hatred fairly fully the only sign of the hatred will be in the behavior of the child.

Parental rejection may be complete; i.e., the parent may dislike the child totally. It may occur during a certain age period; i.e., a parent may dislike all his children during infancy but become quite fond of them when they arrive at school age. The parent may not dislike the child but may be antagonistic to certain phases of normal childish behavior. For example, he may be strict about finger sucking, or dirtiness, or untidiness, or masturbation, or independence. The child is not able to distinguish clearly between the parent's rejection of his traits and the parent's love for him as an individual, and so feels totally rejected.

Parental Overprotection

There is a type of parent who is completely unconscious of his hatred of the child. Some time early in the child's life he became conscious of his hate and dislike for the child and felt horror at having such—to him —unnatural feelings. This reaction of horror caused him to repress his feelings of hatred from consciousness. Soon thereafter he started to become troubled by fears that some terrible catastrophe might happen to the child. He has a panic every time the child has the most minor ailment. He cannot permit the child to take part in any activity or sport in which there is the least element of danger. In fact he is only content if the child sits quietly and does nothing. He is incapable of applying the mildest discipline because he fears he will not be able to control himself and thus injure the child. If the child is especially naughty he may punish him and then he does it so severely as to really hurt. In all of these fears and inhibitions the parent shows that he has the wish to get rid of the child but he keeps such wishes unconscious because he is so horrified by them. The child of such a parent is in a worse situation than if the parent openly and consciously rejected him, and the effect on him is more serious. We believe that some of the worst instances of maladjustments in children come from such an attitude.

Parental Indulgence

It is self-evident that the parent who indulges his child does not love that child with a real adult love. He knows that when he permits his child every liberty and every satisfaction that he is not training him to be able to tolerate the many frustrations and deprivations that will be his lot in life, as indeed they are of all human beings. Furthermore, although the parent grant all the child's requests that he is able to, we have seen in previous chapters that there are many wishes and desires that cannot be gratified. Such a parent, therefore, not only does not prepare the child to be happy in his future life but incurs the child's resentment because he will not gratify his unreasonable requests.

The son of a weak, indulgent father—and usually these terms are synonymous—develops exactly the same personality difficulties as does the son of a harsh, rejecting father. This result comes about in the following way. The weak father makes a poor model of masculine aggressiveness for the boy to copy. The boy does not have the opportunity to express his antagonisms to his father, not because (as with the cruel father) he will suffer retaliation of a painful nature but because he feels so remorseful and ashamed to be hostile to such a kind, considerate person. The kinder his father treats him the more guilty he feels about his aggressive antagonisms, and so it continues until the conflict becomes so intolerably painful that he solves it by repressing not only his hostility to his father but all his masculine aggressiveness as well. A similar result follows with the girl whose mother is too weak and indulgent. If the mother is too indulgent to the boy he anticipates that he will be victorious in his struggle with the father and develops in the same way as the boy who has no father. A similar result will occur if the father is too indulgent to the girl. It might be stated in passing, however, that mild indulgence is infinitely less harmful to the child's development than a similar amount of strictness.

Parental attitudes toward children are a form of behavior and like all other behaviors have causes. Adverse parental attitudes do not usually occur through ignorance but are the result of personality problems in the parents. They are symptomatic of the parents' maladjustment and must be treated as such.

Psychiatrists have noted that the types of neuroses most prevalent today differ markedly from those reported as most prevalent during the latter part of the nineteenth and the early part of the twentieth centuries. At that time marked cases of conversion and anxiety hysteria and of compulsion neurosis were extremely common. At present these are rarely seen; what are seen are mostly character neuroses. Waelder believes that this change is the result of a real change that has taken place in parents' management of children. During the latter part of the nineteenth and the early part of the twentieth centuries parents were strict and trained their children to adjust to rigid routines. As a result a great deal of instinctual repression took place which manifested itself in neuroses with dramatic symptomatology. About the time of World War I parents were learning that such strict training produced unfavorable results and the pendulum swung far to the opposite extreme of indulgence and no real training at all. This type of management produces an individual who is ill equipped to bear the anxiety that results from the unavoidable frustrations and deprivations of life. He molds his character in such a way as to avoid situations that will arouse his anxiety. The best type of management seems to be midway between these two extremes, with the parents' training inclining slightly to the side of indulgence; but at the same time good parents do not protect the child too much from the unavoidable and necessary frustrations and deprivations that occur through living in a real world inhabited by real people, real customs and mores.

THE EFFECT OF PREMATURE OR EXCESSIVE
SEXUAL STIMULATION

Over half a century ago Freud was surprised to find from the psycho-analytic investigations of his patients that there was as active a sexual life in early childhood as there was after puberty. He was impressed with the frequency with which sexual seductions by adults and older children occurred in the early childhood histories of his patients, and also with the fact that their neurotic symptoms seemed to start shortly after these episodes. In many instances he was able to corroborate from other sources that these episodes actually took place. Although he was later forced to reach the conclusion that many of the uncorroborated episodes might have been only fantasies of the little child, yet it is generally agreed, and from our experience amply proved, that actual sexual seductions have a definite effect on the child's development. The small child may be sexually seduced by an older child or by an adult of the same or opposite sex. If the child is a boy he may be masturbated, may be induced to attempt intercourse or may be used as a passive object in one of the perversions. If the child is a girl she may be induced to submit to the same procedure, but more commonly, if the seducer is a male, she may be induced to permit vaginal intercourse.

It goes without saying that the child experiences a degree of pleasure during the seduction. A variety of other emotional reactions are often, however, combined with the pleasurable feelings. The child is afraid, partly because so much secrecy is insisted on by the seducer, partly because the child has probably been warned against exposing or showing an interest in the genitals, partly because the seducer may threaten him so as to force him to submit to the seduction, and partly because the experience is an unfamiliar one and he does not know what to expect. In many instances, particularly when a small girl submits to intercourse with an older boy, the experience will be somewhat painful. Combined with the pleasure there will be a great deal of excitement, and the child is left greatly excited and tense because the act itself is not likely to culminate in complete gratification and relaxation. However, the pleasure is so great, even if not complete, that the child does not mention the occurrence to the parents lest they interfere with a possible repetition of the experience.

It is interesting that this often happens even though the child has been somewhat severely hurt. This is strikingly different from the child's usual behavior, for almost invariably he will run to his parents for comfort if he has been hurt. Partly because of the incomplete gratification and partly because of the need to hide the experience from his parents the child begins to feel guilty, and often, in order to assuage this feeling of guilt, will begin to act in a naughty manner to induce the parents to punish him. This relieves his feeling of guilt, as he expected it would, but the relief is only temporary and the feeling of guilt soon recurs.

As can be seen, the effect of seduction of this type is to bring the child into a state of intense excitement which is pleasurable but out of which he cannot obtain relaxation. He feels nervous and tense and attempts as soon as possible to repeat the experience in the hope of obtaining the complete gratification, which never comes, however, and so he is left constantly frustrated. This vicious circle attracts all his energy, leaving little or none for the other phases of his life and development; furthermore it becomes so painful that he is forced to escape by repressing all memory of the incident and all his sexual feelings. In order to maintain the repression he has to avoid all situations and actions that might remind him of the incident or arouse him sexually. He enters adult life, therefore, poorly prepared for sexuality because of this repression. Also his first experience of sexual excitement has been associated with other emotional reactions—fear, guilt, pain, shame, feelings of disobedience, etc.—all of which are unpleasant and not validly connected with sexuality. When the repression occurs these emotional reactions are also repressed and if he later becomes sexually aroused the other uncomfortable emotional reactions are aroused also and make his later sexual experiences not as pleasurable as they should be.

Definite sexual seductions of younger by slightly older children are common, but because so much of the activity is really only sex play the traumatic effects are not very serious. Sexual seductions by much older children and by adults are less common but occur frequently enough to warrant the suspicion that such has occurred if the child suddenly becomes very frightened or quite naughty shortly after being alone with an older child or an adult for a period of several hours.

Indirect sexual seductions of children by their parents or nurses are very common. A mother bathes the genitals of her baby son most zealously in order to be sure they are clean. As he grows older she continues to do so. She may continue to bathe him, paying particular attention to his genitals, when he is four, five, six, seven, eight years old and even older. (We have heard of instances where the practice continued even well past puberty.) This type of mother usually expresses great horror and disgust if the boy gets an erection through her ministrations. The child therefore is being pleasurably stimulated by his mother but at the same time has to repress any physical reaction lest she become displeased with him.

There are parents who are obsessed with ideas of cleanliness and will not tolerate any mucus secretion anywhere on the body of the child. The child's ears, nose, vagina (if a girl) and undersurface of the prepuce (if a boy) are rigorously cleaned daily. This cleaning, which of course is unnecessary, gives the child sensual pleasure, but if he attempts overtly to get his mother to repeat it she regards him as naughty. Children are avid for sensual pleasure and once they have received it try to seduce the parent to give it to them again. A little boy of three, playing with a stick, fell on it and hurt his groin. His father, a physician, examined him carefully to determine whether he had injured his genitals. No injury was found and in a few hours the boy was quite all right. Several days later when the father was sitting in his study the boy came in and said, "Father, I have a very bad pain here," pointing to his genitals, and dropped his pants down. The father, who was wise, recognized that the boy had no pain but was attempting to seduce him to re-examine him. He did not do so but told him he was all right and that he should button up his pants and go and play. This type of attempt to seduce the parent is quite common with all small children. Less common are the instances, although they occur, where the child actually attempts to have intercourse with the parent. Such children later frequently develop strong guilt feelings about these acts and try to repress their sexuality lest they repeat them.

Similarly, older children who seduce younger ones eventually develop feelings of guilt and stop their behavior. In many cases the feeling of guilt is associated with the fear of being found out. The fear and guilt may be so great that all sexual feeling has to be repressed in order that the child may feel comfortable. Such severe repressions have a detrimental effect on the future sexual life of the individual.

Another traumatic sexual experience that may have far-reaching effects on the child's future life is the observation of parental intercourse. When the child of three or four sleeps in the parents' bedroom he will be awakened by their movements and speech during the preliminary sex play. Children of this age sleep lightly. The room is usually half lighted, for the average bedroom is not really dark at night. The child observes what looks to him like a struggle between the two people for whom he feels the most devotion. He hears sounds that do not seem those of pleasure. He realizes that something is going on that he does not understand. He is interested and excited by the mystery. He feels frightened and bewildered. He is certain something terrible is happening, and because of these feelings he dare not express his emotional reactions lest the parents learn he is awake. If he is going through the Oedipus period he wishes to participate with the most loved parent in whatever that parent is doing with the other parent. His jealousy of his rival is great. He feels resentment toward the loved parent because he is excluded in favor of someone else. He is thus filled with intense and conflicting emotional reactions which he tries not to express because he is interested in seeing exactly what goes on and because of his fear of his parents who seem so monstrous. Often the only form of emotional reaction he allows himself is to wet or soil the bed. The next day his memory of what happened during the night is so unpleasant because of the unexpressed emotional reactions that he has to repress the memory and the associated feelings. From this point on the repressed feelings begin to govern his daily activity and in adult life his behavior is very different from that of the person who did not undergo this experience. It seems to us most inadvisable for a small child to be subjected to this unnecessary trauma.

THE EFFECTS OF A TRAUMATIC EXPERIENCE

What are the effects of a traumatic experience? If one takes a series of cases of children who show symptoms of a neurosis one finds that they fall into two groups: those whose neurosis started at a definite time and those whose neurosis seems to have been present almost throughout the child's whole life. In the first instance it is found always that the neurosis follows a traumatic experience or several traumatic experiences, all occurring about the same time. In the second one finds that mild traumatic experiences have been the child's lot throughout his life. The more severe the traumatic experiences the more severe will be the neurotic illness.

What course does the child's development take after a traumatic experience? Since such an experience is one that arouses intense feelings and strong emotional reactions with which the child is incapable of dealing, he will first feel anxious and helpless; i. e., he will have an anxiety attack. This in itself is painful and in order to avoid the pain he will go through certain maneuvers. He will try to repress the memory of the traumatic experience, the feelings engendered by the experience, and the feelings, thoughts, and desires that seem to him to have produced the experience. In order to keep the painfulness of the traumatic experience repressed and to avoid doing anything that might cause a repetition of it, he may try to avoid all situations or actions that may remind him of what he has repressed. In technical language he will impose inhibitions on himself.

The repression, when reinforced by the inhibitions, tends to break down and the repressed material begins to reappear in consciousness. Perhaps the repression of the impulses and ideas remains effective, but the feelings of fear break through. The child will then suffer from recurrent anxiety attacks and be unable to understand of what he is afraid. Instead of feelings of fear his feelings of guilt may break through, and feeling guilty without knowing why, he may be forced to behave in an overconscientious manner in order not to add to the guilty feeling; or he may tend to seek to assuage his guilty feelings by open naughty behavior which will cause him to be punished. If the repression of the underlying impulses breaks down, the impulses dare not seek their usual form of gratification lest the pain of the traumatic situation be reexperienced. Ordinarily in a situation where the child's inner impulses were frustrated of gratification he would attempt to find new methods of satisfaction but any attempt to find new methods is banned by the fear that they might lead to a repetition of the traumatic situation. Under these circumstances the inner desires have only one course, i. e., to flow backward and seek earlier and now relinquished modes of expression.

Which one of these modes will the impulses find most ready to undertake this task? In the life of most human beings the course of development is not an even one. For example, if the child has had a short nursing period he will still be desirous of obtaining complete oral satisfaction; i. e., the oral zone will still be energized to a greater degree than in other children. This zone will therefore continue to be a weak point, for the energy still attached there is only held in check by strong repression. When the inner desires at a later period are frustrated by the fear of repetition of a traumatic situation and so have to be repressed, they will be attracted by the energy still attached to the oral zone, and add their energy to that already there; the repression will break down and the child will attempt to find satisfaction from the use of the oral activities. This phenomenon is known technically as *regression,* by which is meant that the individual attempts to obtain gratification in a way that he found satisfactory when he was younger. For example, although he has long since given up finger sucking he may now revert to it. This is known as a *perversion.* A perversion may be defined simply as the use of an infantile form of obtaining sexual gratification at an age when sensual gratifications should be obtained in a more adult way.

If he feels a strong antipathy to obtaining gratification through a perversion he may begin to show disturbances in the usual uses of his mouth. The attempt at gratification shows itself in a *disturbance* of oral function because by the time the child attains the age of which we are speaking he may have learned forcibly and definitely that it is not proper to use his oral zone as a means of obtaining this type of gratification. He cannot therefore extract pure pleasure from this gratification; but he has to feel pain in the attempt in order to bribe his disapproving conscience. It is as if he said to himself, "Look here, you are too grown up really to have pleasure from a babyish method of gratification so if you want that mode of gratification, instead of having only pleasure you will have to suffer pain for your desire to be babyish. Each time you wish to gratify your sensual impulses by taking something into your mouth you will vomit instead and at the same time you will feel nauseated just to show you that you shouldn't be a baby." This attempt to obtain gratification of an inner impulse in a childish way, and the punishment for attempting to be a baby again, forms the basic structure of all symptoms.

As noted above, energy will remain attached to an infantile sensual zone if there has been frustration of the optimum period of gratification. It will also remain attached if the pleasure of this type of gratification has been allowed to continue too long; i. e., in connection with the oral zone if the child has been nursed over a very long period. This attachment of desire to a zone through which the infant normally experiences gratification because of too little or too much gratification, and which lasts long after the time when such modes of gratification have been relinquished, is known as a fixation on that zone. If in later life the individual experiences a severe frustration he will tend to show neurotic symptoms connected with that zone.

These are the main methods of reaction to a traumatic situation. However, as the child begins to use one or the other he has to develop modifications of them in order to get along better in life. Besides these modifications he often combines several different methods of reacting, with the result that his neurosis develops a very complicated structure which often requires a long, painstaking piece of work to unravel. We have felt it necessary to introduce the concepts of traumatic situations at this point—and the reactions to the situations by anxiety, repression, inhibition, guilt, regression, perversion and symptom formation—because not to do so would be to make the discussion of the true emotional illnesses during the phallic and latent periods complicated and difficult indeed.

THE EMOTIONAL ILLNESSES OF THE PHALLIC PERIOD

There are two disorders that are most frequent during the phallic period—fears (and phobias) and temper tantrums.

Irrational Fears and Phobias

Childhood is a time of life when the human being is haunted by numerous fears. He is little, weak and helpless and the world in which he lives is filled with many objects and situations that can really do him harm. In fact parents have to spend considerable time warning the child of objects and situations which, however attractive they are to him, are really full of deadly peril. The busy street, fire, sharp knives, sparkling broken glass, electric-light sockets, electric fans, and other appliances—all are fraught with real danger of bodily harm to the child, against which he must be protected until he learns how to protect himself. In addition to these real dangers (which interestingly enough the child often seems to disparage), the world of every child is haunted with unreasonable fears. He is overafraid of falling, of physical punishment, of accidents and injuries, of dying; he is afraid of rough games, bad people, magic, giants, corpses; of the dark, being alone; of strange places and persons, deformities, lights and shadows; of strange noises, scary stories and movies; of ghosts, goblins, bogymen; of birds, insects (harmless or otherwise); of multitudinous objects and situations which in reality either could cause him no injury or are not at all likely to do so.

Jersild in his exhaustive study of the subject found that only 19 of 400 children (comprised of 25 boys and 25 girls at each age level between the ages of 5 and 12) admitted having no fears. The remainder of the

400 admitted one fear and often several. In a later paper he reported that three-year-olds admitted an average of 5.5 fears; four-year-olds, 6.3; five-year-olds, 4.3; and six-year-olds, 3.2 fears each. Children during the phallic period were more commonly frightened by strange objects, persons, situations and noises, by sudden unexpected visual disturbances, by animals and bad people. Boys of all ages were more commonly afraid of bodily injury, and girls were afraid of the dark, solitude, and strange sights and noises.

The unreality of these fears (for what sensible child could really be afraid of a butterfly, or of the motes floating in a sunbeam, either of which could send certain sensible and intelligent children we have seen into a state of severe panic) indicates that they are not really fears but phobias. What is the mechanism of the phobia?

In the phobia the child is conscious of a certain feeling tone which we call fear, and he ascribes the feeling tone to the presence of the phobic object or to the dread lest the phobic object become present. No amount of sensible reassurance, even by an adult whom he loves and trusts, can reduce the feeling of panic or can change his assertion that the phobic object is the cause. In order to discuss the reasons for this compulsive type of reaction and the mechanism by which such phobias occur we will refer to the case presented in our previous book:

A four-year-old girl had a pronounced phobia of dogs. If one appeared three blocks away she became panic stricken and rushed into the house or clung to her mother screaming. It made no difference whether the dog was large or small, friendly or hostile, good natured or vicious; its appearance produced an anxiety attack. This fear of dogs did not follow any attack or injury by one, but began suddenly. When she was convalescing from an attack of pneumonia, she suffered a night terror. In the early hours of the morning she began to scream and did not seem to recognize any person in the room. When her father came toward her she shouted for him to go away. When her mother asked what the matter was, she said there was a dog under her mother's bed. When the father again approached her, she screamed, "Go away. You're a dog." After some little time her terror subsided and she fell asleep quietly. On waking the next morning she was perfectly calm, but from that day on her fear of dogs was present.

What happened to this little girl? She was sexually attracted to the father and as a result was jealous and antagonistic toward the mother whom she loved also. She has had the wish to destroy the mother and rid herself of her by biting her to pieces. During a severe illness she had received a great deal of very pleasant care, affection and attention from the mother, to which she responded with love. But she had also received increased care and kindness from the father and some actual physical handling which had increased her sexual attraction to him. The increased desire for the father in turn increased her hostility to the mother. She thinks, "If I were alone with father he would give me all the attention he now does plus all the attention mother gives me. So why not plan to get rid of mother altogether?" But the little girl relishes the attention and kindness she gets from her mother. If she got rid of her these would cease. How can she get rid of the mother and keep her at the same time? The problem is too complicated for her immature ego to solve.

Why is this, when it is a problem that every human being has to find a solution for, and for which the majority of children do find a satisfactory one? But most children are not exposed to the increase in feelings that were brought about in this little girl by her need for nursing care during her illness. Also before she took sick she learned that her mother and father were not a united couple. They were superficially on good terms, but the mother was being induced by a former lover (whom she still loved) to leave her husband. On Sundays the mother refused to go with the father to visit his relatives. The father went and took the children and the child realized that this separation on Sundays and holidays was not a matter-of-fact occurrence but resulted from a difference of opinion. It is as if the mother were saying, "I can't get along with your father, let him go his way and I will go mine." At her grandparents' she heard much malicious gossip against the mother, with the constant strain that the father should not have married her and that the mother was not really interested in the father.

The mother stayed with the father for the children's sake and occasionally was troubled by conscious ideas of getting rid of the children. These ideas appeared more frequently in her dreams, indicating that she had a great but unconscious desire to do so. There is no question that the child could sense this underlying feeling since, being largely conscious, it expressed itself in the mother's daily handling of the child. The child then felt somewhat as follows, "She is my mother but it is all right for me to want to get rid of her because she doesn't like me anyway and she really wants to leave father. He would be happier if she did leave. My grandmother and aunts all think so. Surely I would make a better wife for him than mother does and with me he would be much happier."

The child was thus all prepared for the possibility that her desire would come true; i. e., she was certain that her wishes were magical and that in a short time they would act, the mother would disappear and she would be completely happy. She took sick and she noticed that her mother was greatly concerned, that she did everything possible for her and that she seemed worried about the illness. (It is to be assumed that the mother would be more anxious than usual because she would feel guilty about the possible fulfillment of her own unconscious wishes to get rid of the child.) This whole situation confused the little girl. She now thought, "I thought my mother hated me as I hated her, but now I find she loves me and tries to make me happy. I must have been mistaken. How could I ever have had such bad thoughts about my dear mother? Perhaps this illness itself and all the discomfort I am suffering are a punishment sent on me for my wickedness. But I still have these bad thoughts of wanting to get rid of mother every time father is nice to me. I have wanted to bite my kind mother at these times. I must be a dog. Perhaps mother is a dog too. Perhaps if she knew what I thought about her she would bite me. I wish I were a dog. Dogs can do all kinds of bad things, things that little girls are forbidden to do. If I were a dog and father were a dog we could do as we liked and then it wouldn't matter about mother. Mother likes dogs. Perhaps father is really a dog part of the day. [It is easy to see here how close such ideas approach to the superstition of the werewolf.] Perhaps mother is a dog part of the day. If they were both dogs I could stay away from them and then would not be so uncomfortable. My father really is a dog." And the dog phobia begins.

We do not mean that this little girl thought this all out consciously. We mean that if her feelings were translated into concepts the concepts would follow the line stated above. Anyone who knows children knows how frequently they play they are animals. If the adult joins in the game and pretends he is a dog or bear and if the game becomes too exciting one can observe the pleasure changing to a thrill and the thrill to a panic, as if the adult were rapidly transformed into the animal he is portraying. The pretense from the child's point of view ceases to be a pretense and the child suddenly loses all perspective of reality. The child enjoys pretending to be an animal because he admires the animal's courage, skill and power, and its freedom from cultural restrictions.

In our opinion the closer the dread of the phobic object (in this case the dog) approaches a reality dread (i. e., dogs really may bite or hurt a child) the less serious is the phobia. We have observed instances where the phobic object was something that did not exist in reality—such as a strange dinosaurlike animal—and in those instances the child was very sick emotionally. In all instances the choice of phobic object depends on an accidental concatenation of circumstances (in the case cited above, on the fact that the mother liked dogs) but the formation of the phobia is a result of the projection of the child's insoluble emotional conflict and has nothing to do with the phobic object itself.

This is important, for both physicians and parents are often misled in regarding the phobic object as of great importance. We are thinking now of the number of instances where parents are certain that the cause of the child's anxiety is due to a movie he saw, a frightening story he read or heard, perhaps over the radio. We remember one little girl who developed an acute panic during the movie of *Jack and the Beanstalk*. The parents blamed the movie. Actually the movie would have had no effect on the child whatsoever if she had not been in the throes of an insoluble emotional conflict about her mingled love and hatred of her mother. Often in therapy with a child who has such an idea it is difficult to get him to realize that his difficulties lie in his feelings about his parents and are not the result of seeing a frightening picture.

All little children have phobias. They disappear when the child has solved his particular emotional conflict. We remember one child who solved his most dramatically. He got out of bed in the middle of the night, shot the bear that troubled him and was no longer troubled by a phobia of bears. In reality he had apparently acquired enough courage to admit and play out his hatred of his father. These phobias are not prognostically serious but are what Freud calls "the normal neurosis of childhood." They become serious only if circumstances make the child's Oedipus problem insoluble for him. In the case cited above the insolubility of the problem lay in the fact that the parents had a real marital difficulty and so could not furnish the security of a stable home in which the child is compelled to work through his conflicting feelings to the satisfactory solution that was mentioned in the previous chapter. The Oedipus situation was made insoluble by a traumatic experience. It is interesting—although Freud does not make any reference to its importance—that in the first case report in which a child's phobia was analyzed the parents of the little boy later separated. Obviously if the separation took place they had a marital problem at the time of the boy's phobia. Also in Freud's case of the man who had the recurrent dream of the seven wolves and who suffered during his childhood from numerous phobias, being particularly panic stricken by the picture of a wolf in a storybook, there had been definite traumatic experiences: the sight of parental intercourse (the most traumatic form of them all), the absence of the parents, the seductions by the older sisters and the quarreling between the servants.

The prognosis of the usual phobias of childhood is good. The child grows out of them. Reich points out that the development of a phobia is a sign that the ego is too weak to control the libidinal strivings. It really implies a splitting of the personality. Sometimes, perhaps always, this splitting is overcome by the accentuation of certain character traits, which accentuation acts by unifying the personality, and this strengthens the ego. However, the unification may take place at the expense of further repression. This probably takes place with the resolution of all the phobias of childhood and if not too marked does not have a serious later effect, which is what happens if the child has not had too many or too severe traumatic experiences. If there have been too many traumatic experiences or if they have been too severe the phobia may disappear but the healing character formation will show very serious scars of inhibitions, accentuated repressions and regressions. Such a personality is predisposed to a breakdown later in life as occurred in Freud's Wolf Man.

All the phobias of childhood merit consideration, if not necessarily treatment, since they indicate that the child is having difficulty in coming to terms with his inner strivings. It is not sufficient to pass them by with the light statement that he will grow out of them. He may need some help in order that his later adjustment may be as adequate as possible. Jersild and Holmes have made a study of the methods of treatment usually used by parents and teachers and group them into three classes:

1. Ineffective:
   (a) Ignoring the child's fears. This is effective only if the child is using his fear to gain the adult's attention.
   (b) Forcing the child into contact with the phobic object.
   (c) Removing the child from the phobic object or the feared situation, or offering him bribes to make him less aware of his fear.
2. Auxiliary measures, which are sometimes effective alone but work best if used in conjunction with other measures:

(*a*) Verbal explanation and reassurance.

(*b*) Practical demonstrations of the harmlessness of the phobic object.

(*c*) Demonstrating examples of the lack of fear that other children have toward the phobic object.

(*d*) Positive conditioning.

3. Most effective:

(*a*) Helping the child to develop skills so that he will be able to cope with the phobic object or situation.

(*b*) Gradually bringing him into active contact with the phobic object and into active participation in the feared situation.

(*c*) Giving him the opportunity gradually to become acquainted with the feared object or situation under circumstances that permit him to inspect it and ignore it.

These methods only deal with the conscious situation. The child is afraid of dogs. Dogs are a usual part of civilized life, and are not often harmful. The child must learn therefore not to be afraid of dogs. We suppose in all phobias that these methods should be followed because it is essential that the child become acquainted thoroughly with all the realities of his environment, and learn how to deal with them. It is important to recognize that all the effective methods depend upon being used slowly and gradually—a very important point in all child training.

But these measures are only supplemental to the aid the child should receive about the real causes of his phobias. Since they center around his attempt to solve the Oedipus situation there are ways of helping him do this. The parent of the opposite sex should gradually decrease the amount of physical attention he or she gives the child. This comes about very naturally in teaching the child himself to look after the clothing and care of his body. It is perhaps better to allow him to be a little less clean or to be occasionally constipated than to have the parent of the opposite sex help him out or pay too much attention to these matters. He should be encouraged to do things for himself and be given the opportunity to spend as much time as possible in association with children of his own age instead of with his parents or other adults. Sleeping with the parent of the opposite sex should be definitely discouraged even though the circumstances may be unusual, such as occur during traveling or visiting. The open expression of hostility to the parent of the same sex should not be suppressed if it is within reasonable bounds. Verbal hostility should be permitted without any retaliation either verbally or physically. Motor hostility against the parent of the same sex should also be permitted to some extent. At the same time the child should have the opportunity for a great deal of motor activity, and if during this activity he indulges in murderous games, such as war, cops and robbers, etc., he should be allowed to do so without adult interference.

Sometimes, and this suggestion is advanced with great trepidation lest it be misused, an intelligent, understanding parent who is well aware of what is going on may talk with the child concerning the phobia, pointing out that his phobia is nonsense, that he is afraid of his feelings to the parent of the same sex and endeavor to get the child to verbalize these feelings. This kind of discussion between parent and child will, over a period of time, result in the child's producing his sexual fantasies and his fears of castration. It will be a relief for him to talk about them. At times during the discussion the parent may assure the child that all children have similar feelings, fantasies and fears, and all grown-up people had them also when they were children.

How can we determine when the phobia of an individual child may be considered pathological and merit professional treatment? There are several criteria for this. If the phobia is severe and is crippling the child's life, treatment is indicated definitely. For instance, the little girl who became panic stricken after seeing the movie *Jack and the Beanstalk* spent the next month clinging constantly to her mother. She would not play with other children, and in fact would not stay anywhere unless her mother were with her. It would not do even if the mother were only in the next room. If it is known that the child has suffered a serious traumatic experience—acts of fate, adverse parental attitudes or seductions— the case usually merits treatment even though the phobic manifestations are not very severe. Particularly where there are adverse parental attitudes treatment is imperative. As mentioned earlier, if the phobic object is bizarre and the phobic reaction severe the case merits treatment.

What treatment should be applied? The really curative treatment will follow the lines so carefully described by Freud in his report on the case of Little Hans. Anyone attempting to treat a phobia in a child should read these *technical details* very carefully. In this connection also the report of Kubie is very helpful.

There are several successive steps in the treatment of phobia. The child must be convinced that his conception of the cause of the phobia, i. e., his idea that he really is afraid of the phobic object, is nonsense. This is usually quite difficult because such a concept makes the child admit he is ill, an admission that neither child nor adult wishes to accept. This can be done either directly (i. e., if the child has confidence in the therapist he may be willing to accept the idea from him) or indirectly as the child begins to understand and work out his conflict about his feelings toward his parents. The child must be helped to indicate to the therapist either verbally or in his play the precise nature of his conflict. This is a rather fumbling process because the therapist is seldom able to read the child's unconscious as accurately as he may be able to read that of an adult, who co-operates to a much greater extent. The child is encouraged to be freer in expressing his sexual and aggressive feelings and the therapist attempts to relieve his sense of guilt about them. Treatment of childhood phobias proceeds along more clear-cut and more definite lines than does the treatment of many other childhood neuroses because the defense mechanism—projection—is a comparatively simple and uncomplicated one, and because little or no regression has taken place.

Temper Tantrums

If the phobia is the normal neurosis of childhood the temper tantrum may be considered the normal psychosis. Let us describe a simple instance of a tantrum which must have been observed by many of our readers who have any association with children. It is five-thirty and dinner will be served at six o'clock. The child desires a piece of candy. The parent refuses the request, telling the child that he will have dinner shortly and that he may have the candy after his dinner. The child again asks and is refused. The child demands that he get the candy now. The adult patiently refuses. The child begins to cry and scream. He stamps his feet, clenches his fists, begins to jump up and down, and hits or kicks at the wall or door. His frenzy increases. He throws himself on the floor, kicks and screams, pounds his head or his body with his fists or bangs his head on the floor. He pays no attention to what the adult says to him. Neither threats, cajolement, bribes, promises nor scoldings make any difference. If he is severely spanked or placed in a tub of water he will stop. Otherwise he will continue for some time. His screaming gradually subsides into low sobbing, his hitting and kicking stop, he lies quietly for a few minutes, then gets up rather languidly. He sobs for a little longer. Perhaps he feels remorse for his behavior. He seems exhausted. After a little while he seems all right again. Of course the whole proceeding may be less severe but at times it is even more dramatic.

There are certain outstanding behaviors in this symptom complex. The first and most important is that the child is completely oblivious to reality and his surroundings. He neither hears nor pays any attention to anything that is said or done to him unless it causes a sufficient shock to penetrate his consciousness. He acts as if he had given up all contact with reality, as he really has. It is this that makes his reactions comparable to those of the psychotic. In this state he uses a great deal of muscular energy either directed aimlessly or against his own body. (We once saw a child with a severe hematoma on her forehead which resulted from the pounding she gave herself with her fists.) Almost never does he attack the adult who has refused him. He cries and screams as if he were suffering the greatest torment. What has caused the reaction? He was to be frustrated for a period of about an hour from obtaining the piece of candy he wanted. Thus it can be easily seen that the reaction is out of all proportion to the apparent cause. Often his speech during the tantrum shows that he is reacting disproportionately. He wails, "You are an old meany. You *never* give me *anything* I want. You want the candy *all* for yourself. You don't want me to have *any* at all."

Before we discuss the significance of this behavior we feel it would be interesting to describe the usual reactions to frustration. These seem to make a series starting from the usual normal reactions and ending with pathological ones. When a person has been frustrated in obtaining something he wants he first has a feeling of disappointment. This disappointment urges him to stop and consider whether he cannot get what he wants through some other method. If he believes he can he then uses that method. If he can find no other method he considers whether it might not be possible for him to obtain the gratification he craves at another time, and if this seems feasible he waits until the new opportunity arises. If this is not possible he is often willing to take a substitute that will gratify his desire in another way; e. g., if he can't get cake he may satisfy his hunger with bread. If he finds none of these possibilities open to him he begins to feel irritated and this heightened annoyance may enable him to see possibilities of satisfaction which he had not observed before. If this does not happen his irritation increases and he becomes angry, and because of this anger he tries to destroy the obstacles that interfere with his satisfaction. If these obstacles are human beings the feeling changes to hate and he tries to remove the human depriver or destroy him. If this is not possible and the need for gratification is very strong he becomes enraged, tries to destroy everything about him and eventually may try to destroy himself. Before this happens another reaction may set in. His rage may become so great that he may lose consciousness and have an epileptic convulsion.

It can be seen that the temper trantrum appears in this series as equivalent to the reaction that occurs just before the individual loses consciousness or has a convulsion. So again we are puzzled as to why there is such a severe reaction to a simple deprivation, and also why there is no attack on the real frustrator, i. e., the adult who has denied the child the piece of candy. He does make an attack but it is on himself. Therefore he and not the adult is the real frustrating person. In this he is realistic—just as all behavior is realistic. Furthermore, most of the force of the attack is directed against his head so that it must be his head that is depriving him. To all of us the head is the seat of self. Therefore it is the child himself who is the depriving person.

Why does the child react so disproportionately? He has been asked to postpone the satisfaction of his desire for a piece of candy for a period of an hour. Even if he is very hungry he knows he will get something to eat long before that time. Furthermore, he is not denied having candy. The denial is only for now. He acts and talks as if he had been denied any further candy for the remainder of his life, and as if the adult denied it to him in order that he have it all for himself. He thus accuses the adult of greediness. Now the child is really a very greedy person and has had to learn with much suffering that he has to control his greed. He does not want to do so but knows it would be better for him if he did. The best way to control greed would be to get rid of it altogether or to deny himself completely its gratification. It is as if the disappointment of the denial increased his desire for the candy. (This is the purpose of the feeling of disappointment.) Now he does not want one piece of candy; he wants the whole box. Furthermore he does not want it later on; he wants it now. The disappointment therefore arouses his greed, over which he has not yet, being a child, very good control. The arousal of his greed overwhelms his sense of reality and, consumed by it, he withdraws his sensory contact with his real environment. The picture of his greed is not pleasurable to his idea of himself as a human being. He does not like himself as the base, greedy person he now appears. He tries to remain in control and project his greed onto the adult whom he accuses of wanting to have the candy all for himself.

This is not a satisfactory solution so he would like to rid himself either of his greed (then he would never want any more candy throughout the remainder of his life, hence the feeling that he has been deprived forever) or of his controls (which were imposed by his parents and which he felt at that time were imposed not for his greed but to satisfy their own greed). He has made his parents' training part of his own personality so that the only way to get rid of it is to beat it out of himself. This he attempts to do. Not only has he withdrawn from reality deliberately but the intensity of the struggle within himself leaves little if any energy to maintain contact with the outside. Only as he becomes exhausted in the struggle or is able to reach a new adjustment of the problem does the temper tantrum subside. He becomes really remorseful for having allowed himself to get out of hand in this babyish fashion.

It would be expected from what we have just said that temper tantrums would be common in early childhood because at that time the child is only gradually learning to control his desires, and consequently is exposed to many and severe reality frustrations. So it is. Tantrums are less common during the latent period. There is a slight increase during the early part of adolescence because of the reactivation of the infantile situation. From that time on they gradually diminish, occurring in adult life only under the most unusual cicrumstances, such as during a severe painful illness or under great deprivation. In reality many adults have temper tantrums, for though such persons are adult chronologically they are not so emotionally.

Since temper tantrums are universal in childhood their status as a pathological manifestation will be determined in the same way as is done for the phobias. If they are very severe and prolonged or if they occur too frequently the child's development is not proceeding properly. There are always good reasons for pathological temper tantrums. If the child has been indulged too much and has been given little opportunity to learn to control his impulses, never having had the necessity to do so, his control system is weak and he reacts primitively to deprivation no matter how hard he wants to behave differently.

There is no question in our minds that a child needs some support from his parents' insistence (kindly imposed) that he learn to adapt himself to culture. It is usual to say that spoiling is the cause of temper tantrums, but in our experience severe tantrums occur when the child has been forced to be too cultured, to exert too much control too early, or to become independent before he is really able to be so. The control system operates satisfactorily but the amount of unsatisfied hungers is great and deserves the title of starvation rather than greed. The child is too much on the side of his control system and regards natural and not excessive desires for satisfaction as an indication of his greed. If the parental demand for too early independence and too much control is the result of a rejective parental attitude to which the child tries to adjust by doing everything possible to behave in a way that will make life with his parents at least tolerable his temper tantrums will be most severe.

Treatment in the first type will be directed toward helping the child gain more control of his infantile desires and making him want to get more mature forms of satisfaction which will compensate for the infantile forms he has to relinquish. He does not need psychotherapy by a psychiatrist so much as he needs mild training by a kindly, friendly, consistent teacher or nurse who can make him feel more pleasure in pleasing her than giving way to his inner impulses. For the second and third types treatment will be directed toward ameliorating the severity of his standards so that he will feel more comfortable in being his age. Children of this type require intensive psychotherapy by a psychiatrist. Under the influence of his benign presence the child is able to play freely and in doing so to learn that even adults do not regard the high standards he sets for himself as necessary. We would say that the main technique in this therapy would be to give the child freedom to be himself at his age level.

There is no treatment for the tantrum itself. Since the child is inaccessible to persuasion and reason it is perhaps best to put him in a room by himself and leave him until the tantrum has passed. This is not done as a punishment but simply because there is nothing else to do. There is no point in scolding or punishing him after the tantrum. The tantrum is not induced in order that he get his own way; hence it is wrong to grant his every request with the hope that he will not have a tantrum. This is more commonly done than might be thought. Tantrums often occur in situations or under circumstances that are rather humiliating to the parents and many parents would rather give the child what he wants than risk the possibility of a tantrum. If the child becomes aware of this attitude on their part he will feign a temper tantrum when he wants something. The practice of ignoring the tantrum of course will cause the child to lose interest in feigning.

BIBLIOGRAPHY FOR CHAPTER VI

English, O. S., and Pearson, G. H. J., *The Common Neuroses of Children and Adults,* Norton, 1937.

Freud, Sigmund, "The Analysis of a Phobia in a Five-year-old Boy," *Collected Papers* III, Hogarth Press, 1933.

Freud, Sigmund, "From the History of an Infantile Neurosis," *Collected Papers* III, Hogarth Press, 1933.

Jersild, Arthur T., and Holmes, Frances B., "Methods of Overcoming Children's Fears," *Journal of Psychology* 1, 1936, 75.

Jersild, Arthur T., and Holmes, Frances B., "Some Factors in the Development of Children's Fears," *Journal of Experimental Education* 4, 1935, 133.

Jersild, Arthur T., Markey, Frances V., and Jersild, Catherine L., *Children's Fears, Dreams, Wishes, Daydreams, Likes, Dislikes, and Pleasant and Unpleasant Memories,* Teachers College, Columbia University, 1933.

Kubie, Lawrence S., "The Resolution of a Traffic Phobia in Conversations between Father and Son," *Psychoanalytic Quarterly* 6, 1937, 223.

Pearson, Gerald H. J., "The Effect of Operative Procedures on the Emotional Life of the Child," *American Journal of Diseases of Children* 62, 1941, 716.

Reich, William, "Character Formation and the Phobias of Childhood," *International Journal of Psychoanalysis* 12, 1931, 219.

Waelder, Robert, *Lectures on Various Theoretical Departures from Psychoanalytic Theory Given before the Philadelphia Psychoanalytic Society,* 1943.

Chapter VII

DEVELOPMENT OF PERSONALITY DURING THE LATENT PERIOD

THE LATENT PERIOD of personality development in the child's life is between the ages of six and ten, or from the sixth year to the onset of puberty. The word "latent" suggests that this period is a quiescent one in the development of the individual, and so it is, relatively. In comparison with the periods covered so far—the oral, the anal and the phallic—the latent period can be called relatively quiet. We have seen that the first three periods are unusually critical, that a great many events of emotional importance take place, and in rapid succession. When we come to the discussion of adolescence, which is also a stormy period, we will find that many of the adolescent's problems have their roots in the latent period as well, and that a problem that is acute during adolescence was present year after year in some mild, unnoticeable form in the child from six to puberty.

The School Situation

During these years most children are in grade school. They are years in which the family delegates a great deal of the child's training to the school system. In fact, a great many parents are often too relieved when the child enters school age. They rush him off to school with the expectation, or hope, that the school system will fill the child's time and direct his play, will solve his problems, answer his many difficult questions, and they are glad not to have to concern themselves so much with the child's development. The parents often consign to the teacher the major responsibilities for the child's development at this time. Some fathers and mothers actually say to the child when he asks a question, "Ask your teacher." Perhaps the reader has heard a parent say, "I'll be glad when my child gets off to school," as though the school were a kind of organization that will absorb much of the child's energy and relieve much of his insatiable curiosity.

These attitudes on the part of parents foster a tendency already present in children of the latent period to seek the company of their own sex, to have chums and to form groups, gangs and secret societies. They advance their own theories among themselves of life, birth, death, adventure, etc., and relate to these topics what they learn about the world in general. Many false theories and much misinformation concerning physiology is present—particularly in relation to the question of sex. The gangs and groups fight each other, either in a supervised way on the sand lot or in football games or under the auspices of the school athletic plan, and thus work off much hostility and aggression. This is particularly true of boys. Society provides better outlets for boys to work off their aggression than it does for girls. We doubt that girls have less aggression than boys but suspect that they have less opportunity to work it off in acceptable social ways. This lack of pleasurable self-expression helps explain why the incidence of psychoneurosis and the anxiety state of so-called menopausal psychosis is higher in women than in men. This fact also has bearing on the neuroses and the many conflicts growing out of inhibited sexuality in women.

Sex Antagonism and Indifference

Boys and girls are not very friendly to each other during the latent period. They show a disinterest in each other which is often extreme and occurs consistently enough to make us ask ourselves why this is so. Of course, one general reason is that adults do not expect children to become completely socialized this early in life. Children have not had enough contact with friendship, goodwill and social customs to enable them to talk in a polite manner at all times or to enable them to behave with consistent consideration and thoughtfulness.

However, we surely do not want to believe that the consideration and thoughtfulness they do learn to manifest as they grow up are merely a veneer. Let us take an example. During the latent period, a child is behaving inconsiderately (he is between the ages of seven to ten). As the parent is taking him to school he says, "You must be nice to Johnny and not repeat the rudeness of yesterday." The child does not heed the admonition. From this fact we must realize that through indifference and dislike of other children he is really acting exactly the way he feels and the parent ought to ask himself why this is so. Let us see why. Children of both sexes have a great many problems to solve in the three preceding periods and—as we have indicated—we do not pay enough attention to them during these phases. So they emerge from the oral, anal and genital periods into the latent period with considerable hostility and much leftover aggression against authority (parents). Having been on poor terms with their parents, they cannot show more consideration for their contemporaries than has been shown to them. They have been hurt, neglected and ignored, and they get satisfaction out of doing the same thing to others. In the solution of the Oedipus complex parents are not always wise enough in the manner in which they relate themselves to their children. Often fathers do not make as good friends of their daughters as they should. So girls and boys suffer a disappointment at the hands of the parents, not having learned enough of friendship to pass it on to each other.

Each sex seems to have its own language. They become segregated. They seem to need someone and something to hate so they look down rather disdainfully upon the opposite sex. Boys say they do not like "those silly girls" who cannot play games. Girls say they do not like "rough boys" who do not have consideration. Not until puberty when the activity of the sexual glands gives a certain impetus to the erotic components of the personality do they turn their interest to each other. However, we are sure the reader has seen boys and girls whose indifference to each other in the latent period changes very little at puberty, and these girls and boys are never able to show very much interest in the opposite sex at any time in their lives. This is partly because from birth onward they did not receive enough kindness and affection from their parents, and partly because there had been so much trauma during the genital development or specific trauma in the solution of the Oedipus conflict during the genital period. Boys and girls who do not have disagreements in play and who get along amicably all the time are probably the exception rather than the rule.

The wise parent accepts the feeling of hostility as a natural outgrowth of what has preceded and realizes with good reason that he should not allow this period to be such a "latent," quiescent period, but one in which he should take even more interest in his child, regardless of what the school is doing. During the latent period most children come home and tell their mothers about the happenings in school, about their successes and disappointments. The mother listens more than anyone else, she comments most and is most interested. Our observation is that this interest of the mother is not enough and that the father shows practically no interest at all. All too many fathers know scarcely anything about their sons and daughters during this period of development.

A patient who was in her third mental depression was asked why she had not had a happier life, since she was well trained in music, had nice manners and had had enough opportunities to have adjusted herself better. She said that her husband was a very quiet man. He never wanted to go out but just remained at home evening after evening behind his newspaper. She had no help from him in establishing a social life: either she had to create it by herself or have none at all. He was not the cause of her depressions, of course, but his attitude undoubtedly contributed to them. A book about marriage by David Cohn has recently appeared, *Love in America,* in which the author stresses the lack of interest of the American husband in his wife. The husband tends to come home to hide behind his newspaper, or to go to the golf club, or play bridge or poker with the boys and to be disinterested in his wife. If the wife cannot interest him, the children are even less likely to do so.

We have talked with college and medical students of both sexes who showed surprise when we said that the adolescent should be fairly well decided upon the kind of work he or she is going to do in his lifetime. Some students thought this was asking too much of the adolescent and argued that thoughts concerning a career occurred casually, perhaps during the senior year in college. We feel that not only should the adolescent be doing a great deal of thinking and planning about what he is going to do but also that the subject should be brought up and discussed from time to time by the parents during the *latent period,* while the child is in grade school. Nothing is decided all at once; at least nothing so important as one's life work should be decided without some thought and reflection. Therefore an interest should be shown in the child's play and work and inquiries should be made to find out whether he is observing how the workaday world operates and where he can fit in. Parents should find out whether he is observing butchers, mechanics, engineers, doctors, lawyers and what they do in order that he can at least make a start in thinking of where his place in the world is going to be.

Gangs and Juvenile Society

Before leaving the matter of sex, remember a great many children enter gangs and groups. They do this as a kind of protest against the parents for not having been very good truth tellers. Since the parents have not been companionable and friendly, have not answered their questions and have not been as interested in them as they could wish, the children seem to group together during the latent period more than at any other time. They have their secrets which they tell only to each other. They do not confide in their parents because their parents have disappointed them by not being confiding enough in them. They are trying to find out about life in their own way.

Sometimes a parent shows an air of concern and remarks that it worries her a little that her grade-school child keeps his thoughts so much to himself. He stays in his room a great deal, or even if he plays with others, she cannot find out very much what he is thinking or talking about. One hears this complaint more often from the parents of adolescents, since the adolescent is frequently sullen, close-mouthed and difficult. He will not confide or share his life with his parents. The reason is quite obvious. The adolescent does not share his feelings and ideas with the parents because they did not share their ideas with him when he was a child. The drawing away from the adults into daydreams, into fantasies, into having only one or two friends, all of which ultimately results in marked social inadaptation or frank mental disease, may have had their beginnings during the latent period.

Cruelty and Aggression

During the latent period schoolchildren tend to be little bullies and tyrants. They want to control or feel that they can control someone. A certain amount of this is worked out in games, but even in spite of games the phenomenon of "being picked on" occurs during the grade-school period. Perhaps there is not much of it before latency because the play of young children is usually supervised, but there is always some of it. In the latent period, when girls and boys are less supervised by older people than during the previous periods, they can be extremely cruel to each other. They form cliques, punishing those they dislike by excluding them. They hate their rivals, verbally castigating each other because they want to feel important and because it is important to them that they affect other persons and affect them rather painfully.

Actually children do not limit cruelty to each other. Often during this period boys will be critical of grownups, especially if the latter are too weak or helpless to retaliate. A certain amount of accepted boyish pranks is directed toward older persons in the neighborhood, which may merge into actual delinquency at times. If anyone asked these boys and girls why they cannot be more considerate of each other or of older people they might not be able to state the reason. Perhaps a few could do so. The parents, in order to be able to give them the understanding necessary to enable them to improve the situation, must know the answer. They must be able to interpret to the children the reason for their cruelty and dislike of each other. The explanation is that older people have not been especially kind to the children, have not shown them the value of kindness, consideration and "giving the other fellow a break" by example as well as by precept.

Even from the most understanding family we must expect a certain amount of residue of the resentment for this previous treatment. The resentment has to be worked off, absorbed, or "cured" during this latent period. It is important that it be recognized and that something be done about it through friendship and closer attention, in order that the resentment, hostility, tendency toward exclusion, loneliness and homosexuality do not increase to too great a degree and reach a point where there is no turning back.

Up to now we have considered the tendency during latency of getting together in groups of the same sex. This tendency in the development of the human being for boys to seek the company of boys and girls to seek the company of girls is referred to as a "natural homosexual period." They feel their own sex is desirable and the opposite sex is more or less worthless. Not until later, and with some of the work that we have indicated, do they emerge naturally out of this homosexual period into heterosexual interests.

The Superego

Another phenomenon of the latent period lies in the development of conscience, or the superego. The part of the personality that comprises the instinctual impulses of aggression and sexuality leading to the tendency of human beings to be egocentric and selfish is called the id. When toilet training begins, if not before, the child comes to feel that he is a separate entity and must become responsible to society. As we have said before, the parent cannot always be present in order to keep reminding the child to be considerate and to do what society expects. For this purpose the child must erect within his own mind some mechanism that will keep him doing the right thing automatically. This part of the personality is called the superego or conscience. Thus three theoretical divisions are erected in order to help our understanding of personality development: (1) the instinctual forces referred to as the id, (2) the ego or "I" which we know as our "selves," and (3) the ideals and dictates of society referred to as the superego. The system makes clear the relations of the three main forces at work and shows that the ego, or self, is always the center of the struggle.

During the latent period a great many situations and events occur that help the developing human being to form a conscience, to make of him a good citizen, to enable him to be a capable person, and to mold him into a considerate person. Up to now the child has been concerned with weaning, toilet training, being neat and clean, and generally involved in a great many questions concerning sexual problems. During the latent period he begins to go to school, he acquires a larger vocabulary, begins to read and to hear about the people who have lived before him and how they behaved. The parents are usually the most important people to the child during the first three periods of development and they still should figure as most important in the formation of the super-ego. However, when the child enters the latent period the parents' influence is enhanced by the educational procedure during the grade school. The school curriculum teaches the child about our national and international heroes and their achievements. He learns about soldiers, statesmen, writers, poets, inventors and philosophers, and the important contributions they have made to society. He wants to be like these heroes because they have brought credit upon themselves, and he feels that if he follows the same kind of life and method of handling himself, if he does a similar piece of good work he will bring credit to himself. And just as his history books relate the adventures of military heroes, so do his geography books tell about courageous navigators, his mathematics books reveal the intellectual ability of the mathematicians, his radio at home tell him about Superman and all the other "heroes" that manufacturers of contemporary products have created in order to sell their wares. The motion picture plays its role, too. Probably more regulation of movies for children will be enforced as time goes on in order that more suitable material may be available for them. The movies make a great impression upon the child.

The Role of the Teacher

In addition to what he hears from his parents and at school, the teacher and the character of the teacher exert a profound influence upon the mind of the child. Human beings of every age want to have heroes, and there is a great deal of hero worship in the world. It is said that there is more hero worship in America than in any other country. We worship our movie stars, our baseball players and our boxing champions. Just as

adults need heroes to worship, so children need them even more, because the child's life is smaller and his interests less diverse. For this
reason the teacher becomes an unusually important person. In fact, she
can be next to the most important person in the child's life—the parent
—during each year or every year of school.

We need to pay attention to the character and personality of our
teachers. Boards of education attempt to do so now, but in a too limited
way, and every once in a while the newspapers report controversies regarding the eligibility of certain teachers. We personally feel that only
those persons who have a well-rounded personality and are well adjusted emotionally are desirable as teachers. Surely we would all agree
to that, considering the important role teachers play in the formation of
the child's personality. Nevertheless, it is a fact that some areas exclude
women teachers after they marry, when through marriage and possibly
having children of their own they may be in a better position to understand and inspire children than the unmarried teachers. We are all
aware of the unfortunate fact that there have been and continue to be
teachers who have no interest in children themselves but who consider
teaching a fairly good vocation, with short hours and long vacations in
summer, and one having more prestige than office or factory work. And
then there are teachers who if they take interest in a child at all, do so
to show favoritism for their "pets." Children sometimes suffer a great
deal from this kind of teacher.

On the other hand the person who is really interested in teaching
and inspiring children, in being a friend to them, aside from imparting
knowledge, can mean a great deal in the development of their personality. Uncles, aunts, neighbors, friends of the family may also play an
important role in forming the child's personality. Perhaps the reader
can look back and remember the interest of some person outside the
family—perhaps a teacher at college, or a Boy Scout master, or some
friend of the family—which influenced him profoundly. The reason is
that during the latent period a great deal of emphasis is still being put
upon the process of imitation, or that process which is more intensive
and more thoroughgoing than imitation—identification. Children will
talk about being some prominent person. For instance, boys may talk
about being a General MacArthur or a well-known flier such as Jimmy
Doolittle. Girls may identify themselves with a nurse or a teacher or a
movie star. In doing so they are playing the role of someone they have
seen and admired, all of which contributes to character building through

the tendency of human beings to imitate and identify with older persons. This process goes on more intensely during the latent period than later. During puberty, for instance, children have come to the point of being rather skeptical and feeling that they have been through the age of illusions. Many have reached an age of regrettable self-sufficiency by the time they are fourteen. A great many adolescents feel it is silly and childish to be too interested in imitating other people and regard it as a sign of weakness. They too readily assume they can learn nothing more from adults; they know practically everything already. Children of grade-school age, on the other hand, have not reached this stage. They are willing to be interested and inspired by other people.

During the latent period much religious influence enters the lives of children. They learn of biblical characters, of the accomplishments and beliefs of religious people and tend to take them seriously and will, no doubt, continue to take them seriously if the adults around them live according to the golden rule themselves. When children get away from the better parts of religious teaching it is usually because of some disillusionment about it suffered at the hands of adults.

A certain slight distinction is made in textbooks between superego and ego ideal. The superego pertains more directly to the concepts of right and wrong, the concepts that hinge around the do's and don't's, the concepts that have a moral turn to them; whereas the ego ideal pertains more to the kind of person one wants to be, the kind of personality characteristics which one will have and which do not relate so specifically to conscience. Mannerisms, for instance, are picked up by children in imitation. The way other people walk, the way they dress, the words and pronunciations they use are not characteristics directly related to right and wrong. These are matters of choice and undergo change from time to time and pertain more to what we call the ego ideal.

We have sometimes questioned whether it is necessary to make this fine distinction between superego and ego ideal or whether the nature of the superego and its functions merely needed study to be understood; we feel that extra names do not substitute for study and understanding. Freud made the statement, for instance, that the superego was the heir to the Oedipus complex. This meant accepting the fact that the boy cannot possess his mother and must accept the incest taboo which is a moral issue imposed by society. Having accepted this bit of social law within his mind as superego material the boy then has to go through a further task of repressing his hostility to his father, using what goodwill is available to love him and imitate him and to regard his qualities as good. This latter task illustrates ego ideal which has been called a precipitate of the superego.

Play and Work Experience

Finally, another point to be taken into consideration during the latent period is the matter of play and work. Children need something to hold their attention during this period; they need to be occupied; they need something upon which to expend their energies. Some children seem to be naturally more resourceful about play than others. We maintain that the child who is resourceful at the age of eight or nine is the child whose mother was resourceful when he was two or four. He has learned to play because his parents have helped him and given him some ideas about it in the beginning. We sometimes hear a parent say to the child, "Run off and play." The child does not know what to play with; perhaps he does not have any toy within reach or has not known enough of the pleasure of playing with others to enjoy playing by himself. Children of the latent period still need help with their play, and here is where the father and mother should come in. A boy of fifteen may be excluded from the baseball game simply because when he was seven or eight his father was too busy to play with him and get him used to throwing a ball in good form. Girls may not know how to enter into dancing classes, picnics, tennis games or other activities because they were not helped by recreations with the mother when they were younger.

Children become embarrassed about their lack of dexterity and poise in comparison with other children and become sensitive to remarks made about their abilities and so begin to be left out of activities by others, or because of sensitivity leave themselves out. Whenever we encounter a person who is suffering from a psychoneurosis or a psychosomatic disease, we ask if he enjoyed school. Practically never do we get an answer in the affirmative. This is not necessarily because the patient did not like the teacher, or had difficulty in learning, but because he did not know how to get along and be popular with the group. The patients felt outside of the group, which means they began to have difficulty in social adaptation at an early age and missed the emotional nourishment that comes from a well-rounded popularity even in childhood.

It is also important to help children to work. It is difficult, we will admit, to have children do a great deal of work in the city, especially in some homes. Primitive peoples teach the children to work along with them, the girls to cook and weave, the boys to hunt and fish. When our country was less industrial and more agricultural and with small trades flourishing, there were always things for children to do. They were expected to do them, and they got pleasure in helping the parents and working along with them. In the city today there is less work activity for children but there is still an appalling disregard on the part of parents in helping children to work at what is available. Often mothers are in a hurry to get the dishes washed, or afraid a glass will be broken, or do not want the little girl around making a mess, so the child is never allowed to help about the house. At twenty-one some girls are most inept at homemaking.

Likewise, there are boys who are not only awkward at play but also in the use of their hands. They have missed the fun of working or, rather, the pleasure in working is not a part of their personality makeup. Some of the serious work difficulties we encounter in patients are among those who have never learned to work with pleasure on small things at home, even once in a while.

In the home of a friend we once saw a child of six whose father had brought him a present of a sandbox that had not yet been put together. The child wanted it put together, but the father did not want to do it at that time and kept putting the child off with such statements as, "We'll do it later." The child pleaded and pleaded with the father, urging him to let them do it together. The father still insisted that he was too busy. Later we heard that while the child was out walking with his mother, the father hurriedly put the sandbox together: he wanted to be spared the trouble of having the child around, annoying him with his youthful awkwardness and eagerness to help! So the child had neither the opportunity to use his hands nor the enjoyment of the pleasure of work in the company of someone he loved. This was not a wise procedure for, as the reader can see, the father missed a real opportunity to have the child erect the sandbox with him, letting him find pleasure in doing it.

Later in life this same father may be astonished that his son is not willing and eager to help him with some project of his business, and will think his son ungrateful for all he has done for him. The son's attitude will not result from the one instance of the sandbox but from the father's general attitude during the boy's childhood. The son will then be doing to the father the same thing the father did to him in regard to the sandbox—and other projects—and in this way will be imitating his father's earlier behavior. When the boy had the energy and enthusiasm for work it was not caught hold of by the parent and directed in a constructive way.

The progressive school has fostered the plan of the child working along with the adult—a close physical and emotional tie being interwoven with the activity. Whenever this is possible to work out in the home, it is important for the parents to sacrifice time and to create projects in which parent and child work together. The ritualistic sending of the boy or girl to do a piece of work for work's sake alone is of questionable value. One well-to-do woman we knew always had the idea that her son should have a paper route and deliver papers. She had been impressed with the stories of successful men who had started life as newsboys. She thought if her son could have some contact with newspapers when a boy, his success as a man would be practically assured. So she sent him forth to deliver papers which he hated because none of his friends did so. He was alone and conspicuous and doing something obviously unnecessary, merely gratifying an impractical whim of his mother's that had no value in character building. In fact it was more harmful than beneficial because it was no fun—only an abstract discipline which caused him to lose respect for his mother's good sense. If she had herself gone to work in her own garden, for instance, and besought his help in something mutually creative, the result would have been better. He could have at least been helping her, which he knew he was not doing when he was delivering papers.

These are some of the things we should think about in this so-called latent, quiescent period when nothing much is supposed to be happening and the children are "just attending school." As the reader can see, important situations and events occur which, if understood, can be made to be contributions to the child's personality, and which he can use to merge with what has gone before and with what is yet to come. If the events of this period are not understood or are neglected, they can leave a weakness in the personality which is corrected with great difficulty later in life.

BIBLIOGRAPHY FOR CHAPTER VII

Cohn, D., *Love in America*, Simon and Schuster, 1943.

Flugel, J. C., *The Psychoanalytic Study of the Family*, International Psychoanalytic Press, 1921.

Chapter VIII

EMOTIONAL DISTURBANCES THAT OCCUR DURING THE LATENT PERIOD

ALTHOUGH in the previous chapters we discussed the most common types of psychological illnesses that occur during each of the periods of infantile development, we left the formal discussion of the neuroses, psychoses and behavior problems of childhood until this point. The reader will understand that such illnesses do occur in younger and in older children.

General Considerations

Preliminary to a discussion of the neurotic symptom complexes we shall discuss the methods of history taking in children's problems, the examination of the child and some of the general principles that underlie treatment.

The medical approach to the study and treatment of emotional illnesses in children differs not at all from the medical approach to an organic illness. It consists in the collection of data concerning the child and his illness (i. e., the child's history and examination), the comparison between that data and the data that would be obtained from a well child (i. e., the psychopathology) and the grouping of the data and its comparison with the data known to indicate the various forms of illness (i. e., the diagnosis). Finally, it consists of a consideration of the measures that will help to restore the child to health and how to employ them (i. e., treatment).

History Taking and Diagnosis

It is advisable to have the parents or parent come without the child for the history interview. If the child is present at the interview, neither the parent nor the doctor will feel entirely free to discuss the child and his history. The child may become annoyed or frightened by some of the discussion. If he sits for an hour in the waiting room while the interview is taking place, he tends to become bored, to consider what terrible plans are being made for him and become frightened. All this unnecessary emotional turmoil is easily avoided by having the parents come alone.

Although there are certain questions to which the doctor requires an answer, it is better to start a history interview by asking the parent to tell all she knows and thinks about the child and his symptoms. With this general question and a little encouragement, the parent will usually launch into a description of both. This description will be infinitely more reliable and valuable than any history obtained by the question-and-answer method. As long as the parent continues to talk there is no need to interrupt except to ask for the dates of the various events she is describing. When the parent has related all she can, then the doctor can ask any questions that still remain unanswered. Not only will the history obtained through this method be more reliable but the doctor will also get more valid impressions as to the attitudes of the parents to each other, to the patient, and to the other children in the family. The patient's history should be recorded chronologically.

The history should include a description and history of the presenting symptoms. In many cases there is one presenting symptom for which the parent brings the child, but it is improbable that it is the only evidence of pathology. It is necessary, therefore, to obtain a complete picture of all phases of the child's activity in order to ascertain the presence of other symptoms. This is doubly necessary because the doctor may note certain phases of behavior which are undoubtedly pathological but which the parents may regard not only as nonpathological but even as admirable characteristics. Inquiry must be made concerning the child's adjustment in school, his educational achievement, his habitual emotional reactions, his fears, habits and physiological status.

Having obtained this data we next obtain the story of the life experiences to which the child has been subjected—acts of fate, parental attitudes, any excessive sexual stimulations, the importance of which we discussed in Chapter VI. At the same time we obtain the history of his psychosexual development.

It must not be expected that this history will be complete in any way. An accurate history of a psychogenic illness can only be given after the illness has been cured. This is inherent in the nature of the illness, which consists of an attempt on the part of the patient to avoid remembering and so knowing the painful experiences which have caused him to alter his psychological adjustments to his real life. Moreover, since the history of the child is obtained mostly from the parent, who does not know all the details of his experiences, the most significant data is obtainable only from the child himself. However as much material as possible should be obtained from the parent, particularly regarding the child's psychosexual development and traumatic experiences and his objective reaction to the latter.

Having obtained as much history as possible from the parents, it is now necessary to examine the child. In most cases the examination must be threefold: physical, intellectual, and emotional.

It is not necessary in every case to have an accurate estimate of the child's intellectual ability. Only if the description of his physical development and symptoms—difficulties with schoolwork, etc.—indicates that there may be intellectual retardation is such an estimate needed. This is done best by a competent psychologist, who knows how to use the standard tests of intellectual ability.

Special care should be taken—especially if there is an apparent unevenness in the child's development—to avoid the sadly common practice of gauging the intellectual capacity by the result from a single test, however good that test may be or however expertly administered. It is the rule, rather than the exception, to discover differences of considerable magnitude among test results for a given individual; and these differences are often of major value in diagnosis.

The tests most commonly used are as follows:

1. *The 1937 Revision of the Stanford-Binet Intelligence Test.* The most widely used intelligence test is the Terman-Merrill Revision of the intelligence test first developed by Binet. Although applicable to adults, the test was standardized on children and adolescents. Intelligence quotient and mental age are obtained by the test. The so-called "scatter," the kind and number of problems the patient is unable to solve, has proved in our experience to be of diagnostic importance. The diagnostic indications obtained appear to agree with the findings of the personality tests and have proved valuable in differential diagnosis of mental delinquency and psychosis as well as of psychoses and neuroses.

2. *The Cornell-Coxe Performance Test.* This test, the newest of its kind, is a nonverbal test, and hence can be used in cases with speech or language difficulty. It is used to measure practical reasoning and visual-motor co-ordination and is standardized only on children and adolescents.

3. *The Bellevue Adult Intelligence Scale.* This test was developed by D. Wechsler and is the first test standardized on adults. It consists of a

verbal and a nonverbal part, each of which can yield an intelligence quotient; thus it unites the advantages of the two tests described above. We have found that the "scatter," the numerical relation of the scores of the ten groups of tasks of which the test consists, has diagnostic significance.

4. *The Minnesota Preschool Scale.* This test for preschool children fulfills the same needs that the Bellevue Test does for adults. It consists of a verbal and a nonverbal part.

5. *Chicago Nonverbal Examination.* The age range is from eight years through the superior adult. It yields scores that may be transmuted into M.A. and I.Q. and also percentile rank.

6. *Kohs' Block Designs Test.* The age range is from six years through the adult; it yields M.A. and I.Q.

7. *Carl Hollow Square Scale.* It is designed particularly for use with adult subjects but is usable down to ten-year levels. The results are expressed in terms of M.A., I.Q., and percentile rank.

8. *The Rorschach Test.* This gives valuable information as to the characteristics of the child's psychic reactions and indicates the severity of the illness from which he suffers. It is often of great value in helping to decide the difficult question as to whether the presenting symptom, such as a phobia or temper tantrums in a young child, merits intensive psychotherapy. It furnishes a flood of light on underlying inner drives and defense reactions which may not be easily obtained otherwise except through a prolonged study. If the result of the test is to be valid it should be administered and scored only by a trained person. If it seems warranted the special tests dealing with educational achievement of special abilities—artistic, mechanical, musical, etc.—should be given.

The examination of the child's physical and emotional status is made by the physician. How should this be conducted? The purpose is not at this point to alter the child. If such is the doctor's purpose in the first interview with the child, he will not accomplish it except through a lucky guess, nor will he accomplish the important purpose of understanding why this child is ill and the nature of the illness. Unless he does the latter, he cannot embark upon a scientific treatment program. Of course all of us, as physicians, have the wish to cure our patients as completely and speedily as possible. If, however, this wish becomes more than a guiding urge and begins to compel us to act even before we know where, when and how to act, then we ourselves are suffering from a neurotic compulsion to obtain relief for ourselves from some feeling of anxiety of which we may be conscious or, as is more often the case, unconscious. The successful therapist is one who has the wish and purpose to cure the patient as thoroughly and speedily as possible, but not the compulsion to attempt to do so without regard to common sense and scientific procedures. The young physician, just starting practice, has a greater and more understandable anxiety in this respect than the older, better established one. Although this is understandable, the young physician should be aware of this feeling of anxiety and learn to cope with it, or his practice will suffer.

The real purpose of the examination is twofold: to ascertain with what kind of child the doctor will be dealing, and to help the child to feel friendly toward the doctor. These two purposes can very easily become mutually antagonistic and exclusive. In the child's unconscious, an inquiry into what he thinks and feels is regarded as an assault and the child reacts to this unconscious feeling of being assaulted by an attitude of hostility. If the physician is largely urged by the purpose of finding out about the child and pays little heed to the second purpose of the examination, the child becomes frightened and hostile and the purpose ruined. If the physician is concerned mostly with having the child be friendly to him, he may avoid methods of finding out what the child is like and so the examination becomes stultified. Both purposes have to be maintained at the same time. Practically, it is desirable to pay more attention to the second than to the first purpose, for the result will not be as detrimental to the treatment of the child.

When the parent brings the child for examination, it is best to see the child alone. There is usually no difficulty in separating the child from the parent. Occasionally one meets a very upset, sick parent—usually suffering from a mild paranoid psychosis—who will not permit the child to be alone with the physician. Occasionally the child is openly afraid to leave the parent. In most instances, however, if the separation is made gradually, the fear is readily overcome.

Which part of the examination—the physical or the emotional—should be made first? The physical examination should be made last; it should be done by telling the child that the physician has to know also about his physical health, with reassurances that he will not be hurt. Most physicians are accustomed to start with the physical. This is a mistake, since the physical examination produces so many frightening ideas in the child's unconscious mind. His unconscious regards the physical examination as even more of an attack than questioning is, and therefore it is no wonder that so many children act as if they dreaded the physical examination even when they know they are not going to be hurt. As every pediatrician knows, examination of the throat, ears and genitals should be left till the last, and if the child becomes very frightened may be omitted unless there are definite indications that organic pathology in these organs may be present. Fear of the examination of these parts is due to the fantasies all people have in regard to them, fantasies that started at early age, particularly in regard to the mouth and throat, as we mentioned earlier. We believe that when a physician is asked to examine a child for a definitely organic illness, it is well to spend a little time first getting acquainted with the child—a procedure that is often carried out by the pediatrician in his private office but seems to be invariably neglected in outpatient departments.

In urban centers, laboratory specimens are usually taken by the laboratory worker, so the physician usually does not have to deal with this procedure. Laboratory tests should not be done routinely on a child but only when they are necessary. The decision in this respect has to be left to the judgment of the physician in the individual case. The electroencephalogram also is useful, although the results of the test are not as reliable as could be hoped for. Certainly when the electroencephalogram shows a disturbance in the brain waves, the pathology is more serious than when it is negative.

How does the physician proceed in making an examination of the child's emotional reactions? The technique of establishing a friendly relationship with the child consists in treating him as a reasonable human being. The small child often has difficulties expressing himself verbally, so it is well to have a small supply of toys on hand. Three dolls (father, mother and baby), blocks (to build a house), one or more toy automobiles, airplanes, guns, some modeling clay, crayons, and paper are best. Usually it is sufficient to draw the child's attention to the toys and tell him he can play with them. Everything he does from that point on is of importance in understanding what he is like. In the record, one should list whether he plays with the toys or not, and if he does, what toys he selects and what play he performs with them. A preschool child's span of attention is short and may go from one kind of toy to another, but if he constantly wants to go back to his mother or if too often he seems bored with the toys, he is feeling anxious and this fact is important.

The child of school age, and often this is true of the preschool child as well, senses something strange if a new adult tries to cajole him into being friendly. In our opinion, it is well to begin the interview with an older child by telling him who the doctor is, the kind of cases he treats, giving a short description of some of the problems that have been treated, explaining that the children all came to the doctor because they were upset and knew he could help them. We tell the child that we can only help him when we know as much about him as he knows about himself and therefore he will have to tell us everything about himself. We reassure the child about being hurt—unless we know he will have to be, when we make this fact clear. We assure him that the interview is confidential, that we are not going to tell his parents, teachers or any-one anything he tells us. He can report this interview if he wants to, but we will not do so without his permission. We also assure him that he can tell us anything in any way he wishes and we will not criticize, scold or punish him. We tell him that we do not expect him to believe this because he must have found already that adults frequently promise one thing and do another, but that we are going to try to be honest with him and he will only be able to find out about our honesty through experi-ence. We then tell him that to help him we have to know everything about him and he can tell us starting with anything he likes. If he feels hesitant about talking, we have toys and perhaps in his play with them he will be able to show us himself. We ask him if he wants to ask any questions about treatment or about ourselves. If he has no questions we suggest that he go ahead.

Everything he produces after this is important because what he says or does represents his reaction patterns and often indicates the factors that have caused these reaction patterns. It may not be possible at this point to say what his type of play or conversation means in respect to the causative factors, but this is not important at this time. More impor-tant is an estimation of his reaction patterns, i. e., of the kind of child we have to deal with.

Having examined the child and his environment, the next step is to come to a decision as to the direction of the major treatment emphasis. Is this child's illness the result of traumatic situations that are still oper-ating or is it the result of situations that operated in the past—situations which the child has made part of his personality and to which he con-tinues to react *as though* they were current?

In many cases the traumatic situations—particularly those due to ad-verse parental attitudes—are still current and are day by day forcing the child to develop unhealthy reaction patterns in order to enable him to live with his own desires and the demands of his parents. In these cases treatment has to be directed toward the child's environmental situation, since he is little, dependent and helpless and can neither change the attitudes in his environment nor leave of his own volition—if he runs away he will be brought back by the police. (The adult is in an entirely different position. If his environment is uncomfortable he can change it voluntarily, except, of course, in such circumstances as military service.) If the child's difficulties call for a drastically changed environment, even the physician himself sometimes encounters difficulty in arranging that the child live in another home and often he will find this impossible.

If treatment is to be directed toward the environment—i. e., toward the adverse parental attitudes—how can it be done? As mentioned earlier, the parents' attitude to the child is a form of behavior and therefore has to be treated as such. The more the physician understands the causes that have led to the adverse attitude toward the child the better he will be able to apply effective therapy. It is therefore decidedly helpful to devote some time to permitting the parents to talk about themselves and their life experiences. The several techniques of therapy by which changes in the adverse parental attitudes to the child may be brought about are the same as those used in the treatment of neurotic persons. They are discussed in Chapter XVI.

Treatment for the parents does not necessarily always accompany treatment for the child. If the child is of preschool age treatment for both parents and child must occur simultaneously because the child has to live with them. He is small and helpless and has to conform to their attitudes, and if he is cured of one neurosis and the parents have adverse attitudes he will have to develop another in order to get along with them. During the latent period it is usually best to follow the same plan. It is not so necessary in adolescence; particularly in late adolescence, there is little real need for it as far as the child himself is concerned.

Although we are firmly convinced that adverse parental attitudes arise as a result of conflicts within their personalities we feel that some parents show what seem to be adverse attitudes toward the child simply because they are unaware of the propriety of certain phases of the child's behavior and emotional reactions. A parent may believe that it is improper for a child ever to become angry or fight and may with the best motives in the world curb every such display. If the parent knew a little more about human beings he would not condemn the child so severely, and thus what appeared to be an adverse attitude would disappear.

We wonder if such situations could not be prevented by courses in the grammar schools, high schools and colleges in the emotional life of human beings. In grammar school and the early part of high school the courses might be confined to the emotional reactions of children and adults, and in the latter part of high school and in college they might be devoted to the emotional needs and reactions of children and to the relationships between parents and children. Such courses could very well be part of the social sciences. All this presupposes that the teacher be conversant with the subject matter. The more contacts we have with teachers the more firmly we believe that they should be selected on the basis of the degree of intuitive understanding they have about human behavior, and that those who do not show much should either be asked to undergo a personal psychoanalysis or choose another profession. It seems curious that such courses have not always been included in curriculums. We wonder if this is not because adults—both parents and teachers—are unwilling to have children learn about the emotional reactions of human beings, because then they would realize that the adults also have emotional reactions and feelings like they do. The adults are afraid they might lose their authority if the children realized this.

There are some parents the adverseness of whose attitude toward the child cannot be ameliorated by treatment. There are other situations where the problem between the child and the parents, originally perhaps caused by the parents' adverse attitude, has reached such a degree of bitterness that no amelioration can be expected until parents and child are separated for some time. In these cases, if treatment is going to have any value for the child, he must be separated from his parents. We do not believe that in every case treatment for the child should enable him to be able to adjust himself comfortably to any situation. We do realize that separation of the child from the parents produces another traumatic situation for the child, but we believe that this trauma can be dealt with during treatment. We do not believe that mere separation of the child from his parents is always a useful treatment measure, but we do believe that just as psychiatrists and social workers have erred in the past in considering it a treatment measure in itself, so they tend to err in the present in not utilizing it sufficiently as an adjuvant form of therapy.

Therapeutic separation of the child from his parents may be either partial or complete, and if complete may be either temporary or permanent. Partial separation is useful often in the case of young children, i. e., of preschool age. In large urban communities there are many families who live in small apartments on busy streets where the children have no play space. Often parents do not have sufficient money to hire a person to take the child to a place where he can play or to look after him so they can go out. In such situations the child, lacking opportunity for adequate play, feels shut in and becomes angry and resentful. He expresses this resentment through annoying behavior. The mother also feels shut in and resentful toward the child, and his bad behavior increases her resentment. A vicious circle rapidly develops which is popularly described as getting on each other's nerves. In such instances, if the child can spend part of the day in a day nursery or nursery school, where he has adequate play space, he feels less resentful and behaves better, and the mother being less shut in feels less annoyed at him. This breaks the vicious circle and their relationship improves. In some cases this is all that is necessary in the way of treatment. In others, treatment for the child and the mother can proceed more effectively as a result. It goes without saying that the teachers in the nursery school and day nursery must be well-trained professional people who understand and can deal adequately with the problems of child development.

This is one important use of nursery schools as a therapeutic aid. Nursery schools are becoming an integral part of American life and it seems important at this time to consider them as an educational and community function. We realize that nursery-school teachers may not agree completely with our opinion, but we believe we should present this opinion in order that the psychiatrist and the educator may be able to come to some agreement. In the first place we believe that under ideal conditions (i. e., the presence in a home of two parents; a feeling of love by the parents for the child; adequate knowledge on their part as to the needs of the child, as to what is and what is not important in child training and the ability to make practical use of that knowledge; sufficient space and opportunity for the child to exercise his energies; and the opportunity to play with other children of the same age and of both sexes) a nursery-school placement is unnecessary. If any of these factors are missing the nursery school may be very useful in supplying the deficiency. If it is necessary for the mother to work outside the home, the child of preschool age is better off if he is placed in a nursery school. Here he is supervised by trained adults who understand the needs of the child. If the mother has rejected the child or if she or both parents use unwise and unnecessary measures of child training the child should have the benefit of a nursery-school experience. If there is insufficient play space or little opportunity for contact with other children the nursery school will make up these deficiencies.

It should be remembered that the placement of a small child in nursery school involves two traumatic experiences—the separation from the mother and acquaintance with new people. It is necessary for the child to weaken his attachment to the mother and to make an attachment to a new woman. During this period of adjustment he suffers anxiety and shows all or certain of the clinical symptoms; and his fears of being deserted, lonely and not being loved are increased. As a consequence the transition from home to nursery school should be made gradually so that he can become adjusted to the change without being hurt too much.

Any parent who contemplates placing his child in nursery school should give these facts about the traumatic possibilities in the placement serious consideration and determine whether the reasons he intends to make this placement are sufficient to outweigh the disadvantages. Similarly, any physician who prescribes nursery-school placement for a small child should weigh all the pros and cons.

In our opinion, as a treatment measure for certain problems and as a means of providing needful satisfaction for children who are underprivileged [1] in certain ways, nursery schools are an essential part of the educational system of urban communities. They are not essential in the suburbs or in nonurban districts. They should not exist simply as convenient places where parents can park their children while they are engaged in interests that exclude their family responsibilities.

In older children this type of therapy is accomplished through their compulsory school attendance so that as a therapeutic measure partial separation of this sort is valueless for them. In cases where there is a great deal of antagonism between the parents and the child, or where the management of the child or his problem by the parents interferes with the progress of therapy, a temporary separation between the two, at least until treatment for both can get under way, is desirable. Boarding schools, camps and hospitals are all useful places for such a temporary separation. Which one will be selected depends largely on the child's

---

[1] By *underprivileged* we do not mean living in a low financial status but mean that the child, because of where he lives or with whom he lives, does not have the opportunities for adequate management, love, play space and companionship.

symptoms, for this type of placement is not curative but is only an adjuvant to treatment. Children with marked chronic aggressive symptoms or delinquent behavior or those who have enuresis, or soiling, are not acceptable in most of these places, although hospitals are more tolerant of enuretics than schools or camps are. We believe temporary placement in a foster home—and by temporary placement we mean for a period of less than a year—to be inadvisable. The return home from a foster-home placement will be much more traumatic than will the return from a camp, school or hospital. The foster home, being a home, has an aspect of permanence about it that is not the case with the other placements; hence the child, knowing that it is not customary to remain for years in a camp, school or hospital, but feeling that it might be possible in the foster home, tends to allow himself to form less strong attachments in the former than he does in the latter.

Permanent placement of a child in a foster home is a serious procedure. The most important item is the personalities of the foster parents. It is for this reason that there are child-placement agencies, whose business it is to study foster homes very carefully before making a placement. If foster-home care is deemed necessary one of these agencies should be consulted. It goes without saying that it should be the best one in the community. If the child shows marked chronic aggressive or delinquent symptoms, foster-home placement is usually valueless, for there are not many foster homes or many communities in which such foster homes are located that can tolerate the depredations of this type of child. The usual history is that after a short period of time the child has to be changed to another home and on top of his original troubles there is superimposed the trauma of another broken relationship.

The Treatment of the Child

The treatment of the child depends on the treatment of the causes of his illness. If the child is languid, tires easily, fretful, whiny and undernourished, and if the examination reveals a definite vitamin deficiency or an anemia it will be obvious to any physician—but somehow, curiously enough, not so obvious to the parents—that the child's vitamin deficiency or his anemia must be treated. If the child is having difficulty in school and the examination discloses that his intelligence quotient is very much above or below the average, treatment will be directed toward a school placement that will be more adequate for his intelligence. If the examination discloses that the child's difficulty is an emotional conflict the treatment must be directed toward helping him to a better solution of the emotional problem.

How is this to be done? From a study of the child's history and from the examination of the child it is possible to estimate the nature and extent of his emotional conflict. The child is not aware that he has such conflicts. He knows only that he has been brought for the treatment of a particular symptom. He has had the first interview, and regular treatment has been decided on. How is he to be approached? He is told that there is a cure for his symptoms and that it will lie in finding out the cause. The cause is due to some worries and fears he has—perhaps he knows about them, perhaps he doesn't. The only way to find out about them is for the physician to know him as well as he knows himself— much better than his parents know him—and usually better than he knows himself. Adults can talk and tell about themselves—so can children, but they usually find it more difficult to do than adults. Therefore if he can't talk he can play with the toys in the playroom, as we saw earlier; in so doing he may dramatize his worries and fears and then the psychiatrist and he can talk about them.

These preliminary hours serve as an introduction to treatment. During them the child often tests the psychiatrist to see if he means what he says. It takes the child some time to develop a confidential relationship with the psychiatrist and often the latter has to demonstrate three things —that he is *able* to help the child in his life difficulties, that he is friendly to him and *wants* to help him, and that the child *is ill* and needs help.

This introductory period is of varying duration, depending on the nature of the child's problem or on the personality reactions he has developed as a defense against his psychic problems. It is an extremely essential part of treatment, and with certain illnesses requires the greatest skill and initiative on the part of the psychiatrist. During its progress the behavior of the child may show no change. It comes to an end gradually as the child learns to develop a feeling of friendliness and confidence toward the physician.

The second phase of the treatment consists in uncovering the child's conflicts and in helping him understand and solve them. The former is accomplished by observation and discussion of the data produced by the child either conversationally or dramatically. The psychiatrist's activity is directed toward helping the child to express himself freely and is accomplished by seeing that the necessary materials are available for the child to use in abreacting his repressed impulses (e. g., a child whose anal impulses have been repressed too much must have the opportunity to play with sand, water, clay and paints); that he has sufficient time to play out these impulses without interference; by explaining to him what desires and what fears of those desires he expresses in his play and productions; by correcting whatever misinformation he expresses, particularly regarding the facts of sexuality, and helping him to be completely frank and confidential. If it is apparent that the child feels that his father is mean and petty it often helps the child in verbalizing his feelings to say to him, "You know, you think your father is a pretty mean man." Along with this—and different from what is done with an adult—a certain amount of education is necessary; e. g., it is all right for the child to express his frustrated anal desires by dirtying up the playroom, but it is better for him after a while to learn to use finger paints constructively and also to use them outside the playroom.

The actual techniques and the means of employing them during this period of treatment are difficult to describe. They can be learned only through personal study with cases and are not susceptible to didactic presentation.

During the period of treatment the child's behavior at home may seem to the parents to be worse. Since parents often are upset by these changes they should be warned in advance that they will occur.

When the child has worked through his problems and is nonsymptomatic the question of the termination of treatment can be discussed with him and he can be allowed to take the responsibility as to how much longer he will continue to come. There are special ways in which treatment has to be applied to special types of cases and special adjuvant methods. These will be discussed under the appropriate illnesses.

At some point in this book the reader may say, "These descriptions of the emotional illnesses of childhood are very interesting and the discussion of their causes is very ingenious, but for each condition depicted there is advised a method of treatment that is often time consuming and expensive. Is this really necessary? What would happen if the child were not treated? Would he go on being sick or would he get well? I have seen children who suffered from some of these symptom complexes and after a time, often when they became adolescent, all their symptoms disappeared and you would never have known them for the same children. Also I have known adults who seemed to be reliable and truthful who related that they had suffered some emotional illness in childhood or even had behaved in a chronic aggressive manner, and yet as adults they seemed to be adjusting fairly well. Do not psychiatrists as a rule regard these childhood maladjustments too seriously and prescribe treatment that is really unnecessary, for if nothing were done would not the majority of children grow out of their illness? Also are there not children who show no symptoms during childhood but who suddenly out of a clear sky become ill during adolescence, and are there not adults who in adult life suffer from a neurosis or psychosis who have been perfectly well adjusted during childhood and adolescence?"

In reply to the questions we agree that the reader's observations seem to be correct, but we would have to question him as to his understanding of the process of "growing out of." We have endeavored to point out that the child at birth is simply a bundle of instinctual desires which demand immediate and complete gratification. This gratification has to be supplied by some person other than the child because the latter is not well enough developed to obtain it himself. If the other person does not gratify him the child feels unhappy and uncomfortable—he feels anxiety. As the child develops more neuromuscular skills he does not need to suffer as much anxiety because he can gratify his own needs or can actively induce other people to gratify them. In this sense, therefore, as he develops he will grow out of many of his feelings of anxiety because he is less dependent on the whims of other people. A simple example: The baby is uncomfortable because he is hungry. He cannot obtain food for himself but has to depend on his mother to feed him. The child can feed himself but has to depend on his parents to provide the food. The adult has learned to work, knows how and where to obtain food and gets it himself.

Much of this progress is due to the simple process of physical and intellectual development—he grows out of his infantile and childish helplessness. This is only one part of the process, however. Certain drives in all human beings are in conflict with each other, certain methods of gratifying certain drives are in conflict with the possibility of getting along with other people, and certain methods of gratification are in conflict with the social organization. In order that these conflicts be solved or at least that a working compromise be evolved, the inner drives have to be checked, redirected and sublimated. This is accomplished through the action of the ego and the superego. Each time that a drive has to be checked and then redirected or sublimated the individual feels anxious. With the appearance of the anxiety the ego has to develop new techniques by which the drives can obtain gratification through redirection and sublimation. As these new techniques become habitual they form part of the character of the individual.

This development of new habit patterns by the ego is also part of the process of growing up and of growing out of infantile behavior. Since each new technique as a method of avoiding anxiety becomes habitual we can say that all children grow out of anxiety situations. Is this growing out always equivalent to growing up, i. e., to the development of new techniques that will allow the gratification of inner drives in a more mature and socially acceptable manner? We should like it to be so in every individual instance, but quite frequently this does not happen. The nature of the drive and of the environmental situation may be such that the ego has to seek methods of defenses against the drive or against the dangers that would result from the environmental situation if the drive were expressed. These defense methods, such as reaction formation, etc., also become habitual and form part of the character. Thus the ego intimidated by the environment may first try to check any expression of the inner drive. This causes anxiety. The ego, in order to avoid the anxiety, tries to allow the drive expression—sufficiently disguised so as not to meet censure—or to allow its expression but at the same time to punish itself for the expression. We will discuss the way this happens in the case of the chronically aggressive child—the aggression is turned from the external world onto the self and a compulsion neurosis results, in which case the child has grown out of his direct expression of aggression but into a hampering and false conformity. In the first case he can use his aggressive drives, in the second he cannot use them at all. The result is a growing out, *not* a growing up.

Another interesting example of growing out of rather than growing up is found in the histories of childhood phobias. As we saw in an earlier chapter, the phobia is an attempt by projection to solve the conflict between the hostile and loving feelings for the parent of the same sex. The conflict between the feelings is painful and so both feelings are feared. The child's ego is too weak to deal with the situation, therefore he projects his feelings into the phobic object, from which he can then stay away. Often as he approaches adolescence the phobia seems to disappear, but fairly soon after we notice that the boy, who while he had the phobia was doing well at school, now does poorly. He is no longer projecting his conflict. He is dealing with his aggressive ambitions by acting as if they did not exist. However, he no longer feels anxiety although he may be worried by his lack of success in school. He has not grown up and solved his phobia. He has simply changed his technique of dealing with it, and his basic problem remains unaltered.

As one follows the life history of a child with a severe neurosis one observes that spontaneous cure or cure produced by changes in the environment seldom occurs. True, the symptoms change and one group disappears—only, however, to be replaced by another group. Squeezed in the iron glove of his intrapsychic mechanisms, the individual ekes out a precarious existence, with at best a narrow margin of reserve for adjustment. If some common but rather marked change (such as change of occupation, marriage, loss of money or of a loved person, induction into the armed services) occurs in his life, his reserve adjustment fails, his defense mechanisms are no longer effective and a neurosis develops whose symptoms are often the very ones that served in his original attempt to solve the problem. As the years passed he grew out of the neurosis into a complicated system of defenses but he has not grown up. These changes in symptoms correspond to the erection of the various types of defenses. After a period of years so many different types of defenses are superimposed on the original conflict that it may require a great deal of hard work for the psychoanalyst and the patient to discover the original conflict and the situations that brought it about.

The child who suffers from a neurosis thus may grow out of the symptom complex but he does not grow up, unless some kind fate so alters the circumstances of his life that he has a chance to start over again. This does not occur often. It is interesting to observe that children often realize this themselves. They will tell you that everything would be all right if they could be born again, and some even seek religion because they feel religion offers them a chance of rebirth. Of course the child may be fortunate enough to obtain psychiatric treatment through which he receives a new solution to his conflict. We have never seen an adult suffering from a neurosis whose history did not reveal a similar neurosis when he was a child.

This capacity on the part of the ego to alter itself and take up new methods, use old techniques in new situations and change its relationship to the environment, lethal as it becomes in the neurotic person, is both helpful and hopeful, for it indicates that with adequate help the individual's problems of adjustment can be solved. In fact were it not for this capacity and for the fact the unconscious urges are always striving for expression, psychiatric treatment would be impossible and there would be little possibility of progress or improvement for anyone.

We have emphasized, chapter after chapter, the importance of adequate therapy for the sick child, rather than letting the disease take its course, because we believe that sick children usually do not grow out of their sicknesses, that although they may grow out of one symptom complex into another, they may do so without actually growing up. We realize that our treatment methods at best are not as efficient as we could wish and that in many cases they seem to fall lamentably short of their goal, but they are the best we have at present. Only by use can they be made still more competent and efficient and perhaps less time consuming.

We have mentioned in another connection one point that has to be observed carefully in the treatment of every child and adult. The capacity of the ego to change is an asset in treatment, but at the same time it is a liability. Its tendency is to try to use methods with which it is familiar; e. g., the ego very often uses repression. Now in treatment the patient's ego may make use of this mechanism instead of finding a real solution for a difficulty. The therapist may be fooled by this into thinking that the patient is better whereas he is only less aware of his problem. Similarly the therapist may feel the naughty child has improved when he has stopped his naughtiness whereas he may only be developing a reaction formation against it.

The therapist also may depend too much on the patient's will as a mechanism for growing up. Often a child will suddenly state that he feels he does not need any more treatment and that he is going to stop. If the therapist is fooled by this behavior and regards it as a sign that the child feels capable of independence and is more grown up he may allow the child to set a termination for treatment. By looking carefully, however, he may find that the child is about to bring a difficult part of his problem into treatment but that his ego shrinks from the task and suddenly determines to avoid thinking about or discussing it. The child would therefore leave treatment with his problems unsolved and perhaps more convinced than ever of the efficacy of his obstinate will power. By continuing treatment the therapist could gradually accustom the child to think and talk about his real problems and so learn to solve them. It is this preference of the ego to use well-tried techniques, rather than to learn new ones, that furnishes one of the greatest barriers to the success of treatment and that is responsible for its taking so much time. And the tendency becomes more marked the longer the problem exists, being most evident in persons past middle age who often can receive little real benefit from psychotherapy.

As a result of the experience of many psychiatrists and of our own as well we have come to believe that every neurosis in childhood is a serious condition and that the situation should be studied carefully by a competent child psychiatrist who can decide what type of therapy is most suitable for the individual case. If this were done in all cases and the treatment actually carried out there would be a noticeable diminution in the number of breakdowns that occur in adult life.

Classes of Psychological Illness

We commonly see more children with neurotic manifestations during the latent and early adolescent periods than we see during the preschool period. It is for this reason that we are discussing the commoner neuroses of childhood at this point.

The psychological illnesses of childhood can be classified as follows:

1. Acute and chronic anxiety states.
2. Anxiety hysteria.
3. Conversion hysteria:
    (*a*) Pregenital.
    (*b*) After the phallic phase is attained.
4. Compulsion neuroses.
5. The chronic aggressive reaction states.
6. Delinquency.
7. Character neuroses.
8. Juvenile schizophrenia.

As in the case with adults, at the present time it is more usual to find a mixed neurosis than a clear-cut case of one type. However, we feel that for purposes of presentation it is better to discuss the etiology, psychopathology and treatment of the symptoms for which children are usually brought to the physician than to discuss the neuroses of childhood under this classification.

Anxiety States

During the height of the Christmas-shopping season in a department store it is common to see a small child standing among a group of adults, crying bitterly or perhaps screaming, with his face contorted by an expression of grief and terror, and inconsolable despite all the efforts of the adults to make him feel more comfortable. He is lost. If he is observed carefully it is found that his expression of terror mirrors the state of his feelings. He is really very frightened. He is restless and trembles. Both his pulse and his respiration are increased in frequency. He feels hot and cold alternately. He sweats profusely. If he is offered food he refuses it because he has no appetite. He may complain of feeling nauseated or actually may vomit. He may wet or soil himself or if he is old enough to control these activities he will suffer from diarrhea or frequency. If he should fall asleep through exhaustion his sleep will be restless, wakeful and filled with frightening dreams.

A similar problem, though perhaps not quite so dramatic, is seen in the older child who has arrived for the first time at camp. He cries a little (usually with deep sobs that shake his body), stays by himself, has no appetite, may have diarrhea or urinary frequency, and sleeps restlessly the first night. When he is asked to describe how he feels he states that he feels afraid and wants to go home. Any adult who has been by himself in a strange city can verify introspectively the unpleasantness of this feeling.

Both of these children feel frightened in a strange, unfamiliar world. It is a feeling all children have when they are separated from the persons they love. The feeling is very painful and upsets the child greatly. The fact has been particularly emphasized by the studies of the children who were evacuated from London before the blitz. It was plainly evident that the children were psychically more harmed by the separation from their parents than they could have been by the sights and sounds of the blitz.

A similar painful feeling that upsets the small child greatly is seen when the mother goes out to work. The child, even though placed in a good day-care center, becomes very frightened and many phases of his development and adjustment become upset. The following case is another good illustration of the same reaction. A father had decided to enlist in the armed services. He talked the matter over with his wife secretly lest his seven-year-old daughter be upset by the news that he was going away. Shortly after he had told his wife the date when he would leave, his daughter came home from school in the middle of the afternoon very frightened. She verbally attributed her panic to the fact that the teacher had scolded another child. Her sleep that night was fitful and broken by frightening dreams. The next day she refused to return to school and became nauseated and vomited when the parents tried to insist that she go. Although the parents thought they had discussed the matter secretly she had overheard and had become frightened by the knowledge that her adored father was going to leave her. Since she had learned a secret which she was not supposed to know she could not tell her parents why she was so frightened and therefore was not able to find relief by discussing the whole matter with them. (This case again emphasizes the concept we have tried to make clear in this whole book. It is better for children to know and to discuss their knowledge fully with their parents than for the parents to try to protect them from the knowledge of unpleasant facts.)

The feeling these children have is one of anxiety. The *feeling* is the same as the feeling of fear and is accompanied by the same bodily changes: trembling, restlessness, an increase in the rate of the pulse and respiration, alternating hot and cold, sweating, loss of appetite, nausea, diarrhea, frequency, and sleep which is fitful and broken by frightening dreams. (Sometimes these dreams become so frightening that the child begins to refuse to go to bed or if made to do so will dread falling asleep lest he have horrible dreams.) This reaction occurs when an individual believes himself to be in danger, either in a real danger or in danger of doing something or of wanting to do something for which he believes he will be punished either by physical pain or by the loss of love. In what real danger is the child lost in the department store, the child during the first day at camp, the child sent from London to the country, or the little girl whose father is going away? In all these cases the child is being separated from the person he loves and on whom he is dependent. He knows that he needs food, shelter, comfort, and love and he is accustomed to get them from his parents. In some cases, as in the case of the little girl, he desires the love of one parent much more than that of the other. These needs cannot be satisfied except by another person. He becomes afraid that if he is separated from this person his needs will remain unsatisfied and he will be uncomfortable, miserable, and perhaps die.

It is interesting that the child usually blames himself for the separation regardless of its real cause. He has done something or wanted to do something that is forbidden and now his feelings of loneliness because he is separated from his parents are his punishment. It is our constant experience that when a child is placed in a foster home because of the sudden death of his parents he denies that this is the cause. Instead he feels that he is being punished for some offense, perhaps as trifling as taking a piece of candy at a time when he was supposed not to. From this point on every desire for gratification will be regarded by him as something forbidden and dangerous and its presence will appear in his consciousness as a feeling of anxiety. It is the burnt child who fears the fire. These acute anxiety attacks, then, are a signal that the inner desires and needs of the individual are in danger of not being gratified because their gratification is impossible owing to the environmental circumstances or because the person believes that if he tries to gratify them he will be punished. The purpose of the attack—i. e., of the feeling of anxiety—is to warn the individual that he is in danger from his need to satisfy his inner desires.

Why is there such a danger? In the cases we have cited the danger lies in the fact that the child has been or is about to be separated from the person whom he loves and whose love he craves. He reacts to his feeling of anxiety by crying in order to bring the loved person back. If this does not work he may attempt to cling to the loved person, as the child did who refused to return to school. If this is not effective he must find new love objects. This is possible if the separation that produces the anxiety is not permanent. If it is, then he must first undertake a period of mourning, whose purpose is to detach the bonds of love from the person from whom he has been separated. All these activities remove the painful feeling of anxiety.

Anxiety will arise, also, if the child wishes to do something or does something for which he believes the person whom he loves and from whom he desires love will punish him, either by inflicting physical pain or injury or by ceasing to love him. During childhood the child has many desires and impulses which he cannot be allowed to gratify in the way he wishes because such forms of gratification would be harmful to him and to his family, or would conflict too much with the culture in which he lives. Consequently children have frequent feelings of anxiety until they learn ways of gratifying their impulses which will be less dangerous and more cultural.

Naturally anxiety arises as a result of the Oedipus situation. The little boy fears to love his mother lest he become torn by his feelings of jealousy and hatred for his father, his love for him and his need for his protection and favors. We have mentioned earlier with what frequency the child attempts to deal with this anxiety by developing a phobia. The anxiety engendered by this conflict is increased if there are real marital difficulties between the parents. For example, it would really be very painful if the little girl of divorced parents who is living with her mother should express her passionate devotion to her father. The mother, who may have been ill treated by the father, would be very likely to become extremely angry at the child.

Even when the parents really love the child and are reasonable in the cultural demands that they place on him the child will have frequent feelings of anxiety. If the parent is overstrict and demands that the child conform to too high a standard or if the parent rejects the child, the latter has a constant feeling of anxiety lest he do something that will cause the tenuous bond he feels with his love object to snap. In these instances the anxiety results from the intrapsychic conflict—the natural need to gratify childish impulses and the fear that if this is done he will lose the parents' love. This is well illustrated in the case of a girl of twelve whose mother regarded any form of pleasure—dancing, movies, parties, association with boys, association with other girls, games, sports, etc.—as wicked and threatened to punish her or to expel her from her home if she engaged in them. Any time this child felt the desire to join with her companions in any of these activities she became immediately very anxious and frightened. In this case the anxiety was heightened by the fact that the mother actually did not love the daughter. She preferred the son, who was younger and to whom the girl had always to give in and go out of her way to see that he got the best of everything. If she did not do so her mother expressed extreme disapproval.

Anxiety feelings are increased if there is a long absence of one parent or the other or if the parents have been too restrictive or too indulgent. They arise, also, if the instruments for the expression of inner desires are incapacitated or if the child fears he will be punished if he uses them. If the small baby cannot suck his fingers because his hands are tied or because he is afraid they will be cut off if he does so, he cannot gratify the desire for nonnutritive sucking. The ungratified desire appears to him to be a very dangerous impulse and he reacts to its presence by anxiety. In fact his tendency is to try not to be aware of the impulse and to feel only anxiety if the impulse stirs. Since the impulse may be active all the time, he may be anxious constantly; we say he is jittery. The impulse may stir only at certain times and we say the child has an acute anxiety attack. Often these attacks occur at bedtime or when the child is asleep. If we observe a small child who of his own accord is in the process of relinquishing his finger sucking we find that he abstains all day but as he becomes fatigued puts his fingers in his mouth. Later he may abstain from this even though he is very tired, but may suck them as he falls asleep or in his sleep. This is because the control exerted voluntarily by his ego becomes weak as his ego becomes fatigued and to some extent is absent during sleep. For this reason acute anxiety attacks are more likely to occur when the child is fatigued or during sleep although they may occur during the waking hours.

Acute attacks during sleep are known familiarly as nightmares or night terrors. We have used the example of finger sucking in the foregoing discussion. Anxiety attacks do occur because of finger sucking, as they may because of any other inner impulse whose expression is frustrated. (When the frustrated impulse is an aggressive one the feeling of anxiety takes a particular form which we describe as a feeling of guilt.) However, because the cultural restrictions in American society fall heaviest on expressions of childish sexuality, the most common source of this type of anxiety is some interference with masturbation. When a child has been severely punished for masturbating or has been frightened by the threat of what may happen to him if he masturbates, he will try to stop the masturbation. He may succeed in doing so during the day, but again when he becomes fatigued at bedtime or while he is asleep the impulse tends to get out of hand. He is so frightened, however, that he cannot permit himself the gratification and struggles to remain awake or awakens himself from his sleep with a frightening dream, and thus he will be sure he does not touch his penis. The content of the dream is almost invariably the repetition of the masturbation threat. He dreams that a ghost with a sharp knife is chasing him. The ghost is really his mother in her white nightgown and the knife is the result of the threat that if he masturbates she will cut off his penis. The dream does not gratify the wish to masturbate but gratifies the punitive conscience and stops the masturbation.

Anxiety attacks occur often when an active sex life has been interrupted for external reasons. Widowers and widows are prone to suffer from them, as are also married couples whom circumstances separate and whose morals forbid either extramarital relations or masturbation. Adolescents who stop masturbating either because of fears or because they are in love and feel masturbation is childish suffer similar attacks.

What is the result of an anxiety attack? This question would be more correct if put thus: What is the fate of the inner impulse that threatens to carry the child into behavior which he believes might cause injury or loss of love? or: What is the fate of the inner impulses of the child who really has been threatened with or exposed to loss of love? There has been a frustration and because of it the inner impulse cannot obtain gratification. The feeling of anxiety is painful, so the individual's aggressive activity is called into action. The aggression may be used to remove the frustration. The child may go ahead and obtain his gratification regardless of its cost or he may attempt to force the loved person to stay with him. If this is not possible or advisable the aggression may act by causing the child to change the method of gratification from the more primitive type (which would cause him to lose love) to a more mature type through which he can obtain gratification and retain the love of his love object at the same time. If a child is angry at his father he does not need to express his anger by killing or injuring him. This would be a primitive method of gratification and would result in the actual loss of the father and his love. Instead he can tell his father that he feels angry with him, and why. In this way he can express his anger and yet retain his father's love. The child gives up his finger sucking—a primitive method of obtaining gratification—because he wants to be grown up and to act like his father who does not suck his fingers. He begins to masturbate—a more mature method of obtaining gratification. He gives up his gratification for play with his excretions (a primitive method) and gets gratification from playing with mud pies (a more mature method). The aggression may act by causing the child to find another love. (The child at camp becomes acquainted with the counselors, finds they are friendly, and his homesickness stops.)

If the aggression cannot direct the individual into activities that will remove the anxiety he tends to return to earlier forms of gratification. If his masturbation is too dangerous and he has to stop it he then begins again to suck his fingers or to wet the bed—both of which are more infantile ways of getting gratification than masturbation is. They are, of course, neurotic manifestations and consist in the return of the repressed. All neuroses start with some frustration which produces a state of anxiety. In short, all neuroses start with an anxiety attack.

So far we have stressed the fact that anxiety is a painful warning that the individual is in danger and that because of the pain he is forced to do something about the danger. A child has a very frightening dream and wakes in terror. He starts to cry and his mother comes and comforts him. Since he seems so frightened and clings so to her she decides to lie in his bed till he falls asleep. The next night the same thing happens. After this has been repeated several nights he again wakes in *terror* from a *frightening* dream. He *cries* for his mother and she gets into bed with him. Now the whole tenor of the experience has subtly changed. He knows that if he *wakes in terror* from a *frightening* dream his mother will sleep with him. This is very pleasant and comfortable and accomplishes his wish to possess her and to take her away from his father. He can well afford to suffer the *real* pain of the anxiety attacks in order to secure the secondary pleasure it brings him. The anxiety attack is no longer a warning signal, it is an end in itself. It has the dual purpose of gratifying an inner and partly forbidden wish (to possess his mother and separate her from his father) and a punishment because the wish is forbidden (the pain of the anxiety). From a warning signal the anxiety attack has now become a neurotic symptom. This can happen if the original dream which was so frightening was an incestuous one. The inner impulse (desire to possess mother) about which he was so frightened has become transformed into a gratifying experience about which he feels guilty. If such a situation continues the child soon learns to avoid paying attention to the attack as a danger signal. Every time he has a feeling of anxiety, he disregards the underlying reasons for the anxiety and instead uses the pain of the feeling to gratify another but prohibited desire—his wish to sleep with mother.

Treatment for anxiety attacks, whether acute or chronic, diurnal or nocturnal, lies in helping the child to become conscious of the nature of the inner impulses and in helping him to find acceptable ways of gratifying them. Sedation is useless as a cure. It is silly to force the child to overcome his fear reaction to a particular situation—e. g., to make the child who says he is afraid to go upstairs alone do so—when the real problem is his fear lest he be separated permanently from his mother. It is equally silly to waste a lot of breath explaining to the child that there is nothing upstairs to be afraid of. The first step must be to ascertain from the child the nature of the danger which he feels threatens him. Since often he is only partly conscious of its nature he may only be able to state it in a vague way. He may say that he is afraid someone will go away. On the other hand he may be entirely unaware of its nature, in which case the answer will have to be ascertained by studying his behavior. For example, if he becomes panicky only when he watches traffic it is reasonable to surmise that he is afraid of separation. Such a surmise must be substantiated by a close scrutiny of the family situation: is there a marital problem which the parents are contemplating solving by separation or for which separation would be a good solution? In such a case the child is entitled to be upset.

If no real cause for his dread of separation and consequent loss of love can be found in the environmental situation it is necessary to examine the child's feelings toward his parents, particularly toward the parent of the same sex. Through conversations with the child he is encouraged gradually to talk about both his love and his hate for that parent, until both phases of his ambivalent attitude are made conscious. At appropriate times he can be reassured that all little boys feel that way toward their fathers, that father wouldn't be angry if he knew of his hostility, that his wishes are not going to make father die. He can be told that the reason he wants father to die is that then he would be free to marry mother; but that is impossible. However when he grows up he will be able to find a woman as desirable or even more desirable than mother and he will then be able to marry her. Through this process of making conscious the dreaded feelings and discussing them and other possibilities of gratification objectively, the child's anxieties cease.

Severe anxiety attacks require intensive psychotherapy which in effect follows the lines mentioned above. The main techniques consist in methods by which the therapist can learn from the child what are the inner impulses for which he fears he will be punished, and then to give him opportunity to discuss them and to act them out; thus the impulses no longer feel strange, dangerous and alien to his ego.

We all know from experience that we are sometimes puzzled, worried and anxious when we do not understand something and that the anxiety disappears when we begin to understand, either through our own efforts and observation or through conversation with someone who does understand and who can explain it to us. The situation no longer seems strange but becomes familiar. This is particularly true regarding our feelings. In technical language, we are worried and anxious as long as a situation or feeling is isolated from our ego. It is interesting that although we experience this phenomenon daily it is our habit to place taboos upon the discussion of certain feelings and factual situations, and consequently expose our children to anxiety and leave their egos isolated from certain everyday facts of life. In America these taboos fall heaviest on the phenomena of birth, death, physiological processes, anatomical details and emotional reactions and feelings (particularly the emotions and feelings of adults). Through withholding a free discussion of these matters we keep the ego of the child weakened and leave him anxious and apprehensive whenever he comes face to face with them. Do we do this because we ourselves wish to maintain a position of supremacy and fear that if we enlighten him we will then lose our authority over him?

All children feel anxiety more often than adults. They meet so many strange and new feelings and situations with which it takes time to be familiar; they often have desires which they cannot gratify because they are physiologically immature. In our experience, however, they develop severe anxiety attacks only when they are exposed to unreasonable and unnecessary emotional strains, i. e., to experiences which we have already discussed as being traumatic.

DISORDERS OF ORAL FUNCTIONS

There are children whose presenting symptoms involve the function of the mouth and the upper part of the gastrointestinal tract. Anxiety, the result of an intrapsychic conflict, may produce disturbances of the functions of these parts or the anxiety may be removed by converting the intrapsychic conflict into a disturbance of these functions. We know that such a conversion takes place but we are not sure how it is brought about. The following case is a good illustration of what we mean.

A seven-year-old girl was referred to the Child Psychiatric Clinic because she was very tense, easily upset, suffered from feelings of nausea without adequate cause, was excessively clean and had few friends. She vomited whenever she saw someone blow his nose, heard someone clear his throat, heard any conversation that mentioned blood, pus, etc., saw food not carefully arranged on a plate, or saw cooked cereal. Both parents felt nauseated in similar situations. The father was easily sickened if the children were too "messy" or if some distasteful subject was broached at table. The patient was excessively clean about her person. She refused to indulge in any play activity that would soil her hands. For example, her mother bought her some modeling clay and a sandbox but she refused to use either, saying she disliked the sticky, dirty feeling on her hands. She would not go to the toilet alone because she could not bear to touch her genitals, and when she took a bath her mother had to wash them.

She reacted with a great deal of anxiety to the idea of going away from her mother. When she was asked if she would like to go to camp she cried hysterically as though her heart would break. She said there were lions and tigers in the woods, that the counselors were mean people who wouldn't let her play or do anything she wanted to do, that they would stuff her full of cooked cereal and that if her mother really loved her, she would not want to send her away. It was clear to her that her mother was only trying to get rid of her. She did go to camp and there she was very well mannered and neat in appearance but inclined to be selfish, pious and very avid for adult approval. She was apt to draw adult attention to the faults of others, holding herself up as a good girl. She showed decided likes and dislikes, excelling in things that held her interest but hurrying over those that didn't (washing clothes, making beds). Her craftwork was good, original and neat.

At school she made good grades and was well liked by the teachers. However, she had to miss fifty-five days of a school term because of illness—usually due to nausea and vomiting.

She was the oldest child, having a sister of three years and a brother of ten months. In the interval between her birth and that of her sister, she had a rather close relationship with the mother. They were able to do things together, such as going through Woolworth's (which the patient dearly loved) or to the movies. In that interval, too, the family was in good circumstances financially. Her sister's birth came at a time when the family was suffering serious financial difficulties, and with the birth of the baby the mother no longer had the time to go places with her.

Both parents were intelligent, though not highly educated. The mother mentioned that when she was a child she felt the same as the patient did. For example, when she was only eight years old she was given the task of taking her father's lunch to him. He worked downtown and she had to take a long trolley ride. This made her feel a little carsick. She had to get off in front of a dentist's show window in which false teeth were displayed. This made her feel very ill, and she still continued to feel nausea at the sight of false teeth. When the mother mentioned something "dirty" that the younger children had done—i. e., when either displayed an interest in or desire to play with urine or feces —her tone of voice often expressed shock and revulsion. She disliked having the children play in water or with dirt and sand. She was obviously under severe emotional tension which seemed to be directly related to the fact that the family lived in a tiny three-room apartment. The father was supposed to go to bed at about four o'clock in the afternoon, which was impossible because the children kept waking him up. He would become furious and shout at both the mother and the children. The mother in turn would shout at him and the children, and then the children would shout at each other. Both parents said it was like a madhouse. The patient hated to come home from school and would dash out as quickly as she could. She was ashamed to bring other children home to play. The mother gave the patient little, if any, opportunity to participate in conversation. She seemed to expect the patient to keep still for unusually long periods while she engaged in rather long conversations on purely adult topics, and would become quite angry if the patient broke into the conversation.

The father's father was a strict, rigid person who did not allow his children to have any friends or to bring other youngsters home, even after they were in their teens. His mother was a submissive type, always attempting to shield her son from his father's harsh discipline. The only other child was a sister, who is now married and has children, but has periods of mental illness. The grandfather did not approve of the marriage of either of his children. The father had difficulty meeting strange people. He was a hard worker and very conscientious, but had no initiative or aggressiveness to help him get better paid jobs. Before his marriage he did quite a lot of drinking. The mother had a tremendous amount of feeling about drinking because during her childhood there had been a great deal of friction because her father was a heavy drinker and abusive. So she stormed, nagged, or was coldly frigid when her husband drank, as though it were the most awful thing that could happen. There were many scenes and hysterical outbursts, which affected all three children, especially the patient.

The patient was a nine months' baby and was born after a labor of about an hour. She was bottle fed till nine months, walked at fourteen months, talked at eleven months, was trained both for bladder and bowels at seven months, and got her first tooth at nine months. Because she had many sore throats she had her tonsils and adenoids removed at the age of five.

Her physical examination was negative, though for an entire year subsequent to it she had colds and a persistent cough.

Her psychological examination showed a C.A. of seven years, four months, an M.A. of eight years, ten months, and an I.Q. of 120.

This child was attempting to restrict, inhibit and control her behavior in order to avoid feelings of anxiety and guilt. These restrictions and inhibitions made her behavior different from the usual behavior of children of her age and sex. Her behavior, however, did not bring any realization that she was different from other children or any feelings of pain and discomfort because of the difference. She regarded even her nausea as being correct behavior and not an illness. She therefore did not suffer from a neurotic illness but from a disturbance in her character. This disturbance was partly of a hysterical and partly of an obsessional type. She is diagnosed as having a neurotic character because of her necessity to avoid the suffering caused by feelings of guilt and anxiety. She made a virtue out of this necessity because through it she gained approval from her mother which she would otherwise forfeit. In brief, she altered her character in order to avoid feelings of guilt and anxiety and then avoided any recognition of the resultant real suffering by finding satisfaction through her limiting character reactions.

At this point, she sees herself as well and other people as sick. This mechanism makes her feel that she has no need for treatment, which attitude makes a difficult treatment problem which is increased by the fact that her parents do not regard her character as neurotic but as virtuous and commendable. It is this type of case that for years goes untreated because adults often do not regard as ill the child who is shy, seclusive, good, overly conforming and who needs constantly to please.

Such children are really very ill. A report from a teacher that John is a very good boy because his behavior and deportment are *excellent* may be regarded by both the teacher and parents as a sign that John is getting along well; but it is really a sign that John is a sick boy. The report and the praise he gets from the report satisfy him, however, and he gets pleasure where it would be better if he experienced pain. Perhaps only when such a person grows older and comes to realize that his character prevents his having a satisfactory adult life does he see that his deprivations and sufferings are the result of his own differences from other people.

What is the psychopathology of the girl? She shows certain definite groups of symptoms:

She is overfastidious in respect to cleanliness. So great is this overfastidiousness that it interferes with her recreational and social life, and has even reached the point where she is so disgusted as actually to feel nauseated with anything that verges on her idea of uncleanliness.

She is overconscientious to the degree of priggishness. Her main aim in life is to get adult approval at all times.

She shows marked anxiety at leaving her mother and is afraid consciously that strange adults will treat her cruelly.

She has learned that these pathological reactions have a value in her life. By her overcleanliness and nauseated disgust she can avoid doing things she does not want to do and still be certain of being thought an obedient and not a disobedient girl. Through this and through her priggishness she can demand that her mother and other adults allow her to have her own way. This use of her symptoms to gain control of situations is a secondary reaction and does not necessarily have much to do with the formation of her original behavior. We think it can be seen quite clearly that her symptoms are an attempt to avoid feelings of anxiety and guilt. If she stays with her mother she has no opportunity to feel anxious, while if she is away from her, she suffers from anxious feelings and frightening ideas. Her behavior about going to camp is an indication of her underlying problem. If she is good in school and to adults to the point of priggishness then they will keep her with them and not send her away. That is, her priggishness is an attempt to avoid the feeling that if she behaves like other children, all adults and particularly her parents won't like her. If she is overclean and overdisgusted with uncleanliness then adults and particularly her parents will approve of her and not send her away.

The girl's problem lies in a great feeling of anxiety lest she be disapproved of and sent away. We know from the history that her present behavior is one of which the mother approves and that the mother would disapprove of any other kind. We see no evidence that the mother's disapproval would cause her to expel the child from home, and even if she did, this intelligent little girl knows that she would be looked after and that civilized America is not filled with cruel humans and wild beasts. Why, then, does she have this fear? Taking first the fear-filled imaginings about camp, we see that they are concretized fears of bodily injury—being eaten and torn by wild beasts, etc. She fears, without reasonable basis, that bodily injuries will be done to her.

The mechanism is similar to that of a phobia. The child fears the phobic animal lest it do to him what he would like to do to the person whom the phobic animal represents. The girl is afraid that if she is away from her parents, she will act like a wild animal and tear and devour other people—probably children. Since the recipient of the aggression is probably a child, it is necessary to see what child. Since she knows none of the children at camp, it must be a child or children that she knows well, that is, a member of her own family. When we examine her behavior toward her younger sister and brother, we see that it is unnaturally good and kind and that there are no apparent signs of the anticipated sibling rivalry—which exists in all children, as Levy conclusively proved experimentally. Therefore we can conclude that she has felt at least the ordinary amount of jealousy and hostility toward them but has suppressed the expression of it and also repressed the knowledge of it from herself. Being repressed, the aggressive activity developed and grew, until to her mind it appeared frightening and dangerous and took on an importance that it really does not possess. Suppression of the expression and repression of the impulse does not get rid of the impulse; it only places it outside of the conscious control of the individual and so makes it a dangerous enemy instead of a useful servant.

But this child's hostile feelings are not all directed toward her siblings. Her overcleanliness indicates that she is trying to please the mother; it therefore covers a fear, i. e., a wish to disobey the mother and be dirty. The history shows that the mother toilet-trained the child early and overseverely. The child, resentful of the toilet training, acceded to the mother through fear of her displeasure and therefore repressed the resentment and hostility she felt toward her. This resentment, stored in the unconscious, attracts to itself all the other resentful feelings, which every little girl feels toward her mother—i. e., her jealousy of the mother's relations with the father, of her ability to have a baby, of her more mature physical development, etc. These other resentful feelings have had to be repressed because the first resentment was, but they serve to make the hostility greater and more to be feared by the child. In order to avoid any possibility of the resentment breaking through, the child agrees to alter her life and avoid all ventures which in her mind would be connected with hostile feelings.

The problem, therefore, in this case will be the treatment of the fear of her own hostile feelings so that she can use her aggression successfully in her life. As we stated above, there are two levels of this child's illness: the primary and deepest is her fear of her own aggressive impulses; the secondary is the value that she had found in the use of her endeavors to repress the aggression. This secondary problem has become so great that she now sees her sick behavior as a virtue and has no feelings of anxiety or discomfort about it. The first step in treatment, therefore, will be to convince her that her behavior is not virtuous but pathological.

This may have to be done partly by the therapist but is accomplished more successfully if the parents can be induced to co-operate and to look upon her overcleanliness, her priggishness, her nausea and her overconformity as pathological symptoms. They could help a great deal by refraining from praise or sympathy with these acts and by pointing out that they are symptoms of her illness and that she need not be so different from other people. In this particular case it was done successfully. The mother not only refrained from praising the child's symptomatic behavior but encouraged her to have fun being dirty, etc. (In some cases of the sort this seems to be enough, and after a year or so of experiencing the treatment the child loses his anxiety and is able to behave in a normal manner about his cleanliness and aggressiveness.) For direct therapy of the child she must be seen at least once a week, and the task of the therapist will be to encourage her to get pleasure from playing with dirty things—water, mud, clay, paints, etc.—and from acting out in play her aggressive feelings, that is, her hostilities, resentments, etc. As this is being done, she will be encouraged to express verbally her feelings toward her siblings, her mother, and her father, and the nature of the fears she has about such verbal expression will have to be ascertained and relieved.

This case illustrates one type of neurotic interference with the function of eating. There are a number of other types. Emotional disturbances of the function of any organ follow several patterns. If the use of the organ is regarded by the psyche as dangerous (it makes no difference whether the individual is aware of this dread or whether it is unconscious, but difficulties are more likely to follow if the latter is the case) the individual will try not to use the organ (use the mechanism of inhibition) or will use the organ in a way opposite to its usual use, or the use of the organ will be accompanied by pain and discomfort (this is the mechanism of symptom formation). If the function of one organ is inhibited because of the dread of using it, the desires that cause it to function may be displaced from that organ to another. There these desires are added to those that usually cause the second organ to function; thus the latter is used for purposes that ordinarily are accomplished better through the use of the proper organ (this is the mechanism of perversion).

The disturbances of the function of eating may be classified as follows:

1. Inhibitions:
   (*a*) Anorexia (lack of appetite).
   (*b*) Dysphagia (inability to swallow).
2. Symptoms:
   (*a*) Rejection of ingested foods—vomiting.
3. Perversions:
   (*a*) Finger sucking.
   (*b*) Nailbiting.
   (*c*) Pica, the ingestion of nonnutritive substances.
   (*d*) Overeating.

Anorexia

We discussed many of the causes of anorexia in our discussion of feeding disturbances of the very young child. The same causes—improper preparation of food (food that is too hot or whose nature and consistency make it too difficult to eat), food that is unfamiliar to the child and that he is forced to eat suddenly, too much excitement at or just before meals, unpleasant experiences at mealtime, feelings of insecurity either because of separation from the parents (homesickness) or because of parental quarrels, hunger strikes which are reactions of rage against what the child regards as unjustifiable demands on the part of his parents—may result in loss of appetite during the phallic and latent periods. To these, too, may be added reactions of disgust which take away the child's appetite. These reactions may be caused by ideas about the person who prepares the food or by ideas about the food itself. Years ago Ferenczi reported the case of a boy who suddenly developed a loss of appetite for his breakfast. Just before the symptoms began he had been told by his playmates that his parents performed sexual intercourse. The boy steadfastly denied this was so, but coming down to breakfast a day or so later he thought suddenly, "My mother prepared this food with her hands; with the same hands, she did 'dirty' things with my father last night." He felt disgusted and suddenly had no appetite.

Loss of appetite because of disgust with ideas connected with the food itself is universally experienced. This is the basis for many food fads—which are particularly common among children and which seem to develop without any reasonable basis—and for many cases of anorexia in small children. Pediatric experience testifies that no child reaches the age of seven years without having had some feeding problem and this universality of feeding problems is caused partly by disgust with ideas about food. If the reader has had the enlightening experience of dining with nursery-school children he will readily understand how these ideas arise. The children compare quite freely and without any feelings of disgust or shame the various articles of food to human beings and animals, parts of human and animal bodies, and human or animal excretions. However as they get a little older and are being forced through cultural restrictions to adopt an antagonistic attitude instead of a predilection for cannibalistic and excretory interests, they have to develop feelings of disgust and shame toward these activities. This is displaced onto the article of food which had been associated in this way in their minds.

A simple example is seen in the varying attitudes of many adults and children toward drinking milk. Some cannot drink it at all. Others can drink it if it is cold but dislike it warm. Some can drink warm milk but not milk fresh from the cow. Others can drink it straight from the cow's teat. Some can drink human milk. The drinking of milk warm from the mother's breast is the greatest joy of the tiny infant, and it signifies a very special relationship with the mother and her breast. All of these attitudes except the last show varying degrees of repudiation of the joy of the infant and his relationship with the mother. The greater the disgust with the drinking of milk, the more the original joy in it and the relationship with the mother have been, the greater is the effort going on all the time to keep the memory of the period of infancy repressed. Anorexia of this type is not very important because it usually involves only certain foods and may not be permanent.

The treatment of all these types of anorexia is really comparatively simple. Find the cause, remove it, and give the child a little time to readjust himself to the changed situation. Every child has natural hunger which arises as a result of metabolic processes and which will reassert itself as soon as the inhibiting circumstances are removed. In the case of anorexia due to the child's disgust with certain ideas he has associated with certain articles of food, complete ignoring of the child's idiosyncrasy is the only necessary treatment. Even if the idiosyncrasy persists throughout life there are so many other articles of food that can be substituted that it seems unnecessary to pay attention to the food fad. Furthermore there is no single article of food the ingestion of which is essential to life and health. Very often if the idiosyncrasy is ignored the food fad disappears after a period of time.

Pediatricians will laugh at our statement that the treatment of anorexia is so simple. Theoretically it should be just as simple and easy as we have stated but practically in many instances such treatment is impossible because there are two parents in the family, and their attitude toward the child's anorexia (or any other feeding problem he may have) after it has started complicates the therapy greatly. In fact the attitude of the parents toward the child's feeding in itself may produce anorexia.

We have had a number of children ten or more pounds overweight referred to us for anorexia. The parent (often the mother, although fathers are not innocent in this respect, wants a child as large or as heavy as her friends'; she feels it is necessary for a child to learn to eat a big meal and to finish everything on his plate at mealtimes; or she has some inner need or anxiety that can only be ameliorated by a child who eats abundantly) conducts the child's feeding in the following manner: A breakfast ample even for an adult is placed before the child. He is encouraged to eat it. As he becomes satisfied and portions are not finished he is given more encouragement to continue. At last with great effort he reaches the point of satiation and cannot take any more. The mother then feeds him the remainder, cajoling or threatening him until he takes it. At this point the overfull stomach cannot contain all the food and the child regurgitates part of it. The parent then prepares another equally large breakfast and tries to get the child to consume it. In order to please her he tries but regurgitates again. Another breakfast is prepared and the same process is repeated. Lunch and dinner are conducted in a similar fashion, and often because of the outrageous length of time each of these meals consumes there is really only an infinitesimal interval between the three meals. The child, being stuffed, has lost appetite for his meals next day, and not many days pass before he has no appetite at all. He would be able to regain an appetite only if he were starved for a day or so when his real metabolic needs would assert themselves.

We realize that such exaggerated parental behavior is not very common but modifications of it are common enough. As a general rule human beings do not have the same degree of appetite for each meal during the day. Some are hungrier for breakfast, some for lunch, some for dinner, depending on the energy they have expended and their metabolic needs. As a simple example, one is thirstier and drinks more liquids on a hot day or during the hot portion of a day than at other times because the loss of water from the body is excessive due to the heat. Although parents may govern their intake of food according to their own needs, i. e., their own hunger, they often forget that the child tends to do the same thing and they try to induce or force the child to devour three big meals every day instead of allowing him to eat as much as he wants at a given time. (Of course it goes without saying that the child should not be permitted to stuff himself between meals because he will then have no more hunger for his regular meals than a woman has for dinner who has spent the afternoon stuffing herself with nuts and candies while playing bridge.)

Often parents feel that certain specific articles, not varieties, of foods are necessary for the child and insist that he eat them. We believe that there are more superstitions about beneficial and harmful varieties of foods (i. e., food fads) among civilized human beings than about anything else in life, with the possible exception of excretory habits. The child should eat spinach, he should eat rhubarb, he should avoid sugar, he needs green vegetables, fish will develop the brain, carrots are good for the hair, etc., etc., ad infinitum. Any scientific basis for these ideas is at best tenuous. They take no account of the scientific fact that they are prevalent only in America and that other cultures have equally healthy people who have been raised by the application of entirely different sets of ideas.

We talk much about certain persons having a sweet tooth, others liking fruit, or meat, or cheese, but we seldom stop to think what these observations mean scientifically. A decrease in the chemical constituents (which are the fuel to produce energy) of the body is felt in consciousness as a sensation of hunger. If the decrease is in the amount of water we call the specific hunger "thirst." Similarly the general sensation of hunger is composed of more specific ones. If the amount of sugar necessary for the metabolism is decreased, a hunger for sugar develops; and so it goes with fats, proteins, salt, calcium (this is the basis for earth and chalk eating among certain children), vitamins, etc. The individual may be aware of the need for the specific substance he requires; he may be able to say, "I feel hungry for a piece of meat." He may not be aware of the specific hunger. Instead he has a feeling of hunger and when he sits down to eat he selects certain types of food in preference to others. In fact, if the meal were composed solely of that type of food he would rise at the end of the meal feeling quite satisfied. The next meal he might not want any of that particular type of food at all. People differ from each other in their specific chemical needs. Some need (desire) sugar, some proteins, some fats. In the words of the well-known saying, "One man's meat is another man's poison." They differ also in their specific chemical needs from day to day. These needs, if they appear at all in consciousness, usually appear only as vaguely felt desires, and the feeling about them can be expressed verbally only with great difficulty.

If the body of an individual knows more about his real needs than does his conscious ego, how much more must the body of the child know about his real needs than does the conscious ego of his parent? The parent's attempt to dictate to the child what his bodily needs are distorts the ancient saying "Mother knows best" into a caricature far beyond the domain of reality. Several years ago Davis conducted a series of experiments with year-old babies. Each baby was given a tray with a large number of different varieties of food. The amount of each food was carefully weighed first. Then the baby was allowed to eat what he liked. After the meal the remaining portions of food were weighed again. For one day one child ate only bananas, another only meat, but when the results were estimated at the end of a year it was found each child had eaten a perfectly balanced diet. Gastrointestinal disturbances were fewer and gains in weight and height larger in the experimental group than in the control group.

From this discussion it is plain that parents do not need to be so concerned about the feeding of their child. It is the parents' duty to see that they provide three properly balanced, well-prepared and attractively served meals a day, that the child does not have access to too much food between meals, and then to leave the child to do with the food what his hunger dictates. They can rely on the chemical needs of the child's body to govern the amount and variety of food ingested. Of course if they themselves have many food idiosyncrasies which they mention constantly they cannot expect the child to be even as free from food fads as the ordinary child, because an imitation of the parents in everything is an essential technique of the child's development. If besides the proper types of food they also see that mealtime is *not* the time or place for scolding or punishing the child for his behavior during the day, or for reprimands concerning his manners, or for the airing of parental quarrels, they can be sure that the child will not develop anorexia, except for the mild and specific anorexias about certain articles of food such as we mentioned above.

If they will adopt the same attitude when a feeding problem has developed or can learn from the physician to adopt this attitude as a means of treatment, the treatment of the anorexias will be quite easy. Some parents are afraid that if such a plan is carried out the child may go on a hunger strike and injure his health seriously or die of starvation. It may be that for the first few days in the treatment of anorexia, particularly if the parents have paid a great deal of attention to the child because of the feeding problem, the child will not eat at all, in the hope that he can coax back the attention that was so gratifying to him. However if the parents will wait patiently the child's hunger for food will overcome his hopes of getting attention through not eating and he will begin to eat. He will never abstain from food long enough to hurt himself. (This only occurs in adolescent girls, who may commit suicide through starvation—a condition technically known as anorexia nervosa.)

The first step in the therapy of anorexia is the removal of the secondary gain, i. e., the extra and gratifying attention the child has been receiving from his parents because of his lack of appetite. The institution of this step often reduces the degree of anorexia markedly and quickly (within two or three weeks). The second step is to ascertain the original cause of the anorexia and then to remove it. If it is due to parental unhappiness, steps must be taken to help them to a better adjustment either with each other or through separation. If it is due to adverse parental attitudes these must be treated or the child removed from the home. If it is due to resentment of the child because the parents have demanded that he become more cultured, as we discussed in the chapter on illnesses arising in the anal-sadistic period, his training may temporarily be allowed to lapse or at least be made less rigid. If it is due to disgust with the person who prepares the meals the child must be helped to come to terms with the facts of sexuality. (This is perhaps better done by a professional person than by the parents.) If it is the result of disgust with certain articles of food then the physician has to decide whether he feels that the repudiation of these foods is a serious enough problem to warrant intensive psychiatric treatment for the child, since only in this way can this type of disgust be remedied.

A really serious situation may arise if the child for reasons of health—allergies, diabetes, etc.—has to be on a special diet that excludes certain articles of diet which he likes or which the body craves. The same problem faces the adult with a similar illness but the adult has greater ability to submit to deprivations than does the child, particularly the young child, who is more governed by the pleasure than by the reality principle. The child is bound to feel unhappy and resentful under these restrictions. He should not be scolded or punished for his resentment but should be helped to recognize that the parents understand how he feels about the situation. As much as possible he should be protected from seeing too many other people enjoying the foods he cannot have. This does not need to be carried to absurd lengths (i. e., no member of the family eating any of the proscribed foods), but he should not be tantalized too much; and if at all practical, the dietary restrictions should occasionally be relaxed. Finally, the physician should not prescribe too many restrictions at once. It is better that the child's health suffer a little than that his emotional development be traumatized too suddenly.

The refusal to take food into the body, the refusal to swallow food (either for conscious or unconscious reasons, i. e., whether the child says he will not swallow it or cannot swallow it), is known technically as dysphagia. It may involve all foods or only certain articles of food. The inability may be complete or there may be only a difficulty in swallowing. Daily speech has translated this refusal to swallow food into psychological terms. We often say we cannot swallow some statement that we are unwilling to believe or that we repudiate. It is as easy under certain conditions to translate this back into physiological terms and to be unable to swallow some food that reminds us of something we wish to repudiate psychologically.

Young children will frequently hold food in their mouths for a long time because they have an aversion to swallowing it and yet want to please their parents and eat it. This usually results from the same situation we mentioned under anorexia, i. e., the child's disgust with the association he has made between the food and some other disgusting object. Another reason for the refusal to swallow certain articles of food or perhaps nearly all foods is jealousy of the new baby. The older child notices that the newcomer does not eat the same kinds of food he does but is given milk only. He wishes he were the new baby and then proceeds to try to act like him. He cannot eat any food but milk, and if other types of food are forcibly placed in his mouth he spits them out because he feels he can't swallow them.

Occasionally a child will refuse to swallow because of a more traumatic situation. We refer to the case we reported in *Common Neuroses of Children and Adults*. A child of six had a severe feeding disturbance. Although perhaps complaining bitterly of hunger she would sit and stare at her meal tray and then suddenly overturn it on the floor. If an attempt was made to feed her, she would knock the spoon away, spilling its contents. If her hands were held and she was fed, she would spit the food out. It made no difference whether the food was that usually liked by children—candy, ice cream, cake, etc.—or not. The behavior was fairly constant although through pressure and forcible feeding she was given sufficient nourishment to keep her from starving, but she lost many pounds in weight. This behavior started rather suddenly at the age of four and apparently without cause.

Study of the child revealed first that she equated her ideas of food with the bodies of her parents, more particularly her father's. Next she equated food specifically with her father's penis. Then was uncovered the following episode in her life. A day or so before the food difficulty began, her father, who was a chronic alcoholic, coming home drunk, locked himself and the little girl in his bedroom, removed her clothes and his own and attempted to assault her sexually. He tried first unsuccessfully to introduce his penis into her vagina. The attempt caused the child some bleeding and pain. Then he committed fellatio—introducing his penis into her mouth where he had an ejaculation. The child was sexually stimulated but also frightened and hurt. She wished the experience repeated, but at the same time recollected the pain, fear, and disgust she had felt. Almost at once she displaced all her reaction of desire, fear, disgust and pain to her oral zone and began to feel toward any object such as food—which she desired to introduce into her mouth —the other painful and disturbing emotional reactions. She refused to eat when she was hungry lest in gratifying her desire she again be frightened, hurt and disgusted. This story was obtained from the child, and following its full discussion and the abreaction of the experience, her behavior toward food became normal. The story was corroborated in most of its details by the mother.

Vomiting attacks without organic cause are common in both children and adults. Their purpose is to get rid of something the individual finds unpleasant. In the case quoted earlier in this chapter the vomiting expressed unconscious feelings of rage against the mother because of the strict way she toilet-trained the child; i. e., the mother had annoyed and upset the child, now the child would vomit in order to annoy and upset the mother, for the child knew that any stomach illness is upsetting to a parent (as we mentioned in connection with the illnesses associated with the anal-sadistic period) and that vomiting made her mother feel nauseated. These feelings of rage were largely unconscious, but children may regurgitate deliberately, being quite aware that they are doing so, to get back at their parents. Sometimes the child may even express himself verbally by saying, "If you don't let me do what I want then I will vomit and you'll be sorry."

The reader must remember that when a child shows this degree of spitefulness and rage his parents have treated him in a way that would make any human being revengeful. It would be no more logical to punish him for his spiteful reactions than it would be for the United Nations to punish the Greeks and the Norwegians for feeling and acting spitefully against the Nazis. The only people who would call this punishment justifiable would be the Nazis themselves. The child does punish himself for these rage reactions by feelings of illness, and the more unconscious he is of their presence the more nauseated and sick he feels when he vomits. These unpleasant feelings are his attempts to punish himself for daring to feel angry and spiteful against his parents.

Similarly vomiting may be an expression of disgust either with some person or with some of his own ideas about articles of food. The child is simply acting out what the adult expresses in words: "It makes me sick to think about it."

Another cause of vomiting is seen in small children of both sexes and in older girls. The mother is pregnant and has morning sickness. The child is intensely interested in the coming baby, is envious of the mother, and would like to have a baby herself. She identifies herself with the mother and develops attacks of vomiting. She may or may not be aware that her attacks represent in her mind her wish to be pregnant. If she is aware of the wish the vomiting is simply a regurgitation and is unaccompanied by nausea. It is as if she were playing she were the mother, and because she is only playing she need not suffer any criticism or pangs of guilt. (One of the functions of children's play is to permit them to pretend to do things that are forbidden without feeling any criticism from their superego, since what they are doing is only "play pretend.") If the child is unaware of the wish, the vomiting will be accompanied by nausea, and she will seem anxious and disturbed. And if she has a gastric upset from an organic cause, the anxiety she feels will be even greater. She has wanted to be the mother and have all her privileges, to do all the things she does. She has concluded that the best way to do this is to get rid of the mother. Since she felt guilty about these wishes she tried not to think consciously about them; i. e., she repressed the wishes. Now her conscience has started to trouble her about her wishes even though she has repressed them. It is as if her conscience said to her, "You are a wicked child. At one time you wished to be your dear mother. Now your

wish can come true. You can be your mother—in her pain and misery."
The nausea and the feeling of anxiety therefore arise as a punishment
by the superego for the hostile wishes.

A similar mechanism, i. e., an identification with the suffering parent
as a punishment for hostile wishes against that parent, is seen frequently
in the headaches and other minor illnesses of children. The father suffers from migraine for which he receives care and sympathy from his
wife. The son starts to develop headaches also. These are real and painful
but are neurotic symptoms and not migraine. We often recognize this
unconsciously in our attitude toward the boy. We say, "Poor child, he is
just *like* his father."

Another type of identification with a parent in illness occurs. A little
boy is passionately in love with his mother who suffers from migraine
headaches, at which times he is solicitous of her and does all he can to
please. However, because his passionate devotion produces too severe
feelings of fear and guilt due to his intrapsychic conflict about his
feelings toward his father, he endeavors to rid himself of his love for
his mother. This endeavor results in another conflict between his love
for her and his desire to be rid of his feelings of love for her. Instead of
solving the conflict by detaching his feeling of love from her and placing it onto another object—an aunt, a teacher, etc.—he changes the
character of his love. The earliest type of love relationship in human life
is identification. "I love you. I want to be like you." The later type is
object love. "I love you. I want to do things for you and please you so
you will love me." The boy we are discussing reached the beginnings of
the second type of love, but under the influence of his fear and guilt he
cannot maintain the position but instead regresses to the first type. Now,
instead of looking after and doing things for the mother when she has
one of her headaches he also has a headache. In this way he accomplishes
several purposes: he can get attention from her without having to feel
guilty at disturbing her when she is ill or without feeling frightened
about his relationship with the father; he is able to express his positive
feelings for her without having to feel guilty about them, since he is
saying that he wants only to be like her, not to possess her; he can remain babyish without having to suffer loss of pride, since he is ill.

This identification with the sick mother, however, starts to produce
further conflicts. If he identifies with the mother in her headaches he has
to identify also with her passive feminine attitude toward the father.
This makes him helpless in any competitive situation with the father

and later with other men in authority. His attitude toward authority will be one not of respect or admiration or a desire to imitate but rather of a flirtatious attempt to get the authoritative person to like him. Such an identification can easily become a passive feminine attitude toward men and lead to overt homosexuality.

From what we have said the reader can see how important it is to pay serious attention to the child who tends to have the same type of illness as his parents. It is not that the child takes after the parent—as is so commonly the opinion—but that subtle psychological changes are occurring in his personality as a means of solving some of the difficulties in the Oedipus situation. If the changes are of a helpful nature they can be left alone. If not—and certainly identification with the parents' sickness can never be an adequate method of solving a life problem—the child should be studied by a child psychiatrist and treatment instituted if necessary. We hope we have made it clear that the purpose of intensive psychotherapy is not to cure the child of the symptoms—i. e., the headache—but to correct the subtle intrapsychic changes, which will thus help him to a better solution of his problem.

We have mentioned the fact that the child is ambivalent. He is able to love and hate the same person at the same time. This is seen readily in all his behavior and is expressed in all stages of his development. During the oral stage he will kiss the mother one moment and bite her the next. If he bites her very hard he may feel remorse. (When an adult does something for which he feels remorse he may say, with a shudder and a faint feeling of nausea, "I feel sick about what I have done.") In the child—and sometimes in adults as well—the remorse, instead of appearing as a psychic feeling, may be expressed organically in attacks of vomiting. He feels antagonistic—perhaps because he is envious— toward someone he loves. He wishes to hurt the person by depriving him of some of his possessions—usually of some part of his body. The child then begins to feel remorse about these antagonistic feelings and in order to relieve his feelings of remorse he tries to make restitution to the person whom he feels he has injured. If the process takes place in oral terms his actions are as follows: He feels envious and antagonistic. He would like to devour (i. e., take away and keep for himself) the object of whose possession he is envious. He feels remorseful and in order to quiet his remorse he would like to spit out or vomit up what he has taken away and devoured.

It is not unusual for children to think in oral terms. During one treatment session a boy of nine enacted the following play: He was a savage and captured the physician. After the capture he played that he tied him to the stake, lit a fire under him and burned him to death. When the physician was properly roasted he ate him and thought that now he would be able to perform the magic the physician performed. Here the play stopped, but if he had become remorseful he would have had to spit out or vomit up the physician's body in order to return to the latter his magical powers. If the child's reaction to the adult is unconscious or if he quickly represses it, the repressed energy may reanimate old oral patterns. These reanimated patterns appear as symptoms; i. e., a regression has taken place—a common cause in many children who have periodic attacks of vomiting. Since the whole process—even, often, the feeling of envy and hostility and remorse for that feeling—takes place below the level of consciousness the child has no idea why he has the attack of vomiting.

We believe that children have attacks of vomiting as an expression of remorse for antagonistic desires more frequently than is generally believed. Sudden acute gastrointestinal upsets are much more common in childhood than in adult life and may be caused partly by the child's tendency to eat anything that attracts him (this is the cause usually assigned, and is done so without any real investigation) and partly as a manifestation of allergy; but we believe that the psychological cause we have presented may be at least as common. This is a subject that justifies and needs further research.

The treatment of dysphagia and periodic vomiting in children must follow the same lines laid down for the treatment of anorexia. If the dysphagia or the vomiting has been severe or long continued the child will be undernourished and will suffer from avitaminosis. In our opinion certain of the symptoms—weakness, tiredness, and emotional instability—shown by such children (or adults) are the result of the avitaminosis, and we believe it desirable to consider all cases where the feeding disorder has continued for any length of time as being complicated with a vitamin deficiency which must be treated. The symptoms of dysphagia or of vomiting must be treated as we advised for anorexia— by ignoring it. In certain severe cases this cannot be done easily or safely by leaving the child with the parents, and it is better to have him hospitalized for a few weeks until psychotherapy can be instituted. In milder cases in young children the child may be entered in a good nursery school where the teacher is trained to observe him carefully and is accustomed to the proper management of children and their eating habits. It is often useful to have a trained social worker live in the home for several days in order to observe exactly what does go on there around and during mealtimes. Of course no parent will behave in exactly the same way in the presence of a stranger who is there to observe as she would if alone, so that the worker does not see what really goes on. However such a person is a great help to the busy practitioner or pediatrician. We say social worker rather than nurse because the majority of nurses have not had as intensive or extensive training in emotional conditions as the social worker has. Of course the ideal person to assist the physician along these lines would be a nurse who also has had training as a social worker.

During the child's separation from the parents a careful study of the whole situation must be made in order to find out the causative factors. If they are problems of the parents they must be treated. If a parent has shown persistent determination to overfeed the child the physician's advice may be helpful, but in certain cases it fails completely because the overfeeding is the result of a neurotic compulsion in the parent. Such a parent needs treatment for her own problems, of which the neurotic compulsion is only a symptom. If the main problem is the adverse attitude of the parents toward the child, the problem must be treated as such; at the same time in most cases the child needs psychotherapy as well in order to free him from the results of having to force his expression of his needs into unusual channels, necessitated by the need to get along with the parents.

One child whose case one of us has reported before had, among many other symptoms, attacks of vomiting. He had had to suppress any expression of his aggressive and sexual interests in order to get along with his mother who had rejected him. During treatment he expressed a strong desire for the therapist to feed—i. e., love—him. Later, when he was assured of the therapist's love, he was able to express his aggressive feelings and sexual interests both verbally and in play. As he lost his tenseness and became more like a normal boy, and as some treatment was carried on with the mother, she was able to feel more affectionately toward him and thus he was able to carry his increasing freedom to be himself into situations outside of the therapeutic hour.

If the problem is the result of the child's disgust with his own ideas, psychotherapy is called for. As mentioned earlier, it is questionable whether intensive psychotherapy is needed in mild and occasional food fads. Such cases are better left alone. If the problem is the result of an identification with a sick parent or of a regression to the oral phase (i. e., if the vomiting or the dysphagia is an hysterical symptom), intensive psychotherapy for both child and parent is necessary.

The question as to who should treat the child can only be answered on the basis of the severity of the child's symptoms. The results of the Rorschach test are most helpful, since it may reveal deep-seated emotional disturbances that are not apparent on the surface, or it may reveal that the intrapsychic life is fairly satisfactory even though the gastrointestinal symptoms are severe. If the presenting symptoms are mild, not associated with too many other indications of personality maladjustment, and the Rorschach indicates a fairly stable emotional life, the case may be treated satisfactorily by the pediatrician or general practitioner who knows how to conduct the treatment. If the symptoms are severe or are associated with other symptoms, and if the Rorschach indicates a serious personality disturbance, it would be wise to refer the child to a pediatric psychiatrist for consultation and treatment if necessary.

We have seen that the mouth has two functions, the ingestion of food and the pleasure that comes from sucking and biting actions. Both functions—and both are pleasurable—are continued throughout life and do not merit any social condemnation, nor can they be designated as perversions. The function of eating may become perverted if it is used largely to obtain satisfactions other than the need for food. Some time ago, one of us reported the case of a boy who ate enormously. His need for extra food was an attempt to satisfy his longing for the love of his mother and later his stepmother. Whenever he felt her lack of love he would gorge. In adult life one occasionally sees patients who complain of having excessive appetites. When the history is studied it is found that the excessive appetite began just after the sexual life was greatly curtailed. This phenomenon is well known to exist in eunuchs and often in men and women who have passed the menopause. In all of these instances the gorging is a regressive displacement of the need for love and sexual gratification from the genitals to the oral zone. The regression takes place either because the individual is afraid to get genital pleasure or because the circumstances of his life prevent him from satisfying his needs for sexual gratification or for love. In the case of the child, the treatment is not to prevent his eating, even though the overeating may be resulting in serious overweight, but to correct the cause, which is usually a lack of love, for which treatment must be directed toward the rejective parental attitude.

Pica

All children eat nonnutritive substances, a catalogue of which would include all substances that can be put into the mouth and swallowed. Their ingestion can be considered normal if it does not happen too often and if the child is not made ill. When the child eats nonnutritive substances to excess or almost exclusively the condition is known as pica. We have not seen many cases of true pica, but on the basis of those we have seen, we have come to the conclusion that pica usually occurs in children or adults whose diet does not satisfy certain bodily needs. There is recorded the case of a child suffering from a serious feeding problem that resulted in a calcium deficiency, which he tried to correct by constantly eating the plaster off the wall. Similar dietary deficiencies seem to underlie the dirt eating that is endemic to some parts of the southern states. The treatment, therefore, will be directed toward the correction of the dietary defects. When these are corrected the pica will cease.

Finger Sucking

We do not need to refer again to the fact that finger sucking is a normal activity of early childhood and should not be interfered with. Here the physician may ask, "Does it not deform the mouth?" and "If a parent brings a child because he sucks his fingers must I not do something to stop the habit?" In reply to the first question it can be stated categorically that there is no proof that finger sucking deforms the mouth or jaw except under the most unusual circumstances, and that most of such deformities are either congenital or the result of adenoidal obstruction of breathing. In reply to the second question it can be stated as categorically that nothing—neither the use of punishment or scolding nor the application of nasty-tasting substances, bandages, or guards to the fingers nor the application of splints to the arms—should be permitted or suggested. The physician who conducts his practice in an honestly scientific manner will explain to the parent the facts concerning finger sucking and the inadvisability of preventing it. If the parent is dissatisfied and the doctor loses the case he can comfort himself with the assurance that he has been honest and correct in what he has done.

We can be sure that the parent who consults physician after physician for her child's finger sucking and who is not content with the honest advice she receives has an unconscious problem of her own about finger sucking. It may be that as a child she had a problem with her own parents over finger sucking and so does not let her child do what she wanted to do lest her parents punish her. It may be that she has an unconscious desire to suck her own fingers, a desire that is becoming strong because she is not obtaining genital gratification. In such cases any real treatment must concern itself with the parent's own problem, either her fear of her parents or her fear of obtaining genital gratification.

How long does the average child suck his fingers? It varies with the child. Some gradually relinquish the habit about the second or third year. Others continue till the age of five or six. Freud and Burlingham report that children who live in their own homes tend to relinquish the habit of finger sucking much earlier than do children who live in institutions, who tend to prolong the sucking as a means of comforting themselves for several years longer. The process of relinquishing goes something like this: the child first gives up the habit while he is awake, but as he gets drowsy and starts to fall asleep it recurs. Later he abstains even when drowsy, but as he falls into sleep his fingers find their way to his mouth. Still later he ceases altogether. In some cases the child has a constitutional need to suck his fingers, which need is not as easily satisfied as in other children. In other cases the child continues his finger sucking because he is frustrated in some of his other needs. When a child continues his finger sucking past the age of four or five it is wise to study the home situation carefully to ascertain if there are adverse parental attitudes that are making the child too miserable and unhappy to permit him to give up his infantile forms of gratification. If such are found they should be corrected; if they are not found then the finger sucking should be left to the child to stop when he is ready.

Finger sucking, however, may be a symptom of regression to the oral stage. A child may relinquish all his finger sucking by the age of four years. Several years later, perhaps at the age of seven or eight, he may start again. This is an entirely different condition from the finger sucking we just discussed. The child has progressed naturally along the path of his development and then suddenly starts to retrace his steps. The finger sucking therefore is an indication that the child has met an insoluble difficulty in his development and has attempted to solve the problem through regression. The real problem is the nature of the apparently insoluble difficulty that the child has met. In some cases, many of which were seen at the time when so many mothers were starting to work in war industries, the child feels unloved by the mother and his finger sucking is simply a motor cry, "See, mother, I am only a little baby, please stay with me and love me." In others, the child has become desperately frightened about his masturbation and has stopped it: if the phallic stage of development is so dangerous he had better get his pleasure in a safer one, i. e., the oral. An interesting example is one we quoted in our previous book. A girl of fifteen had sucked her fingers since she was seven. She had not dared to stop sucking them because if she did, obsessional thoughts crowded into her mind that were of an unpleasant masturbatory character.

Here again if the physician understands the pathology the treatment will be obvious. The child who returns to sucking his fingers because he feels insecure in his mother's love must be helped to feel secure. If the insecurity is caused by the birth of a new sibling in the family and if the parents are handling the situation of the older child adequately there is no need to take any steps but simply to wait until the child does feel more secure. If the insecurity is the result of separation from the mother then the mother must return to her family or a satisfactory mother substitute provided. If the finger sucking is the result of castration threats the child must be relieved from this fear. In the case just cited the nature of the unpleasant thoughts must be ascertained and her irrational conclusions corrected: she must be educated to a more reasonable view of her sexuality. In none of these cases is it ever necessary to do anything about the finger sucking itself. It will cease within a short time after the cause is removed.

Nailbiting

Nailbiting is very prevalent in America. It is surprising to note the high percentage of inductees at the induction center who give a history of nailbiting either in childhood or in adult life. It is this prevalence that inclines us, falsely, not to consider the habit as an indication of emotional instability. Dogs spend a great deal of time cleaning between their toes and around their nails with their teeth and possibly also biting at the nails themselves. They have no other way of attending to their paws. Children frequently break their nails playing and get rough edges. They feel a certain amount of discomfort when too much dirt collects under the nails. The skin beside the nail often gets slightly torn.

The adult attends to these conditions by the use of nail file and scissors. The child is not anxious to use instruments that would take him from his occupations and interests when he has an instrument ready at hand, his teeth. Parents feel it necessary to stop the child from doing so and often err in trying to stop it too abruptly and too severely. When it is done gradually and the child encouraged to adopt more adult methods of manicuring and given time to learn them, he harbors little resentment, but when it is done in the way described he feels he is being picked on, becomes resentful, tends to continue the habit and even to increase it; thus a simple, childish procedure may easily become a severe case of nailbiting.

To repeat, despite the prevalence of the habit in the population we must regard it as a sign of poor emotional adjustment. Lieutenant Lessee has noted that the sailor who bites his nails now is a poor risk for selection for services that require an ability to withstand long continued and severe physical and emotional strains—such as the submarine service.

Severe cases of nailbiting are motivated in part by the desire of the child to annoy and humiliate the parents—and the parents' reaction indicates clearly that the child does accomplish his desire. At the same time, the fact that the parents do get angry and that often the child bites his nails so deeply that the biting itself is painful, and the fingers afterward, indicates that there is another motive, i. e., the need to punish himself for his resentment. Severe nailbiting therefore has the structure of a neurotic symptom. Essentially it is an aggressive hostile act directed against one's own person because one is afraid to direct it against the real object. In most cases the real object is the parents, frequently the mother.

One little girl began to bite her nails as soon as she went to camp for the first time. She was a child whose mother had indulged and protected her; in fact, until she was five years old she was not permitted to play with other children. The mother also seemed helpless in the face of the child's demands, very often acceding to them when it would have been more sensible to refuse them. The child therefore had never learned how to get along with other people, and when she went to camp for the first time she felt a great deal of social anxiety, which caused her to want to regress to the satisfaction of finger sucking; but she felt this was too babyish. Nevertheless her hands crept toward her mouth. She felt angry at the mother for putting her in a position of being so anxious—i. e., for sending her to camp—and angry because she had babied her so much.

The child recognized that if the mother had not treated her so babyishly and had treated her more as an adult she would not now feel so helpless in a new situation. This feeling of helplessness made her envious of the mother's social poise (which in reality was not very great, although her daughter thought it was) and this envy increased her resentment against the mother. She was therefore in a conflict: if she expressed her resentment against the mother, then she would have no mother to fall back on to protect her against her feeling of discomfort when she was in a new situation and with strange people with whom she had never learned to get along; if she fell back entirely on the mother then she would miss all the pleasures and advantages of a social life and in the future of a life with the opposite sex.

The conflict was insoluble and so she tried to repress it; but she had to do something about the feelings connected with it. Tormented by her social anxiety, her hands crept toward her mouth as a symbol of her desire for the mother's babying and protection. At the same time she felt bitter resentment against the mother, so she began to bite the fingers that symbolized her. The greater the conflict between her two opposing feelings to the mother the more viciously she bit her nails, until they became sore and bleeding. Since the mother disliked the nailbiting, she could now add another motive when she came home: she could use it as a way of expressing openly her defiance and resentment.

In certain cases a conflict exactly similar to the one just described, and solved by the habit of nailbiting, arises if the mother has threatened or punished the child for masturbating. The child stops the act, bitterly resentful of the mother because he has to do so. His inner desires then take a regressive trend toward finger sucking. This regressive trend combines with the hostility and resentment, and nailbiting is the result. The child keeps it up because he knows it humiliates the mother, whom he thus punishes for interfering with his pleasurable activities.

As mentioned above, treatment for the common tendency of the child to use his teeth as a manicuring instrument is to teach him slowly and gradually, more by example than by precept, the use of other implements for manicuring. The gift of a manicure set and the gentle, regular manicuring of the fingers by the mother and occasionally, as the child grows older, by a professional manicurist are all helpful.

We are of the opinion that there are mothers who do not like to manicure their children's nails. They are not very gentle but go about it roughly in their desire to get the unpleasant job finished. This makes the whole process unpleasant to the child. There are three parts of the routine of civilization of which most children complain—manicuring, washing or brushing the hair, and washing the face. Since the mother is not doing these things to herself, she is not guided by her own warning sensations, and the procedure accidentally becomes painful and the child gets slightly hurt. Furthermore, children are not as able to tolerate slight degrees of pain as are adults. Then, too, if the parent is annoyed at the child or if the child is being cared for by a nurse who has been forbidden to punish him and is annoyed because of something he did earlier, she may and often does vent her spleen on him during the toileting by pulling his hair, brushing it hard, cutting the nails roughly, etc.

To these hurts that the child actually may receive during the manicuring is added his unreasoning inner dread that the scissors may really mutilate him. He becomes tense and fearful and tends to pull his hand away at inopportune times. Thus he may really be hurt; or the parent, fearing she may hurt him, scolds him for not keeping still. The combination of these two discomforts makes the child dislike the manicuring process and to prefer to use his teeth instead. Such reactions can only be overcome by gentle, slow insistence until the child begins to take pleasure in his well-kept hands. We are a little skeptical, however, whether any child really cares much about his appearance until he reaches puberty and falls in love—when a revolution in his habits of personal cleanliness is usually produced.

Treatment for the severe types of nailbiting must aim toward a better solution of the child's conflict. He must learn to be less fearful of expressing his hostile feelings, if they are valid, and more able to dispense with his exaggerated need for dependency. When the emotional difficulties have been resolved the course of training that we mentioned for the first type may be instituted. Often, however, it is unnecessary, for the child is avid to be a grown-up person.

There is another point to be considered. Parents who bite their nails cannot expect their children not to follow in their footsteps. In fact, it would be a sign of inadequate development if the child did not do so. The parent may complain of the child's table manners, his neatness and tidiness, his food fads, his temper tantrums, his lying, his grammar, his use of slang or profanity, while all the time his behavior is a correct replica of that of the parent. It is not so strange that the parent should thus complain, for often he is actually unaware that this is the way he behaves. Or he may feel it is correct for an adult so to conduct himself but incorrect for a child; or he may be displeased with the way he himself behaves and not wish the child to follow in his footsteps. (The last-mentioned reaction is seen often in parents recently immigrated to America.) In all of these cases the child is influenced much more by the parent's example than by his precepts and if the latter wishes the child to change he must change his own habits.

When the child attends school, whether it be nursery school, kindergarten, grade or high school, he tends to imitate the habits of the teacher of whom he is fond. These habits will be different from those of the parents, and the wise parent will welcome the tendency as a valuable contribution to the child's character development, as helpful for his future life in a democracy where it will be necessary for him to be able to meet, understand and get along with a wide variety of people. The unwise parent who is either bigoted and prejudiced or has the need to clutch the child too closely to himself will try to interfere; and the child will suffer a totally unnecessary conflict. Such conflicts are important during adolescence and will be discussed later on.

Disorders of Speech

Speech is another function of the mouth and is a much more complicated one than either eating or pleasure sucking. As a result of a sensory stimulus arising outside the body, of physical changes within, or because of instinct energy, an idea forms within the associational pathways of the cerebral cortex. If the idea is to be expressed in speech the stimulus innervates the ill-defined speech centers in the cerebral cortex, which are in the left cortex in right-handed persons and in the right cortex in the left-handed. Impulses pass from here to the peripheral speech mechanism, which consists of two parts—the bellows or breathing apparatus which produces a blast of air, and the vocal cords, throat, tongue, lips and teeth which form apertures that can be varied in size and shape. The blast of air passing through these apertures produces the particular word sound desired. Disturbance of any part of this complex apparatus will injure the perfection of the speech.

The child learns to speak—i. e., learns to modify voluntarily the size and shape of the apertures through which the blast of air passes—by imitating his parents. Through observation he learns that certain sounds made by the parent accompany certain actions and facial expressions, and produce certain results on other people. It is no wonder that the small child regards speech as magical—when he emits certain sounds he can cause other people to do what he wants! Through his observations he associates certain sounds with certain specific results, and when he hears these sounds he expects that the specific results will follow even if he has to bring them about himself. We say he has become aware of the meaning of words, that he has learned to obey commands, etc. This occurs before he can speak himself. The child begins to think in verbal images and he understands words before he can use them. Then he begins to try to make similar sounds to express his verbal ideas and we say he is beginning to talk. He models the sounds he makes on the sounds he hears; therefore if the parents have a speech defect, if they have an accent, or if they talk very fast or very slowly, his speech will tend to copy them as accurately as possible. There are many children who when they enter school are sent to a speech-corrective class because their speech shows the well-ingrained habit of enunciating exactly like the parents. This often is the case with children of foreign-born parents.

Some children tend to talk so-called baby talk and continue the habit for a long time, and in most instances it is because the parents tend to talk baby talk to them and regard their use of the mutilated syllables as cute. Thus such children not only imitate the parents but continue to talk in this way in order to be admired. We feel it is better for children not to hear baby talk, since it may take considerable retraining before they can learn to talk correctly.

In order to imitate exactly it is necessary to hear accurately. Defective hearing is a frequent cause of speech defects, and in every case of speech disorder the child's hearing should be tested accurately. Auditory defects, like visual defects, even if fairly severe frequently pass unnoticed in small children. Otitis media also seems to be increasing in frequency among small children in urban communities, although its severity and serious sequelae have been greatly modified by the use of sulfa compounds in treatment. The great number of draftees rejected because of auditory or visual defects indicates that it would be a wise precaution to have the vision and hearing of all children tested carefully as a routine before they enter school, and then to have instituted whatever corrective measures are necessary and possible. It is too bad to allow a child to go for years with an uncorrected but correctable sensory defect which distorts his whole knowledge of the world and makes it impossible for him to react as efficiently and accurately as can other children. A child with a speech disorder due to defective hearing should be given expert professional care. If the child is totally deaf, either because of some congenital condition or as a result of some serious illness during his first year of life involving either the middle ear or the auditory nerve, he will not talk at all. Most cases of muteness are not the result of any injury or defect in the speech apparatus, but of deafness. The deaf child needs expert training in learning to speak.

Cortical defects or injuries if they affect the speech centers produce speech defects. It is probable that many of the speech defects of mentally defective children are cortical in origin rather than peripheral. Speech defects that result from cerebral injuries are known as aphasias and have a specific symptomatology, which is not necessary to describe here because they are not commonly met with in children. We ourselves have only seen one case of true motor aphasia in a child—the result of an automobile accident. However, we anticipate that in the future there will be more aphasias develop in children with the increased number of serious motor accidents that are bound to occur after the termination of gasoline rationing. Treatment for the aphasia is the problem of the neurologist and should not be attempted without at least a neurological consultation.

Orton has called attention to a specific and important type of speech disorder of cerebral origin. We know that the speech centers are in the left-cerebral hemisphere in right-handed persons and in the right-cerebral hemisphere in the left-handed. There is the anatomical structure for speech on both sides of the brain but the function of speech is located predominantly in the dominant hemisphere, whose presence is indicated by the handedness. If the child is congenitally left-handed the centers that control the function of speech will develop in the right-cerebral hemisphere. Should the parent or teacher decide that the child should become right-handed and force him to learn to use his right hand in preference to his left, she will also be training the left hemisphere to become dominant. This results in a conflict of dominance between the two hemispheres and is revealed in the child's suddenly starting to stutter. There are specific tests designed to determine whether this conflict of dominance is the cause of the stuttering, and treatment for the condition consists in retraining the child to use the originally dominant side of the brain and in retraining his speech defect. Unless both are done together no improvement occurs. We will discuss more fully the neurodynamics of this condition when we discuss another discovery of Orton's called strephosymbolia.

The greatest number of cases of speech defect are the result of some disorder in the use of the peripheral parts of the speech mechanism, i. e., the breathing apparatus or the apparatus that shapes the words. If the child has enlarged tonsils and adenoids he cannot be expected to speak well since the air passages are distorted. We seriously doubt that the so-called tongue-tie really interferes sufficiently to cause a speech defect. It may be so in occasional instances but certainly not as frequently as to justify the frequency with which frenotomy is performed.

If we suffer a painful injury to some part of our bodies, all of us will hesitate to use the injured part for a short period after the injury has healed and our first attempts will be made very gingerly. If this is true of adults it is more true of children who are not as tolerant of pain. Often with a child the dread of re-experiencing the pain remains for a long time and makes his action hesitant and consequently awkward and not well co-ordinated. It is a well-known fact that if a child starting to walk falls and really hurts himself he may abstain from any further attempts to walk for a long time, and his next efforts will show a great deal of timidity. When a young child painfully injures his mouth, cutting either his tongue or his lips, but particularly his tongue, he seems to develop a great deal of anxiety. This is probably the result of the fact that he has injured an important part of his oral apparatus which is almost as important to him at this age as his genitals will be later on. Often he even will not allow his mouth to be opened in order that the extent of the damage be ascertained. Following this he may cease to speak and when he starts again, his speech may be mutilated and in-co-ordinate and remain so for years. In technical language he suffers from a traumatic neurosis. He has suffered a painful injury to his tongue, an organ that is part of the function of speech. He dreads any attempt to use the organ lest he re-experience the pain, so he inhibits the function of speech either totally or partially. (He also may repress the memory of the accident.) The treatment for such a traumatic neurosis consists in helping the child to uncover the amnesia about the accident. At the same time he is encouraged to use his mouth and tongue as much as possible.

Sometimes the traumatic neurosis is not the result of an accident but is inflicted on the child deliberately by the parent as a punishment for some misdemeanor. In one case the child began to use profanity which he copied directly from his father who swore a great deal. The father, angered by the child's swearing, hit him brutally across the mouth. The child ceased talking and when he began again he used mutilated speech.

Treatment for such a case must combine the two goals mentioned above, with a lessening of the child's fear of the father.

The most common type of speech defect is stuttering. There is no need to describe the symptoms, for they are undoubtedly familiar to the reader. We sometimes find it most painful to listen to a stutterer. We feel annoyed and irritated and extremely desirous of helping him out and thus end the pain of listening. Although some stutterers are extremely sensitive about their speech defect, even in some instances to the point of being unwilling to talk at all, the majority go straight ahead calmly and stubbornly to complete what they are trying to say.

The primary dysfunction in stuttering lies in the bellows which furnishes the blast of air for speech—i.e., in the breathing apparatus. In order to speak clearly, smoothly and rhythmically the breathing must be smooth and rhythmical. Anyone can demonstrate this on himself quite easily. If the breathing is increased in rate or if the rhythm is disturbed by muscular exertion it becomes difficult to speak, and if one forces oneself to do so the speech is mutilated and greatly resembles that of the stutterer. We have already discussed the fact that the respiratory apparatus in the very young infant is not well co-ordinated and that he only learns to co-ordinate it gradually as he gets older. We also pointed out that the startle reflex will suddenly throw whatever co-ordination he has achieved out of rhythm. (This happens also in adults when, due to being startled, they catch their breath.) In the child this sudden disorganization may last not only several minutes but even several hours or days.

In most children stuttering starts immediately following a sudden severe shock or fear. The child is startled and frightened at the same time; the startle reflex disorganizes the breathing rhythm; the disorganization persists and expresses itself in the stuttering. This explains the well-known phenomenon of the stutterer who ceases to stutter when he sings or when in some other way he changes the pitch or tone of his voice. In fact, many cures for stuttering are based on imparting a different rhythm to the stutterer's breathing. If the child starts to stutter after a sudden fright and his fear reaction can be treated and overcome within a short time after it begins, his speech will become normal again. Levy has shown this in his work with release therapy.

The sudden startle does more than cause a regressive disturbance of breathing. It causes an arrest of development and a regression to either the anal or oral stage. Some stutterers show marked sucking or biting movements as they speak which interfere greatly with the smooth enunciation of words. Others show marked anal characteristics and have the most difficulty in enunciating words that express sadistic drives. This is best illustrated by the case reported by Spring which we quoted in our previous book. The stammerer, a boy of ten years, was engrossed with the shape of words. He said, "My throat is round and lots of easy words come through like sausages, some are liquid. When I get a word with a corner on it or a square word it sticks in my throat and I have to change the shape of my throat so it will slip through." Fenichel says, "The words have in addition the significance of an introjected object—the conflict which originally took place between the individual and the object is now expressed by means of a conflict between the ego and the speech apparatus or its speech products." Spring's case is an illustration. The boy stammered severely over the name of a teacher he disliked. He said the name had prickles on it—which clearly expressed the fear of being injured internally by the hated object, the name being the equivalent of the object. The name of the loved teacher on the contrary was liquid, therefore not dangerous, and was pronounced without stammering.

The regression causes the child to use speech no longer as a means of communication but as a vehicle by which his erotic and aggressive drives are carried, just as, during the oral stage, he used his mouth and during the anal stage he used his lower bowel and its media of feces and flatus to carry them. It tends to reactivate his old belief in his magical powers and his omnipotence. It tends to return him to the old conflict of ambivalence, the struggle between powerful erotic and hostile impulses toward the same person. He dreads the return of this struggle and tries to solve it by repressing his erotic drives and aggressive feelings. Lest his speech carry any of these charges he tries to inhibit its free, smooth flow. All this struggle goes on underneath the level of consciousness. It becomes what is called technically a case of pregenital conversion hysteria. He is conscious, however, of the inadequacy of his ability to speak, begins to feel consciously inferior, and thus more tense than he was before. This increased tension interferes again with his breathing rhythm and the stuttering becomes worse.

The stutterer has feelings of inadequacy as a result of his stuttering. He has great muscular and psychic tenseness which results from his fear lest he do or say something that will get him into trouble. He tries at one and the same time to speak the truth and please the person to whom he is talking—often an impossible thing to do. He tries to pretend unconsciously that he has no hostile or aggressive feelings toward anyone. It is as if he said in his stuttering, "See, how can I be hostile or dangerous to anybody when I am such an ineffectual person that I cannot even speak plainly?" His character increasingly shows a tendency to emphasize the passive, submissive side of his personality. The suppressed aggression must find an outlet and it does so in the calm stubborn insistence by the stutterer that he finish what he is saying even though he knows that his speech causes his hearer great feelings of discomfort. Children often show their realization of this when they imitate a stutterer for a few days in order to annoy their parents.

The following case illustrates the inhibition of speech—although the symptoms of stuttering did not occur. A boy had learned a slightly risqué song about eating beans. At a picnic where there were a number of girls he began to sing it. They were shocked and ostracized him. He became extremely embarrassed. Later, when he grew up it became necessary, in the course of his business, for him to speak in public; but each time he did so he felt embarrassed, being certain he would not say the correct thing. He had suffered a humiliating experience when he tried to express his anal sadism through speech. (The song had been a sadistic attempt to seduce his feminine audience.) Later he feared unconsciously lest he re-experience the pain of that episode when he spoke in public. (The speech was an attempt to seduce—i. e., influence—his audience, just as the song was, and to him it had the same sadistic correlation.)

Stuttering of this type is the sign of a deep-seated emotional disturbance and if it has persisted a long time the mechanisms may become irreversible. No halfway measures of treatment are satisfactory. Speech retraining is woefully inadequate, for although most such methods depend on helping the patient to relax so that the breathing becomes better organized, he has great difficulty in doing so because the cause of his tensions lies in his emotional conflicts. Psychotherapy may solve his emotional conflicts, but it is usually too superficial to be adequate to help him to a better solution of them. Psychoanalysis furnishes the best method of psychotherapy and must be combined with an intensive retraining of the speech, for the combination of the two methods can cure stuttering. However if the case has been in existence for a long while the prognosis is poor. There may be improvement without permanent cure. This makes it essential that the stutterer be brought for intensive treatment as soon as possible after his symptom appears. He should not be allowed to grow out of it, for it is extremely improbable that he will do so.

Disorders of Bowel Function

Constipation is the outstanding disturbance of the function of the bowel. What is constipation and what are its causes? In the human being at fairly regular intervals the peristaltic movements of the large bowel cause its contents to collect in the rectum. The individual then feels a sense of fullness and pressure. This is slightly uncomfortable, and as soon as possible—because the free exercise of this ability is curtailed markedly by culture—he goes to a toilet and relaxes the sphincter muscles of the anus, and the peristaltic action of the bowel ejects the contents from his body. What are these contents? They are not derived to any great extent from the ingested food, but mainly from the secretions of the gastrointestinal tract. Excluding vegetables and coarsely ground cereals, the contents have a fairly constant composition: water 65 per cent and solid material 35 per cent, the latter consisting mostly of desquamated epithelial cells and numerous dead bacteria. If the diet has contained a proportionately large amount of vegetable substances the stool will be rather soft and bulky because it is composed largely of cellulose—woody fibers that cannot be digested. As the cellulose content of the food is increased, the stool contains more water and solids, more of the ingested food is undigested, and more nitrogen is lost to the body. The increased bulk of this undigested residue stimulates intestinal peristalsis, the passage of food through the bowel is quickened and the digestive ferments have insufficient time to exert their full action. Therefore too much vegetable food in man interferes with the processes of digestion.

If the call to defecation is neglected or impossible to answer, the rectal wall relaxes and the sensation of fullness—which we call the desire to move the bowels—passes off. At what intervals does the need to move the bowels arise? This varies with the individual's peristaltic rhythm. Some experience the desire to move the bowels once in twenty-four hours, others once in forty-eight, and still others once in seventy-two; individual variations are even greater than this. Alvarez does not consider that the condition should be called constipation until there has been no movement for over three days. Does constipation have any detrimental effect on the health? Alvarez has proved that the answer to this question is in the negative. The symptoms that do develop in cases of constipation—foul breath and tongue, impaired appetite, flatulence, nausea, loss of power of attention, depression, headache, insomnia and irritability—are due to the distention and mechanical irritation of the rectum by the fecal mass. Masses of cotton wool packed into the rectum produce exactly the same symptoms—which as in the case of constipation disappear as soon as the mass is removed. The validity of these experimental findings was proved recently by Rickenbacker and his crew and by Dixon and his companions.

We have discussed the physiology of constipation thus fully because the thinking of many parents in regard to it is a mass of superstition. They call the child constipated when he is merely operating according to his normal rhythm, which may be a movement every day, every two days, or every three days. More often they are certain that the child's health will be ruined if he does not have a movement—and a "good" movement (by which they mean a large one)—every day. Obsessed by this worry, they display a tremendous interest in the child's movements, question him about them, and even inspect them every time they occur. If the appearance is not satisfactory they change the child's diet, adding the usual bulk foods—bran, fruits or agar-agar. They forget that in doing so they are speeding up intestinal peristalsis and interfering with the process of digestion, with the result that the stool contains much valuable but unutilized food substance. Since the increased peristalsis is caused by mechanical irritation, such a diet tends to produce a pathological condition of the intestine. (We have seen at least one case of an adult whose intestinal tract functioned badly, with painful flatulence, lack of proper digestion of food, frequent diarrhea and marked anal soreness, because she persisted quite unnecessarily in using such a diet for her so-called constipation.) They become determined that the child shall have a daily movement, and therefore require that he go to the toilet at a specific time to sit there till he has moved his bowels. They encourage him to exert voluntary effort through the contraction of the abdominal and chest muscles and the diaphragm to force the feces out of his body. (The only necessary voluntary effort usually required is the relaxation of the anal sphincter.) This straining is quite unnecessary and results in the forcing of large quantities of blood into the lower pelvic veins—particularly the hemorrhoidal ones. This produces congestion and certainly in adults is a frequent cause of piles. It is not unusual in such a home for the child to sit an hour or even more on the toilet trying to move his bowels. (We have known instances when the child was forced to sit there three or four hours.) He gets bored with sitting and sneaks a book in with him. Now he can sit and enjoy himself reading. When he grows up he spends a long time—perhaps even an hour or longer—sitting on the toilet reading.

In certain instances the parent comes to the conclusion that the child is not really trying—as he probably is not—and attempts to convince him of the dire effects that result from constipation. If the child believes her, he now takes over her attitude and spends his days in a turmoil of worry lest he be not able to move his bowels properly. In other instances the parent feels he is stubborn and punishes him for his stubbornness.

Of course such parents resort with great frequency to medicinal aids —saline preparations, which act by pouring liquid from the blood stream and tissues into the bowel; vegetable cathartics, which act by irritating the intestinal wall and increasing peristalsis; or inert, bulky preparations such as agar-agar, which act by increasing the bulk of the intestinal contents and through mechanical stimulation increase the peristalsis. Some of these have a nauseating taste; others produce irregular peristalsis which is felt by the unhappy child as painful cramps. (It is a pity that certain drug firms have disguised the taste of many cathartics with flavoring and have attempted combining them with other drugs to reduce the tendency to cramps. If the cathartic preparations were only dispensed in a more crude form there would be much less unnecessary and unreasonable self-medication.) However, this self-medication is not as disastrous in its psychological effects on the child as is the indiscriminate and unecessary use of enemas and suppositories.

From what we have just said, one of the important measures in the treatment of constipation in children is first to determine whether the child is constipated or whether the constipation exists solely or largely in the parent's mind. In our own case as parents, we can honestly say that we never knew whether our children's bowels moved or not. Occasionally they would tell us that they were constipated and needed medicine, but apart from that no notice was taken of their bowel activities. We have not observed any ill effects resulting from this form of management and believe that if all parents would follow the same plan much of the so-called constipation in children would cease. Naturally the parent who follows this advice has the duty of seeing that the child's diet is adequate and that he has sufficient opportunity to exercise his body. These are only general measures of hygiene, however, and we are not sure if they have much to do with the regularity of bowel movements.

We realize that the reader who is unfamiliar with the studies of the last twenty years on digestion and excretion, or who is bound emotionally to a fecal fetish, will feel scornful of the views here expressed. We recommend that such readers read carefully the articles of Alvarez.

Although so many cases of constipation in children are really fictitious ones existing only in the parents' minds, true constipation does occur in children. For this there are two main psychological causes. One occurs in the child who has marked feelings of repugnance and disgust with any form of dirt, especially excreta, which are the result of a fear that if he moves his bowels even in the toilet his parents will punish him. This situation usually follows improper methods of toilet training. In this type of constipation the child has lost all sensory contact with his rectum and hence does not recognize when the organ is distended. Since his rhythm has been lost he should be advised to sit on the toilet once a day and try for a few minutes *only* to relax his anal sphincter. If he is unsuccessful he should stop and try again next day. He should be advised to be sure to go to the toilet as soon as he feels any perineal discomfort. A small amount of food containing cellulose or agar-agar should be added to his diet for a short time till his rhythm is re-established. He should be encouraged and even praised for playing with dirt, clay, sand, finger paints, etc., and for getting himself dirty. If this encouragement can emanate from his parents, whose former actions have caused his accentuated feelings of disgust or repugnance, so much the better. If these simple measures fail after being tried honestly for a period of time, then the child needs a more intensive type of psychotherapy.

The second cause of constipation in children is well illustrated by the following case. A boy of seven would go for several days without a motion. Although he was placed on the toilet daily and appeared to try to move his bowels, there was no result except that he appeared to be in great pain. When his bowels did move the stool was not a constipated one, and his shrieking with what seemed to be pain was really from fear. This fear had several components. He had been rigorously toilet trained to the point where he had begun to think of any bowel movement as wrong and displeasing to the mother. He was insecure in her affections and had been made unhappy by the birth of a younger brother on whom the mother lavished attention. His jealousy of the brother was connected with his ideas about defecation, for he stated that if he moved his bowels he made men and boys in the toilet and then killed them by flushing them away. Therefore in his mind the flushing away of his bowel movements was the equivalent of murdering his brother, whom he hated because he was the center of the mother's attention, and killing his father, whom he hated for a similar reason, yet whom he feared greatly. The presence of the fear of the father was readily demonstrated by the fact that when the father returned home unexpectedly and caught the boy sneaking downstairs to talk to the maid (which proceeding had been forbidden) the boy almost lost consciousness on the stairs. The constipation also represented a strong desire for the undivided attention of the mother and grandmother, both of whom were overly concerned with the matter of proper toilet habits. Such cases need intensive psychotherapy which must be directed toward first uncovering the child's fears of his own emotional reactions and feelings and then attempting to remove them.

Constipation in children does not usually wait until the latent period but begins at the time when the cause—be it the parents' attitude toward toilet training or fears the child associates with excretory functions—begins to operate.

Children—and adults—are extremely avid for any experience that brings sensual pleasure. We don't know the intimate lives of our children any more than we know the intimate pleasure lives of our friends. As we stated earlier, small children like to play with their excreta—feces or urine. They have a tremendous desire for sensual pleasure, which can be obtained readily by manipulation of the excretory organs. It is pleasurable to rub the anus and the surrounding skin and to introduce the top of the fingers or some other small object into the anus. Children constantly play at giving each other enemas. (This is not so uncommon in adults, either. Every so often someone is seriously injured because a blast of compressed air has been forced up his anus as a practical joke.) Everyone knows that they postpone going to the toilet as long as possible—often so long that the internal pressure overcomes the contraction of the sphincter and the child soils or wets himself a little—that they adopt many devices to retain the excretions. They hold the anus or the urethral opening, they hop and dance and stand first on one foot and then on the other. They even try to hold back the feces by standing on one foot and pressing the heel of the other against the anus.

This behavior is explained usually by saying that the child is so interested in his play that he does not want to take time to go to the toilet. This is partly true, but partly only, since children often behave in the same way when the call for excretion arises when they are not particularly enthralled by what they are doing. The more important reason is that children derive sensual pleasure from the feeling of bladder or rectal fullness and from holding back as long as possible and then suddenly relaxing the sphincter. The number of excretory games of this nature played by children is legion. Of course one expects these games to be most common during the anal-sadistic period, less common but still frequent during the phallic stage, and still less common during the latent period and adolescence. Although less common, and certainly done in a secretive manner, they are often carried on even in adult life by persons who otherwise are eminently respectable. Their occurrence, therefore, during the latent period is natural and so is not a cause for alarm. Excessive indulgence in them occurs usually because the child has met some difficulty in progressing in his development and so strives to retain the pleasure activities of his infancy. Any treatment must be directed toward ascertaining the reason for the dread to continue with his development. When this is corrected the excessive excretory play will decrease to a normal level.

Disorders of Bladder Function

Just as the historical monuments on a battlefield show where the struggle was most bitter and where the tide of battle ebbed and flowed, so the attitudes and behaviors of the average civilized human being toward the acts of urination (and defecation) are a series of monuments to the bitter struggle that has been fought out in the past between the child's wish to please his parents and his desire to perform his excretions where and when he desired. Few older children and adults, if any, are as un-self-conscious or unconcerned with the function of urination as are animals and little children. One child cannot urinate in front of others. He stands utterly unable to relax his urinary sphincter. Another, going somewhere with friends in a car, is too modest to ask that the car be stopped so that he can go to the toilet. He sits in silent misery and when the stop is made and he finally goes to the toilet, his bladder is so full that he has difficulty in starting to urinate and when he is about to finish the difference in intra-abdominal pressure is so great that he feels sick and faints. Another cannot urinate if he knows someone will hear him. One child refuses to use the toilet at school lest he get ill from germs and another will not use any public toilet for the same reason. Both endure misery till they can get home and relieve themselves. Another child may be perfectly willing to use a strange toilet but be too modest to ask anyone where the toilet is.

It can be seen readily that such attitudes are the most arrant nonsense socially and practically even though they are quite common. During World War I the greatest dread of many soldiers was that they be disgraced by being wounded while in the latrine. A more familiar example is the great difficulty and sometimes impossibility that many Americans find in urinating and defecating in bed, even though lying on a bedpan. When the child's wishes for excretory freedom succumb to the parent's wish that he be toilet trained they succumb completely, and thereafter when the whole procedure has become unconscious they continue to exert their influence regardless of present and practical considerations. These self-imposed inhibitions about the excretory functions are fairly marked in the latent period and perhaps are most imperative during adolescence; and it is always to be hoped that they will lessen as the individual enters adult life.

These attitudes are a sign of a certain degree of neurosis and are not the virtuous manifestations many parents think they are. Besides being bad for the child because of the great degree of unnecessary suffering they entail for him, they often serve as a too direct outlet for excretory pleasures which would be more valuable to him if they were more sublimated. There is no question that this excessive modesty and *nicety* interfere with the process of sublimation and therefore with the cultural development of the individual. If these attitudes are very marked it seems advisable to study the child carefully. He may have many other signs of unnecessary neurotic inhibitions and may need treatment.

The most frequent and distressing—to the parents and indirectly to the child—disorder of urinary function is enuresis. Enuresis is a condition in which the child who has been toilet trained, or has passed the age when toilet training should be completed, wets himself during the day or the bed at night.

Since toilet training is not expected to be complete before the age of three and a half, any wetting done prior to this time cannot be called enuresis; nor can the term be applied to the occasional accident that all children have even after that time; nor to the incontinence which is only a minor symptom of some other illness, such as pyelitis. (The child who has pyelitis has tremendous frequency and urgency. The latter is so great that he may be unable to get to the toilet or to call for the bedpan quickly enough between the time he feels the urge to urinate and the time he is forced to let go.) The child who has enuresis is a healthy child, without any other signs of physical illness or symptoms related to a disturbance of urinary function. When his urine is examined it is found free from any pathological changes. This definition excludes, of course, all cases of bladder and kidney infection and those few cases where disease or abnormality of the spinal cord or vertebral column, such as spina bifida, may cause a disturbance of bladder function associated with disturbances in the motor and sensory functions of the legs and perineum. Nocturnal epilepsy may show itself only by the fact that the child has urinated in the bed during the night. Every case of enuresis should be studied carefully as to the possibility of its being due to epileptic convulsions occurring during the night.

Excluding these cases, which in actual practice are extremely rare, there remains the vast majority of children who suffer from enuresis and in whom no logically scientific physical cause can be found. There are a number of diverse causes for enuresis. In one type which is fairly common the enuresis is associated with other more important symptoms of personality maladjustment. If the patient is a girl she will have many fears, particularly of men; she will be extremely ambitious and if her ability does not exactly correspond with her ambitions she will become frightened and anxious. She must always be first in everything and particularly she must at least equal if not surpass any boy. Instead of showing the natural passivity of a girl she tends to be as active as a boy. On some occasions when she wets the bed, her urination will come at the climax of a dream in which she wants to urinate, but does so as a boy. In short her whole life will be conducted on the principle that she is not a girl, but that she will try in every way to be a boy. The basis of this idea is her fear of being a girl and having a feminine relationship to a man due to the fact that she is afraid of her father, particularly as a sexual person. As a small child she may actually have been over-stimulated sexually by her father or have become frightened of him either because of the way he actually behaved toward her or because of her observations of the way he behaved toward other women. She fears to allow herself to have natural feminine feelings toward him and decides no longer to be a girl. She then tries to be a boy and as part of this attempt wants to urinate like a boy. She cannot do so, so she tries to express the wish in her sleep, and the enuresis results. She usually will stop wetting the bed at puberty with or without any treatment for the enuresis, but her fear of being a woman in relation to a man will continue and in her adult life she will tend to avoid men completely and be homosexual or to fall in love with a man whom she knows she can dominate. If she reaches the point of being psychologically able to have a child and has a boy she will tend to dominate him or even to reject him completely.

If the patient with this type of enuresis is a boy the clinical picture he presents is almost exactly the opposite. He, like the girl, suffers from many fears both in the daytime and at night. He is passive and retiring. He has no interest in any competitive activity, and if he does indulge he tends to deprecate himself when told he does well. He seems to have no pep, no backbone and to be overwilling to let someone else take his responsibilities. In short he prefers to first let George do it. This type of child invariably refers to his bedwetting with the expression "the bed got wet." He takes no responsibility for the situation. And there are parents and physicians who will agree with him. So much so that it is common to hear the statement that children wet the bed because they sleep so heavily, and in recent years attempts have been made, by the use of benzedrine, to help the child sleep more lightly: since he is more easily waked, he gets up and goes to the toilet and *therefore the bed does not get wet.*

Certainly such treatment does not answer the question as to why the child should have to urinate often during the night nor does it make any attempt to deal with the problem of the child's personality reactions. It can be seen that these are not masculine character traits; in fact, when his dream life is examined it is found that his enuresis dream is one in which he urinates like a girl. In brief, in his behavior, personality reactions, and dreams he is trying to be a girl and not a boy, just as the girl was trying to be a boy and not a girl.

The reaction is caused by fear of the mother, who is usually a dominating and harsh person—so much so that he dreads to love her or any woman as a boy loves his mother; he feels he would be safer in loving her if he castrated himself and became a girl. One boy of six with enuresis stated that he had no wish to sleep in the mother's bed. It was too cold. On questioning, however, he explained that if he went into his mother's bed he would have an erection and she wouldn't like that at all. It was better for him to wet the bed because then she would never want him to sleep with her. Just as with the girl, the boy usually stops bedwetting at puberty. The reason seems to be due to the re-establishment of a more active sexual life at this time. However, although the bed-wetting stops he carries his dread of women through adolescence into adult life.

The enuresis usually begins when the child has ceased masturbating through fear of punishment. The frightened cessation of masturbation causes a halt in the progress of the psychosexual development. Since the emotional development cannot progress it regresses to the stage immediately preceding the phallic, i. e., the stage of interest and pleasure in urination. The resurgence of the sexual energy at puberty overcomes this regression to some extent and the enuresis ceases. Of course all these reactions and feelings are unconscious or largely unconscious to the child. Certainly the connections between his fear of the parent of the opposite sex, his character traits and his enuresis are unconscious.

Treatment, therefore, will be directed toward the amelioration of his fear of his own sexual self in relation to persons of the opposite sex. It will not be directed toward the stopping of the enuresis, which after all is only an incidental part of the problem. Therefore the use of atropine, belladonna, alkalies, restriction of fluids at bedtime, waking and taking to the toilet, star charts, apparatuses that ring a bell when the child starts to wet the bed, apparatuses that occlude the urethra by pressure, operative procedures such as circumcision and tonsillectomy which are based on the theory that there is some mechanical irritation that causes the bedwetting—although they may stop the wetting, they are useless as attempts to cure this psychologically sick child. What is called for is intensive psychological treatment that will rid him of his fear of the opposite sex, and in our opinion this is best accomplished through a psychoanalysis, which will take a long time and will certainly have to be continued long after the bedwetting itself has ceased.

The symptom of bedwetting in these cases is often a peculiarly variable one. In some cases the bedwetting ceases after the child's first visit with the analyst, and never recurs. In others it ceases permanently after the parent makes the appointment with the analyst. It ceases frequently if the child is operated on. In other cases it does not stop until the analysis is almost completed. The cessation of bedwetting is not a reliable guide to the progress of the therapy. There are parents and physicians who regard the wetting as the main symptom and so desire to stop treatment as soon as it has disappeared; or they report marvelous cures through the use of methods that, to say the least, have no scientific validity. In these cases enuresis occurs only at night. There are included, also, cases in which the child has been toilet trained and then has relapsed, and cases where toilet training never seemed to have taken place. It is the commonest but not the only type. It is best designated *character neurosis with enuresis*.

We have not personally encountered any cases of the next type of enuresis but a number have been described in the literature on the subject. There is recorded the case of a boy who had enuresis mostly at night but also in the daytime for about two years. A year before the enuresis started his father died of tuberculosis of the bladder. Both the boy and the mother were very upset by the father's death, and to comfort each other they started to sleep in the same bed. Careful analysis showed that the enuresis was an unconscious attempt on the part of the boy to identify himself with the dead father. He had loved his father deeply and wished he would return. However his absence did bring certain advantages, such as sleeping with the mother, which he would lose if the father returned. The conflict in his mind could be solved if he were the father. He could retain him and at the same time get rid of him. Thus on the one hand he wanted to be the father because he loved him and on the other he wanted to be the father because he was jealous of him.

These two conflicting motives made him uncomfortable and feel guilty. It was as if his conscience said to him, "You have always wanted to get rid of your father and take his place. Now he is dead and your wish has come true. You will be your father. But your father was kind to you and loved you and you were a very wicked boy to desire to take his place. So now when your wish comes true you will be punished for your wish by being your father" (i. e., by having bladder trouble as he did). This is a case of *hysterical enuresis*. The hysterical mechanism is unconscious and responds best to intensive psychotherapy for the child. Usually psychoanalysis is the method of choice. Of course the boy should not be permitted to go on sleeping with his mother, and it would be well to ascertain if she is becoming too devoted to him and using him in her life to replace her dead husband.

Another type of neurotic enuresis may be illustrated by the following case. A little girl of five had been strictly and severely toilet trained much too early, after which she began to masturbate. The mother punished her for doing so. She then continued to masturbate but did not use her hands. Instead she sat on a rocking horse and during the rocking masturbated by sliding backward and forward on the saddle. One day she slid too far forward, the horse tipped and she was thrown violently against the pommel. The horn of the saddle bruised her urethra and for a day or two she suffered considerable burning on urination. Since she had acquired the injury during masturbation she dared not tell her parents of her discomfort. She worried a great deal lest she had injured herself permanently and inspected herself to see if she had mutilated her genitals. Since she could find no visible sign of injury she developed the idea that the injury was hidden inside, soon would burst forth, and then she could no longer hold her urine. She started to have some enuresis, which confirmed her fears.

Similar cases of enuresis—and these may include a few where the child wets herself both in the daytime and at night—may follow a painful sexual assault on a little girl by a much older boy or by a man. Since the child is hurt and yet excited she begins to feel guilty. Her guilt makes her believe that she has been injured in some way and that therefore she no longer has a physical organ to retain her urine. As a result of this belief she makes no effort to control her urination and whenever she feels the urge accedes to it on the spot. Since the child does not tell the parents of the sexual episode, the cause of the enuresis remains a mystery and can only be uncovered through intensive psychotherapy; the cure takes place when her erroneous beliefs are corrected. This type might be called *enuresis due to a fancied castration*.

Enuresis may be an expression of jealousy of a new baby, as in the following case. A boy of six and a half had the following history. He was toilet trained before he was two years old. When he was three the mother adopted another baby on whom she lavished much affection. The patient reacted by starting to soil and wet. The mother, much annoyed by this return of uncleanliness, scolded and punished him for it. When a friend told her she was not treating the boy fairly, she gave him more attention, and the soiling and day wetting stopped, although bedwetting continued until he was five. The boy was saying to his mother, "You give my new brother all your love and interest. He gets more attention than I do. See, I am only a little baby, too, and have to be cleaned and changed as he does." In cases such as this there exists, besides the organic plea for the mother's attention, a certain element of revenge.

The child is well aware that his stained clothes add extra work of a distasteful kind for his mother and the maid. They may even complain a great deal about it, but he goes on doing it just the same. One sometimes even gets the impression that the child hears their complaints with a certain amount of glee. This type can be called *regressive neurosis*. The treatment should follow the course suggested by the friend of the mother. Of course the enuresis will not stop right away but will gradually cease after a moderately short period of time.

The revenge element is slight in the type of enuresis just described, but forms the most important motive in the next type, which includes most cases of both day wetting and soiling. (Soiling may also form a part of the symptom complex of the previous type.) In these cases the child's lot is an unhappy one. He is rejected by one or both parents. From the time he arises in the morning until he goes to bed at night he is nagged, fussed at and criticized. Not uncommonly by the time he is ready to leave for school in the morning both he and his mother are in tears of irritation and rage—not over the bedwetting (although that comes into the picture) but over every detail of the daily routine. The father takes the mother's side or else remains aloof. The child has no one to support him against his nagging and unreasonable parents. He has few ways in which he can express his resentment of them. He knows that if he wets his clothes and the bed he will give his mother extra work and thus annoy her, giving himself the excuse that he cannot help his accident. Such a child often awakens at night and then wets the bed, instead of getting up and going to the toilet. He of course denies having been awake or having had anything to do with the wetting. It is only when he comes to have confidence in the therapist that he admits to having done much of it deliberately.

This is *revenge enuresis,* and its logical treatment is to change the parents' attitude toward the child, or if this fails to remove him from them. Often such a child has no enuresis during a stay in hospital, in camp, or with friends (where the child is treated reasonably) but the symptom recurs as soon as he returns home. Such cases are difficult to treat because the rejecting parent has no incentive to change his attitude toward the child. In fact, he unconsciously welcomes the child's enuresis because it gives an added reason for nagging and abusing him. Similarly he seldom wishes to have the child placed because he will then lose an object on whom he can express his hostile feelings, and although he may bring the child to the physician for treatment every effort of the latter is thwarted.

In many papers published on the subject of enuresis attention is directed to the fact that a fairly large number of cases have low intelligence and come from poor economic and social levels. Any large hospital clinic for child psychiatry will have a number of cases of enuresis referred to it by other departments, but many of them do not keep their appointments, or if they keep one, never come back. Investigation often shows that the family is not at all concerned with the enuresis. The child was brought to the pediatric clinic for some illness—a cold, bronchitis, etc.—and only in the history taking is it disclosed that the child wets the bed. Further investigation shows that the parents never attempted to toilet-train the child, nor are they concerned in doing so. All children wet their beds is their attitude, and it is only as they approach adolescence that they gradually begin to toilet-train themselves. In the majority of cases this attitude of the parents is due to their laziness and indifference to the restrictions of culture. Sometimes the attitude is due to the fact that the parents also had enuresis in childhood and "outgrew" it. In a very few cases it is due to the fact that the mother gets sensual pleasure in attending to the physical wants of little children and is loath to have any of her children grow up.

This is *enuresis from lack of training*. There is really no problem in the first group at all. The child eventually of his own initiative will establish bladder control. In the second group the outcome is usually the same. In either case the physician can do little or nothing about the situation because the parents want nothing done and feel his efforts are not necessary. The third group are just as difficult to treat but the physician has more obligation to do so, since the attitude of such a parent is inclined to develop a babyish personality in the child which will make him unfit to be really successful in life. If treatment can be carried on at all it should be directed toward helping the parents find more pleasure in the child's development than in his remaining a baby.

There is one point about enuresis that has not been mentioned. Frequently when a child has enuresis the parents will tell you that other members of the family also had the condition in childhood. There is no certain explanation for this phenomenon at present. We can only make the assumption that such families show an inherited weakness in establishing voluntary control of the urinary sphincter. Whether this is due to the existence of a defect in the mechanism of voluntary control or to the fact that such persons possess a greater need to prolong the infantile pleasure of wetting cannot be stated definitely.

From the foregoing discussion it is clear that unreasonable punishment, shame and scolding of the child because he wets his clothes or the bed are not only not necessary but distinctly contraindicated. Such parental behavior only serves to focus the child's attention to his bedwetting, which can then give him a weapon for use against the parents, such as the weapon of anorexia that we spoke of earlier. It is better for the development of the child that the parents encourage him to be clean and dry as an attribute of being grown up and at the same time give him time and opportunity to do so.

BIBLIOGRAPHY FOR CHAPTER VIII

Alvarez, W. C., "Autointoxication," *Physiological Review* 4, 1924, 352.

Davis, C. M., "Self-selection of Diet by Newly Weaned Infants," *China Medical Journal* 43, 1929, 68.

Fenichel, Otto, "Pregenital Conversion Neuroses. Outline of Clinical Psychoanalysis," *Psychoanalytic Quarterly* 2, 1933, 94.

Ferenczi, Sandor, "Further Contributions to the Theory and Technic of Psychoanalysis," Hogarth Press, 1926.

Freud, Anna, and Burlingham, Dorothy T., *The Freud, Burlingham Reports,* Foster Parents' Plan for War Children, Oct., 1943.

Levy, David M., "Release Therapy" *American Journal of Orthopsychiatry* 9, 1939, 713.

Levy, David M., *Studies in Sibling Rivalry,* American Orthopsychiatric Association Monographs, No. 2.

Michaels, J., and Goodman, S., "The Incidence of Enuresis and Age of Cessation in 1,000 Neuropsychiatric Patients: with a Discussion of the Relationship between Enuresis and Delinquency," *American Journal of Orthopsychiatry* 9, 1939, 59.

Pearson, Gerald H. J., "A Case of Compulsion Neurosis in an Eleven-year-old Boy," *American Journal of Orthopsychiatry* 10, 1940, 136.

Pearson, Gerald H. J., "The Child's History as an Aid in the Psychiatric Treatment of Children," *Journal of Pediatrics* 17, 1940, 241.

Spring, William J., "Words and Masses: A Pictorial Contribution to the Psychology of Stammering," *Psychoanalytic Quarterly* 4, 1935, 244.

Chapter IX

EMOTIONAL DISTURBANCES THAT OCCUR DURING THE LATENT PERIOD (*Continued*)

MASTURBATION

THERE is a type of masturbation that is a manifestation of a child's great unhappiness. It is known as *compulsive masturbation*. Such a child masturbates to the point of orgasm four, five or more times every day. He does not attempt to hide his act from observation. He unbuttons his clothes, takes out his penis and masturbates. He may do it in public or before his parents or the teacher at school. He apparently feels little shame, guilt or fear about his actions, or if he does it is not sufficient to cause him to stop. During the masturbatory act he has fantasies of which he may or may not be aware. Their content is not the simple erotic and aggressive fancies of the normal child but the sadistic and masochistic ones of the child during the anal period and include ideas of obtaining pleasure by hurting others and by being hurt by them. Sometimes the ideas are associated with ideas of suicide, in which case the more he is warned that masturbation may hurt him the more he masturbates, since his desire is to injure himself. Sometimes when the masturbation is done publicly the child's underlying desire is to seduce the adult before whom he masturbates, in which case he has a serious intrapsychic problem and usually is living in a family situation that forces him to extreme efforts in order to adjust to it.

What is meant by this last statement? In the ordinary family where there is mutual love between the parents and between the parents and the child the emotional atmosphere is relaxed and happy. Quarrels and disagreements do occur but they are not constant nor is the emotional atmosphere so tense that each member of the family fears to say or do anything lest he set off an explosion. The child does not have constantly to watch both his father and mother to determine if their mood is favorable, nor does he have to seek the refuge of his own room or of some corner where he can carry out his own pursuits in peace. The parents do things together and often they include the children in their recreations or plan interesting recreations for them. Together they go to the movies, to the zoo, or to a museum. Together, afterward, they talk about what they have seen. The child can talk with his parents about his interests if he wishes, though they make no attempt to pry into his affairs. At times the child prefers to play with other children and the parents feel no resentment, or he prefers to stay in his room and work at something in which he is particularly interested. He does not need to withdraw to his room in order to get out of the way. He knows when his parents wish to be alone or with other adults, and he respects their wishes even if unspoken because they respect his wishes under similar circumstances. The parents see that the child has ample play space and an adequate number of toys. Such a child has little need to feel lonely or unhappy, and therefore he is not so compelled to seek physical gratification from playing with his own body.

The opposite is true of the child whose parents do not love each other, do not love him, or are too fussy and restrictive about what he does. We saw such a child recently. In the playroom, in spite of the many toys provided, he sits in a corner playing with his fingers or clothes. His behavior indicates that he is afraid he will be criticized if he plays with the toys so he prefers to play with his own body. He has developed the habit because of the unreasonable restrictiveness of his parents. In a home filled with adverse attitudes a child has to curtail everything he does lest he suffer from the wrath or disapproval of some adult. As a consequence he can find little pleasure in life except that which he is able to extract from his own body.

Treatment must be directed along two lines. First both in importance and in point of time there is required an intensive investigation of the child's intrapsychic life and of the interpersonal relationships in the family. (In the cases we have seen there has always been a serious marital problem between the parents.) If the problem of interpersonal relationships in the family seems insoluble or if it appears that efforts to solve them will take a long time the child should be removed and placed in an institution. The child needs intensive psychotherapy, usually of the degree of analysis. No other degree of treatment will really be beneficial. Second, after treatment has been started the child should be cautioned against masturbating in public, and if he continues he should be excluded from the group until he ceases. Such treatment requires the services of an experienced child psychiatrist and should not be attempted by any-one else. Above all, operative procedures, prostate massage, bladder irrigations, and cruel and unusual punishments should never be used.

DISTURBANCES OF THE SPECIAL SENSES

We are dependent on our special senses for almost our entire orientation to reality and the external world, and a great deal of our sensual pleasure comes through their use. Among civilized man the most important special senses are vision, hearing and touch. The other special senses such as smell and taste, though formerly more important than sight, have become relegated to the background through disuse.

Disorders of Vision

Vision plays an increasingly large role in our life. Today the technique of servicing airplane and high-speed motorboat engines is taught to the soldiers largely through the use of moving and still pictures, and those engaged in the work have found the method so valuable that they are already planning similar methods of instruction for civilian life in the postwar world.

The sense of vision is a complicated one and can be disturbed in many different ways. Though the reader is probably familiar with the mechanics of the sense of sight we feel that the subject is so important as to warrant a brief review. When the light rays pass from an object to the eye they enter by passing through the lens. This inverts the image of the object, hence when the image falls on the retina it is in an inverted position. The tracts that carry the sensations backward from the retina to the occipital cortex of the brain transmit the image in the same position so that as far as we can trace the progress of the impulses the image continues to be inverted. Furthermore, the image registered on one occipital cortex is the obverse of that registered on the other. An F appears on one cortex as Ⅎ and on the other as ⅎ. If the images of the two occipital cortices are superimposed (in order to make the single object we see consciously) the result is ∄ As far as we can make out the very small infant sees the world upside down.

We have no proof for this statement because we cannot learn from small infants how the world looks to them, but we do have some indication that this is so from older children in their constant game of imagining a topsy-turvy world. In order that sight may be used as a means of orientation with the environment and with reality, such an impression must be corrected to correspond with external reality. This correction is a learned process. If a person puts on lenses that reinvert the image, he sees everything upside down for a short while and then quickly learns to see them in their correct orientation. This learning process comes about in two ways. The child looks at and touches an object at the same time. At first he sees the top of the object while his hand feels the bottom. After a few experiences of this kind he begins to try to see the object in the position that his sense of touch feels it. Gradually in this way he comes to recognize the true spatial position of objects and corrects the visual images of their position until he sees everything in its proper relation to space. Occasionally, following a cerebral injury or in those children whose learning is slow, it is possible to prove that the inversion of the visual image is only corrected psychologically.

The separation of the image on one occipital cortex from its obverse on the other takes place in a different way. Orton has shown that the image on the occipital cortex of the dominant side of the brain is retained while that on the undominant side is consciously elided and simply not seen consciously. The fact that such an elision can take place for purposes of convenience and clarity indicates that the conscious ego can readily alter or elide actual sense impressions—a fact that is well known. At best we only see what we want to see and actually do not see consciously what is repugnant to our minds, what is associated with ideas that are repugnant to us or with feelings that cause us discomfort. Such an ability to repress and deny the evidence of our senses is not very possible before the beginning of the latent period, but it becomes increasingly possible thereafter. This is why the state of the mother's pregnancy is revealed to the whole nursery school by the three-year-old child, while the ten-year-old child, much better able to reason, understand, and possessed of more knowledge than the three-year-old, is quite astounded when he is told that he has a new sibling. He never *noticed*—because he could not help but *see*—the change in the mother's figure. We have seen such an utter obliviousness to visual impressions of the mother's pregnancy even in an eighteen-year-old boy. This ability not to be conscious of visual impressions explains the vehement assertion of an eight-year-old boy that his father, whom he saw nude every day, had no body hair.

These disturbances in the conscious recognition of visual impression because of their association with repugnant ideas or unpleasant feelings are extremely common in the latent period and continue to be rather frequent in adolescent and adult life. The mechanism merits the designation of hysterical repression and is one of the reasons why teachers complain constantly of the lack of curiosity in children of school age. In some children the mechanism becomes so marked that actual disturbances of vision such as hysterical blindness or partial blindness result. In their case the usual condition is a concentric contraction of the visual fields—the child feels as if he were looking through a tube.

Although perhaps more properly placed in the section on the discussion of educational difficulties, it seems well to discuss reading disabilities here because they are so closely related to the mechanism of sight. Research educators have come to the conclusion that children are not able to learn to read until they have reached a certain stage of development, and that the age at which this is reached is specific for each child. It is therefore useless to try to teach a child to read before this stage is reached. It seems probable that it is inaugurated when the intracortical connections between the various brain centers have reached a stage of maturity. The attainment of this stage is known to educators as reading readiness, and may take place anywhere between four and ten years of age. If the parent or teacher tries to teach a child to learn to read before the stage of reading readiness the child does not understand what the whole procedure is about. He tries in order to please the adult, but without result. If the adult gets annoyed by his "stubbornness" or "laziness" the child tries harder, but again without success. Reading therefore becomes associated in his mind with a painful feeling of failure, and when his reading readiness appears, the past association with pain may make him try to avoid any contact with the subject. It may even be years before the pleasure he finds in reading becomes great enough to overcome the memory of the pain of the past. Or he may always be disinclined to read or always be a poor reader. The prevention of such a result will depend on not trying to teach the child to read before he is ready. If a reading disability has resulted from the failure to observe this rule the child should be given a rest from all reading for awhile and then be retaught to read under pleasant circumstances and in ways that will bring a quick sense of success, which will gradually outweigh the painful memories of past failures.

If the child starts his reading when he has attained the stage of reading readiness he usually will be interested in learning. However, if he has interpersonal difficulties with his teacher—if the teacher dislikes him, is unnecessarily harsh and brutal, or is too impatient—then he falls into the same emotional reaction. His dislike for the painful experiences at his teacher's hands is carried over to the subject matter and he begins to dislike that and not want to learn how to do it. He develops a reading disability. For reading disabilities due to this cause the ideal treatment is tutoring by a person who understands the importance of the interpersonal relationship for learning. Much of the tutoring consists in an introduction to the tutoring—an introduction that has as its main purpose the development of a friendly relationship between tutor and child. When this has been accomplished the retraining in reading proceeds quite rapidly.

In certain cases of reading disability that we have seen, the beginning of the difficulty lay in an unpleasant interpersonal relationship between the child and the parent, who, the child knew, had placed a high value on the ability to read. The child was angry and annoyed at the way he was treated and in revenge struck where he knew it would hurt most, i. e., through the matter of reading. Treatment for such cases must follow two routes: the unpleasant interpersonal relation with the parent must be corrected and later the child must be given special tutoring to bring him up to his grade level.

Educators believe that there are effective methods of teaching reading. If they are used after the child is ready to learn, the learning proceeds adequately. If ineffective methods are used the child may develop a reading difficulty. Cases of this kind should be treated by an educator.

As we mentioned before, Orton has discussed an important and special type of reading disability—strephosymbolia. This condition shows itself in both the child's reading and writing. The child has great difficulty in learning to read because at one time he sees the letter E as E and the word SAW as SAW and at another sees E as ∃ and SAW as WAƨ At one time he will write not as NOT, at another as TON. Such children actually often read in a mirror better than when looking at the page itself. This is due to the fact that the dominance of one cerebral hemisphere over the other has not been established. Therefore at one time he tries to elide the sense impression from one half of his cortex and at another the sense impression from the other. This uncertainty in dominance is sometimes associated with the fact that the child was innately left-handed and right-brained and was then trained to be right-handed and left-brained, which made it possible for one cerebral hemisphere to attain definite dominance over the other. Such cases are readily ascertained when tested by the methods developed by Orton, who also has formulated precise methods of treatment for them. All cases of strephosymbolia should be placed in the hands of some person trained in the use of Orton's methods.

There are a small number of children with reading disabilities who show some of the characteristics of strephosymbolia but who do not respond to the specific tests. The disability is the result of complicated emotional problems concerning the use of language—written, spoken and read—as a weapon of offense and defense, and results from the child's reactions of guilt and fear about these uses of language. Such cases can only be diagnosed and treated by a psychiatrist, and the ideal treatment is psychoanalysis.

We have discussed the causes of reading disabilities. When a child has such a difficulty—whatever the cause is—we find that he is not as successful in his school progress as other children. As a result he begins to feel inferior. He tries to evade the inadequacy in various ways. He may, for instance, strain his memory prodigiously so that simply by sitting in class, listening to other children read, and paying careful attention to marks that will distinguish the page on which he is reading, he is able by memory to read the whole page with only a few mistakes. If he is confronted by exactly similar words arranged in a slightly different order on a page that has no distinguishing marks he is totally unable to read it. (We have seen children who had attained the eighth grade who were able actually to read only a very few words.) He may become totally disinterested in all schoolwork and proceed to develop compensations along other lines. He may develop feelings that the teacher is picking on him and that she is responsible for his deficiencies at school. All of these reactions are the result, not the cause, of the reading disability. They may have to be dealt with during any tutoring process, a point of which many parents and teachers seem unaware. The basic essentials of good tutoring are the ability to develop a good interpersonal relationship between child and tutor and the capacity of the tutor to understand the child's behavior and reactions. It is the presence of this particular ability that makes one tutor successful in his work and another not, rather than whether the tutor knows his subject or uses the most advanced teaching methods.

Disorders of Hearing

Just as the obliviousness to visual sensory impressions is not due to so-called inattentiveness but is the result of a deliberate attempt not to see, either voluntary and willed or automatic, so children's obliviousness to auditory sensory impressions also is not due to inattentiveness but to a deliberate refusal to hear. Children are notorious for their voluntary refusal to hear when they do not want to. A child is interested in his play. His mother calls him again and again. The child goes on playing. He has heard and will tell he has heard, but he does not respond because he does not want to. Only when the tone of the parent's voice indicates that there will be a punishment in store if he does not come does he respond. He has an alibi for his behavior: because he has not heard he cannot be accused of being willfully disobedient. The more the child tries to make a picture of himself as a good, obedient child (i. e., to inhibit his defiance of the parent), the more likely he is really not to hear when he is called. By repressing the consciousness of his sensory impressions he can be disobedient and relieve himself of any feeling of guilt about his disobedience.

This condition can become a hysterical deafness; that is, the child can become actually deaf to all or certain specific sounds if they have been associated in his mind with former unpleasant experiences. For example, if the child has overheard parental intercourse and, because the feelings engendered in him by the sounds were unpleasant, has repressed the memory he may have to repress hearing any sounds that remind him of what he once heard. Children often react to this repression as if they were really deaf. (Since they cannot hear accurately they often compensate by developing a greater sensitivity of another sensory organ such as sight or touch. A similar compensatory reaction may follow the repression of the ability to see, or in fact the repression of the use of any channel of sensory intake). We have not seen complete hysterical deafness in children. Of course no treatment is required for the first group. The second (i. e., those children who mask their deliberate defiance under the guise of deafness) need some treatment for their exaggerated need to be good—a good course would consist in the parents' lowering, somewhat, their standards for the child. Real conversion hysteria needs intensive psychiatric treatment.

Any of the special senses may undergo types of disorder similar to those already discussed, and their management will be the same.

DISTURBANCES OF MOTOR FUNCTIONS

Children are ordinarily more restless than adults. They cannot sit quietly for as long periods. They are more inclined to do things than they are to talk or to think. This restlessness is natural although there may be times when parents and educators find it annoying. However there are certain children whose restlessness is different from the average, in quantity or in quality.

Hyperactivity

Some children are always getting into things, always on the go, and so on. Often they are so active that they remain thin, although well developed muscularly and having a good appetite. Their restlessness differs from the average child's in quantity. It usually is not associated with feelings of anxiety and may best be characterized as a state of hyperactivity.

In some instances this hyperactivity seems to be a constitutional trait. There are undoubtedly two classes of adults—indeed of children, of babies, and even of fetuses: those who are constantly active and seem to get most out of doing things, and those who are not so active but prefer quiet pursuits. The constitutionally active child tends to meet more restrictions from his environment than does the child who does not move so much and as a result he often develops antagonism toward the restricting person. This antagonism is met by further restrictions and soon a chronic aggressive reaction pattern develops.

The treatment for this type of hyperactivity is environmental. The child should have plenty of space and opportunity for muscular activity and does best in a rural situation. When he reaches school age he should be placed in a good progressive school, particularly one where games and athletics form a prominent part of the school life. In order that chronic feelings of hostility should not be aroused it is important that there not be too many restrictions on his activity. It has been interesting to us to observe how frequently parents punish hyperactive children by making them sit still for long periods—several hours—or by tying them in one place. This not only increases the need for muscular activity but causes the child to be uncomfortable and therefore hostile and antagonistic. It is probable that hyperactive children grow into hyperactive adults—the type who love tennis, golf, hiking, etc., and who feel uncomfortable and distressed if they have to follow a sedentary occupation.

In other instances the hyperactivity is the result of an organic brain lesion. This type of restlessness became well known following the epidemic of encephalitis of 1919–20. Its pathology is similar to that of the chronic aggressive reaction pattern due to brain lesion. Treatment consists of training new areas of the cortex to take over the task of control of the motor activity. It is not accomplished easily and the prognosis at best is poor. It can seldom be done in the home but will be more effective if the child is in a controlled environment such as a hospital for cases of chronic encephalitis or a training school for the feeble-minded.

Fidgetiness

The restlessness exhibited by the fidgety child differs from that of the average child in its quality. Such a child shows associated anxiety symptoms; his restlessness is not the carefree happy activity of the hyperactive (even if aggressive) child, in whom the hyperactivity is given free expression, but is an unhappy, partially controlled fidgetiness. He is like the child in the nursery rhyme:

> *Fidgety Phil*
> *He couldn't sit still.*

He does not spend much time running and jumping but tends to sit still, with all his muscles in constant but inhibited action. He squirms, moves his fingers, hands, legs or head, pulls at his sleeves or clothes, plays with pencils, table utensils, makes faces, and so on. In such children the restlessness is a neurotic symptom; that is, it is a sign of the presence of an intrapsychic conflict.

We again must draw the attention of the reader to the fact that it is only a neurotic symptom if the child is *really* restless. There are some parents who require a degree of inactivity which is impossible for any child or even an adult to attain. They believe in the old but outworn adage that children should be seen and not heard, and that the proper child is the child who sits still all the time. They regard a normal degree of activity as hyperactivity and accuse the child of restlessness when he really is not restless. The reader readily can see how quickly mutual hate can develop if this type of parent has a constitutionally hyperactive child. Treatment must be directed toward changing the point of view of the parents or toward rescuing the child from their restrictions.

However, there are children who are really fidgety and whose fidgetiness is the sign of an intrapsychic conflict. Long ago Darwin pointed out that animals become fidgety if they are excited, hungry, frightened or angry. Fidgetiness and restlessness form a large proportion of the symptoms of experimental neuroses in animals. The neuroses are produced by conditioning experiments in which the animal is required to discriminate between two closely similar stimuli, or to delay its response to a stimulus too long, or when, after being accustomed to being used as a test animal, the practice is stopped and its cellmate is used instead— in brief, when it is required to control its reactions too carefully or when it develops jealousy. Everyday observation will show that children, and adults also, become restless and fidgety when they are frustrated in satisfying some inner need or hunger and are unable for external or internal reasons to overcome the frustration.

Chronic fidgetiness in a child is a sign that he is being frustrated. Either his anger has been aroused and he is not permitted to express it or he has been refused satisfactions that he feels are necessary. This may occur when he has been placed in a situation where his jealousy has been aroused or when he is being asked to conform to impossible requirements. Such frustrating experiences make the child feel insecure and unhappy and as a reaction to these feelings he becomes chronically angry and has the urge to attack and annoy the persons in his environment. He does so overtly at times, while at other times he tries not to, although he is aware of what he wants to do. At such times he becomes restless because his desire to attack and annoy is greater than can be expressed through his actions, and the excess energy flows over to innervate the general musculature, producing unpurposeful motions. If he tries to remain unaware of his desire to attack and annoy and stops any attempt to put the desire into action the restlessness becomes involuntary fidgetiness. The more the desire to attack and annoy is prevented from being translated into action the more the restlessness becomes fidgetiness and spreads throughout the whole motor system.

What are some of the frustrating experiences that chronically fidgety children have experienced? In many instances the child has suffered one or more serious and prolonged illnesses in a short period of time, perhaps during one year. Such illnesses make the child more dependent on the parents and concentrate their love on him. The satisfaction in such a situation to the child's mind places a premium on being sick and dependent. When he becomes well organically he does not want to relinquish these gratifications. However, if he wishes to obtain gratification by being dependent he has to repress his desire to be active, whose main vehicle for expression is the muscular system. In order to do this he has to place an inhibition on the purposeful use of his muscles. Instead of being active as he wants to be, he at the same time tries to abstain from activity, and the muscular innervation becomes more and more purposeless until a state of in-co-ordination or perhaps tremor is reached. His desire to be active is increased by his illness for as he lies in bed he does not have the muscular system well enough under control (because of weakness, medical prohibitions, etc.) to use it to express his active impulses. Consequently the active impulses are stored up to be liberated later as he gets well.

After a severe illness children are often restricted unnecessarily from too active behavior by their parents who fear a repetition of the anxiety and mental discomfort caused by the loved child's serious illness. Since muscular activity is a part of life, such restrictions tend to make the child restless, i. e., to appear to have a purposeless excitement of the motor system. (This is clearly seen in the expression "tickles in his feet," used for a small child whose activity has been interfered with by a rainy day.) These restrictions also make the child angry. If he could express his anger verbally it would help, but his parents object. He tries to act angrily. The parents object. These emotional outlets being forbidden, the child tends to masturbate. If this, too, is forbidden the desire to masturbate is changed to a desire to touch other parts of the body or to move in ways that will give genital satisfaction. This restlessness enhances the restlessness already present and causes a further conflict with the parents until a vicious circle is produced.

There are children who have suffered a number of traumatic experiences—a birth, a death, a divorce in the immediate family, or marital difficulties in the parents' lives—within a short period of time. Others have suffered from the continual expression of adverse attitudes by the parents. These adverse attitudes are similar to the situations that produce neuroses in animals that we discussed above. A parent whose overprotection is based on rejection of the child frequently trains him in such a way that he has to make too fine a distinction between what is permitted and what is not. Or the parent may be overanxious to make the child conform too quickly, i. e., to learn too soon to replace his use of the pleasure principle as a guide to life by the reality principle.

Treatment of these cases must consist of a search for the underlying conflict. It is not only useless but harmful to try to coerce the child to stop fidgeting by threats, bribes or punishments. It is equally useless and harmful to reduce the muscular activity by the use of sedatives such as phenobarbital. The fidgetiness should be ignored by the parents, the educator and the physician. Instead, intensive psychotherapy for both parents and child should be instituted.

Years ago Freud drew attention to a type of person whose main defense is to act out impulsively a psychic conflict rather than consider it and deal with it rationally. If a series of persons living under essentially similar conditions—economic, social, etc.—is studied, it is found that accidents (fractures, wounds, etc.) occur only in a certain number of these persons. If the histories of this number are studied carefully it is found that they are frequently meeting with accidental injuries. When the accident itself is studied carefully it is found that it presents the picture of a deliberate attempt on the part of the individual to injure himself, though of course he is unaware that he deliberately has hurt himself. Further, it is found that persons who are prone to develop fractures are those who tend to act out or are unable to inhibit impulsive expressions of hostility. They usually have had to suppress their hostile feelings in deference to stern parents. Their muscular tension is great at all times. (It is interesting that this muscular tension disappears when they get relief from their feelings of guilt about their revengeful impulses—that is, if repression of the knowledge of the revengeful impulse has not taken place.) Ordinarily their muscular movements are stiff and jerky and they tend to act out their conflicts rather than consider them.

Similar accident proneness occurs among children. A child who is not accident prone can undertake a hazardous act safely, while another child who is will get hurt in a situation that is not at all dangerous. When the psychic life of the latter is studied it is found that he is in the throes of an intrapsychic conflict which he attempts to solve through an impulsive act. Certain children have strong dependency desires. They wish to be babied and coddled, and to be free from the responsibility of doing anything for themselves. This need for dependency is repressed into the unconscious because it is in conflict with the demands that he grow up and with his pride, particularly if the child is a boy. The repressed need is felt in his conscious mind as a fear that he will be a coward and unable to do the things that the other children of his age do. This feeling is painful and unacceptable to his conscious mind and he sets out to prove to himself that he is not that type of person. He can obtain such proof only through performing daring deeds. If there is a ditch he must jump the widest part. If he rides a bicycle he must ride on the most heavily traveled streets. As long as the need to prove himself brave is uppermost he can usually perform these acts safely, but if at any point the unconscious need for dependency becomes paramount he slips on the rim of the height, he falls in his jump or he is careless in judging his distance from an approaching car. The accident occurs. Through the accident he obtains the attention and babying care he has longed for, but he can always excuse the result by feeling that he had no control over his failure. It was accidental, i. e., the result of fate.

In another type of conflict the child wishes to do something that has been forbidden by the parents or by his conscience. Instead of acceding to the demands of his conscience and abstaining or else getting rid of his conscience and going ahead without any feeling of guilt he impulsively does the action and does it in such a way that he gets hurt. One boy was forbidden (unnecessarily) to play in a certain park. He went impulsively. While there he fell in the creek, lost his shoes and socks, tore his trousers, and injured his hand. When he returned home in this dilapidated state he had to confess where he had been and received summary punishment. His sense of guilt over his disobedience and over his hostility toward his parents' orders haunted him so much that he could not have a good time without getting himself hurt. He compromised by acting in a disobedient way and getting himself punished for it. Accidents due to this type of psychopathology are frequent in accident-prone children. It is interesting that the child who, because of parental rejection, has never learned to love anyone and loves only himself does many dangerous acts safely. He is able to perform such deeds because his feelings of fear have been obliterated through a feeling of personal omnipotence which has been engendered through his self-love. Since he has no feeling of guilt he is able really to do quite dangerous things without getting hurt.

Accident proneness may also arise through an impulsive need to commit suicide. In children such an impulse is motivated often through a desire to take revenge on the parents by making them feel remorseful. This is well illustrated by the case of Tom Sawyer. Angered at Aunt Polly he decided to go away and never come back; hence she would suffer permanent remorse for the way she had treated him. Had he drowned on his expedition—as it was thought he had—his revenge to his mind would have been complete. We say to his mind because in his fantasy he would not be extinct but would be able to observe what went on after his death. In fact the whole story of the episode (the flight, the report of the drowning, the secret return to watch the funeral ceremonies, etc.) resembles the usual suicide fantasy of the child—which he sometimes attempts to act out. Perhaps it represented a real boyhood fantasy of Mark Twain's. In many accidents the child escapes with injury only but sometimes the results are fatal.

We feel that children who show proneness to accidents need psychiatric study and probably treatment. The psychopathologies we have discussed are serious deviations from the normal and unless corrected can cause much harm and suffering to the individual and to his loved ones both in childhood and in adult life. They are not the types of psychopathology that can be expected to be changed by the simple process of growing up or by environmental change.

Children whose restlessness is an attempt to solve an intrapsychic conflict tend to become more restless in the late afternoon and evening. At this time their activity seems more aimless and in-co-ordinate; they are more liable to have temper tantrums and are more difficult to manage. As a general rule such a child is thin and pale. Parents often feel that the child is tired out by his excessive activity and think that if he rests during the afternoon he will be less tired, and therefore easier to control. The child is tired out, but his fatigue is due only to a slight extent to his activity. The restlessness does tire his muscles which are then less capable of serving as a vehicle for the expression of his aggression, but this simple physiological fact accounts for only a small part of the fatigue, for chronic fatigue is caused to a much less degree by physical exertion than by emotional conflicts. It is the interpersonal difficulties between the child and his parents or the child's intrapsychic conflicts that produce his restlessness and fatigue. If he were not restless at all he still would suffer from as great a feeling of fatigue. The treatment for the fatigue state in general is not physical rest but psychic peace. It must consist of measures that will make the individual more comfortable with his environment. Either the sources of discomfort in the environment (adverse parental behavior and attitudes) or those in the psychic life (unsolved intrapsychic conflicts) must be changed.

Tics or Habit Spasms

When one observes a fidgety child one feels that he is fidgeting purposely, that he could control his restlessness if he tried harder. There are a group of conditions, however, wherein the impression received by the lay observer is different, wherein he feels that the muscular movements are not made purposefully by the child. These movements do not involve the whole of the child's body but only one or two groups of muscles. A child may blink his eyes, he may make grimaces with his mouth, he may turn his head spasmodically, or he may make jerky motions with his fingers or hands. It is always a group of muscles with a specific function that is affected and the movement caricatures an ordinary movement of expression.

A good example is the child who has attacks in which he blinks his eyes. He does not blink steadily but only in attacks that last for a few minutes and then subside. This is a caricature of the ordinary movement of blinking which we all do to protect the eye from injury, or to shut out the light because the eye is irritated. However, when this child is examined it is found that his eyes are not irritated by disease, foreign bodies or visual defect. (Children who have defective vision may screw up their faces and blink their eyes in order to help them to see better. Neither parent nor child, however, may be aware that the vision is defective until some chance examination brings the defect in visual acuity to light.) It is true that we do blink in order to protect the eyes from injury, but it is also true that we blink in order to shut out repellent sights and to stop thinking unpleasant thoughts. We often say, about something that we do not want to think of, that we shut our eyes to it. Also we may shut our eyes and refuse to look if we feel that looking is wrong or that we will be punished for it. Such an attitude is illustrated in the well-known folk story of Peeping Tom and Lady Godiva. Thus we close or open our eyes in response to psychic activity and we may do so spasmodically as a result of an intrapsychic conflict.

An intensive study made of a number of children who suffer from spasm of the eyelids shows that the spasm is an attempt to solve an intrapsychic conflict. Often in these cases the spasm of the muscles stands as a monument to some former emotionally upsetting experience—such as some sexual curiosity for which the child had been punished or feared he would be punished but which he now has forgotten. Or the spasms of blinking began at a time when there was a slight irritation of the eye but continued after the irritation had disappeared because the motion became connected with a psychic conflict. Often these children show no signs of personality difficulties other than the spasms of the eyes, which may include spasms of the other muscles of the face. It is as if the entire psychic conflict has been crystallized into one group of symptoms and as long as it remains there the rest of the personality structure is unaffected.

After the symptom has been in existence for a little while its presence becomes noticeable to other people. The parents begin to insist that the child stop the movements and when he seems unwilling to do so—he really is not able to—they begin to nag, ridicule, and punish him. Other adults join in the nagging. The child's friends begin to tease him. This situation develops, usually, regardless of the cause of the child's disability. Even if he is suffering from chorea—which is an infectious disease of the brain—his parents may ridicule and punish him in their attempt to get him to stop the movements. The nagging and teasing are unpleasant to the child. He tries to stop and, finding he cannot, starts to become tense and restless. We say he is very nervous. A certain amount of the restlessness found in chorea is caused by this nervousness, which ceases as soon as the nagging and ridicule stop.

The child, being unable to stop the movements and finding the teasing and nagging unpleasant, begins to try to extract some pleasure from the situation. He begins to desire the attention he receives from his movements, and getting pleasure in this way he no longer minds the unpleasant part. It is remarkable how little shame or embarrassment such children feel consciously about the symptom, although they are ridiculed and teased constantly. In one case we observed, the child felt little shame about the symptoms because certain members of the family constantly remarked how cute his grimace was. Of course when the child comes to find that he enjoys the attention he receives from his blinking he is loath to give it up.

Blinking of the eyes is one of many types of movements that are designated as habit spasms or tics. They most commonly affect the head and neck, although they occasionally appear in the other extremities. Teeth grinding, whether during the waking hours or in sleep, is rather common in children. It represents a desire to injure by biting some person whom the child loves. (He feels guilty about the desire.) Rocking movements are common in babies. They express a desire for physical pleasure and of course are more pronounced in children who do not get sufficient satisfaction of this sort. Head knocking and banging occurs in older children, i. e., at about one year of age. It is important in such cases to examine the ears carefully, for the child may have an otitis media but be too young to be able to tell that he is suffering, and so bang his head in an effort to get rid of the pain in his ears. Usually, however, he bangs his head because he feels resentful—and usually justifiably so—of some person but is too feeble to bang him. Since he cannot bang the person who has angered him he is reduced to banging the first person at hand, i. e., himself.

Certain organic diseases of the central nervous system, such as chorea, the dystonias, etc., produce localized spasmodic involuntary movements. These must be differentiated from cases of habit spasm and psychogenic tic because the treatment and prognosis are different. The diagnosis usually can be made through a careful observation of the movements and a thorough neurological examination by a competent neurologist. In some cases there may be a doubt as to whether the cause is organic or functional. It is better to treat these cases as if the cause were functional, for up to the present there is no curative treatment for the lesions in the central nervous system that produce spasmodic movements, while great improvement and often cure result from treatment of spasms due to psychic causes.

In the treatment of localized spasmodic movements it is necessary first to deal with the child's secondary gain from the symptoms, i. e., the attention, painful or otherwise, which his family directs toward him because of his spasms. They should be advised to refrain as much as is humanly possible from any remark about his movements. The parental attitudes toward the child and the family situation in the present should be studied carefully, and if possible any adverse attitudes corrected or the child removed to another home. Both of these measures should be undertaken in every case where a child shows spasmodic movements whether the condition has an organic or a functional etiology.

Many children suffering from chorea are tense and jerky because the parents, unaware of the organic basis of the disease, nag and scold constantly because of their "restlessness." Or they may live in an unpleasant family situation and the chorea makes life a little more pleasant for them because it brings the kindly attention of the physician, often the comfort of several weeks in the more pleasant atmosphere of a hospital; or if they stay at home they are kept in bed and the parents make some effort to be nice to them because they are ill. When they recover they find their life in the home more unpleasant by contrast, and they begin to wish they were ill again.

In our opinion certain cases of so-called recurrent chorea are really two successive illnesses—the first attack is a true chorea, and the subsequent ones are psychogenic copies of it. In all cases of habit spasm and psychogenic tic it is necessary to study the attitudes of the parents toward the child and to try to correct them if they are adverse. Besides this the child requires intensive psychotherapy, the purpose of which is to discover the impulses that underlie the movement and to remove the fear or distaste the child feels for the impulse. At the beginning of treatment he may be unaware either of the fear and its nature (punishment by physical injury or by loss of love) or of the impulse (curiosity, aggression, etc.). As he becomes aware of both sides of the symptom during treatment the fears can be removed and the proper and adequate use of the impulse can be pointed out to him.

The whole process consumes much time and energy for both the patient and the physician. Tics or habit spasms of long standing require therapy as intensive as psychoanalysis. However, like stuttering, the misuse of the muscles may continue even after the emotional problem is solved, in which case care must be taken that all the secondary gain has been removed from the child's symptoms. If it continues after this is done it is advisable to suggest that the child go through a period of retraining in which he consciously tries to control the spasm. Although tics and habit spasms sometimes cease of their own accord we do not believe that children grow out of them. Instead we think that they use a deformation of character to solve their unsolved conflict and therefore, although no better intrapsychically, do not need the symptom of the spasm any more. This is a pity because deformation of the character produces more real suffering in life than do single symptoms and is much more difficult to treat.

COMPULSION NEUROSES

Little children are notorious for being unable to play together peaceably and happily for long periods. After a reasonably short while they tire of each other's company and turn to other pursuits or to quarreling. If the play is at all vigorous and exciting or if there is an adult present the quarreling starts sooner. This is because they are intensely individualistic and self-centered. They wish to be first in everything, to have the best and to be the most important, and they have little capacity to share or fill any role, no matter how necessary, on which the limelight does not shine only upon them. A great deal of childhood and adolescence is spent in learning how to limit and control this attitude in order to live happily with one's peers, all of whom have, basically, the same characteristics. It takes a long, hard process of learning before the child is able to know when it is desirable for him to consider the needs and desires of others, and when it is desirable for him to assert his demands for himself.

Usually it is only with the beginning of the latent period that the child begins to make contact with real social life with his fellows, and if the reader will watch a child of this age he will see the great variety of struggle through which he goes in his attempts to get along comfortably with his companions. He begins to take part in group games and any-one who has observed these games formulated by children without adult aid will realize that they are governed by rules more rigid and unchange-able than the laws of the Medes and Persians. In the common and sim-ple game of tag the child who is "it" is not chosen by any authority or by any system of democratic voting, but is selected by a method of counting out. This method—based entirely on chance—means that no one makes the selection, therefore there is no superior and each player has the same chance of avoiding being the unwished-for "it." Logically, therefore, there can be no recriminations, no hostility and no jealousy, and if these occur they cannot logically be directed at any member of the group but only at malignant fate. Therefore the process of counting out, the leaving the selection to chance, is a magical method that avoids any personal participation in the result and removes any possibility of the arousal of jealousy or hostility within the group. In this way feel-ings of hostility within the group are checked and kept in control. It is not always efficacious, for frequently the cry of cheating in the counting is raised by some child who has not yet learned sufficiently the rules of social behavior.

Another way which the child uses to socialize his urges is found in the common "game" of walking without stepping on cracks in the pavement. The crack is symbolic to the child of an expression of some inner impulse which would meet with social disapproval. Sometimes the game is accompanied by a rhyme:

> *Don't step on a crack*
> *Or you'll break your mother's back.*

We are not certain whether this game is based on the same inner impulse —i. e., hostility toward the mother—among all children who play it. To step on the crack is to injure the mother. The child uses the idea of step-ping on a crack as a symbol of an inner wish and then avoids the expression of the wish by refusing to step on the crack. The impulse is displaced onto an action toward an indifferent object and then the child can avoid the action.

Not only do children deal with hostile impulses in this way, but they often displace erotic drives from one object to another and then either perform or avoid performing an action to that object, depending on whether the child *must* do it or *must refrain* from doing it. For example, touching is a pleasurable activity. In our culture we place quite severe restrictions on children's touching. We find that the word don't is applied more often to children's touching than to any other single activity. Not only is the child "don'ted" for touching his genitals but also for touching innumerable objects around the house, some of which are fragile and some dangerous—all of which curtails the amount of pleasure the child wants to have from the use of his hands. Children in the latent period have many touching games. They must touch every telephone pole they pass, or every second or third one. If they are prevented from doing so or miss the proper one they feel irritated and go back and touch it. They express their need to touch by saying they will have bad luck if they don't.

Children have a great tendency to bind themselves by vows. Sometimes the vows, voluntarily made, come to have such a hold on the personality that the individual finds himself unable to escape their influence. In many cases they are of a hostile, revengeful nature. A girl was rebuked by her father, when she tried to kiss him, because her breath was offensive. She became furiously angry at the rebuff and vowed never again to show him affection. Another girl vowed never again to tell her father anything about herself. As she grew up she found it impossible to be confidential with any man in authority, even though this attitude was detrimental to her. A boy vowed that when he grew up he would kill his father. When he did grow up he found it impossible to have a satisfactory relationship with his bosses. He either attempted to do them some injury or else he behaved toward them as if no act of theirs could ever anger him. We feel that it is inadvisable for parents to induce a child to make a vow—to love mother always, to respect father always, to dislike a certain person, certain forms of behavior, etc., always. The vow may attain control over the child's ego and the results may be disastrous to the individual.

It might be argued that all the rituals we have described are simply the expressions of excess energy on the part of the child. This would fit in with one theory of play, that play has the purpose of using up excess energy. However this theory does not explain the content of the play or the fact that the child feels irritated if the specific action is interfered with; e. g., he feels irritated if he does not touch the proper telephone pole. Certainly part of the dynamics of play is the pressure of energy which needs utilization. The content of the play, however, indicates that the form of utilization also satisfies a specific need in the child's unconscious. In the touching games, he wishes to touch his or someone else's body. He represses this desire into the unconscious and then displaces it from touching the body to touching an inanimate object. He is unconscious of his displacement. If he touches the secondary object he feels pleasure. If his game is to avoid touching an object he is unconscious of the fact that he avoids because he is afraid of the punishment that he believes would result if he touched.

This process of learning to control the mode of expression of instinctual impulses—through games into whose composition rituals, ceremonials and magical procedures enter—is a step on the child's road to the socialization of his desires and toward the sublimation of primitive impulses into cultural but pleasurable activities. It is after this stage that he becomes able to play real group games such as football, baseball, etc., where team play is important and where rules are laid down that make the play for the good of the whole team more important than the play for the good of the individual player.

Thus during the latent period the child learns to control the mode of expression of his inner urges through the use of rituals, ceremonials and magical procedures. His ego skills and abilities are not well-enough developed yet to help him to control them in other more realistic ways. The personality of the child of this age level therefore has a strong resemblance to the personality of the adult who suffers from a compulsion neurosis, and the reasons for the personality structures in both are the same; i. e., a weakness of the ego—in the child because of immaturity, in the compulsive adult because of extreme fear of his superego. In both cases the personality structure is brought about to avoid painful feelings of guilt.

The tendency on the part of children during the latent period to resort to rituals, etc., to avoid feelings of guilt about the modes of expression of their inner impulses should be seriously considered by religious educators. Many children of this age turn to formal religion not because they understand or wish to lead better ethical and spiritual lives, but because the rituals and ceremonials of religion offer them temporarily an easier way of controlling the modes of expression of their inner impulses than having to learn how to deal with them from an ethical and sociological aspect. A child in the latent period is converted. Having made his peace with his sense of guilt by having placed all responsibility for his actions on the *religious rituals* and *ceremonials*—not on religion—he can then behave as he likes without feeling any guilt about his behavior. He can continue to behave as he likes as long as he performs the necessary rituals and prayers.

He may not react to his conversion in this way. Instead he may rely on his religious beliefs to keep his erotic and aggressive impulses repressed. They therefore remain in a childish state of development and he never learns how to use them or deal with them in an adult fashion. It seems a great pity when a child in the latent period pledges his future life to the church in order to avoid the struggle he must make to socialize himself. If he is allowed to continue with this ambition he can only be an immature and inadequate minister of religion. It is fortunate that many religious educators are aware of the perils that lie in such a course, but unfortunately parents often are not, and give their sanction and even encouragement to such an ambition.

There are certain children who are unable to solve their Oedipus conflict satisfactorily, particularly that portion of it that is concerned with aggression and hostility toward the parent of the same sex. Such children feel that the only way to deal with their guilt, aggression, and hostility is through the accentuation of the rituals, ceremonials and magical procedures so common during this period. Instead of the mechanisms serving as a step toward maturity they become the dynamic forces by which life must be lived. They develop all the symptoms of a compulsion neurosis and behave in the same fashion and with the same difficulties as do adults who suffer from the same illness and whose symptomatology we will discuss later. The treatment for these cases will be intensive psychotherapy, preferably psychoanalysis.

NAUGHTINESS IN CHILDREN

All our readers are acquainted with naughtiness in children, but we wonder if they have defined what they mean by naughtiness. If they introspect carefully they will find that they have their own personal ideas as to what constitutes naughtiness. Each adult and each child has his own personal code, and any violation of that code by himself or others is regarded as naughtiness. For one, disobedience is the deadly sin, for another autoerotic sexuality, and for another untidiness. Overlying this personal code there is the code of the social organization, which is applicable to everyone living in that society regardless of whether the individual considers it appropriate or not. As a rule people do not violate their own personal codes, and regard those who do as being naughty, but they do not feel quite the same obligation to obey the social code and often violate it openly or underhandedly or countenance its violation by others. Even if they do not violate it they may feel that the code needs changing, and will work hard to bring the changes about, while seldom, if ever, do they feel that their own personal code should be changed or any willingness to work toward changing it.

Ideally the code of parent and teacher should be exactly the same as that of the social organization that has been developed through long experience as the best way for individuals to live happily together in a group. Unfortunately such is frequently not the case. Parents are not content with the restrictions imposed by society, but have to impose others of their own. They may even be loath to accept the social code themselves, and so train the child to follow their code and to feel disrespect for society. A child may be considered naughty by the parents because he violates their own personal code, by the teacher because he violates her personal code, by the social organization because he violates the sociological code.

From the adult's point of view, naughtiness consists in the rebellion of the child against the code, i. e., the real sin lies in the rebellious unwillingness of the child to conform. The child is first and foremost an individualist and has little or no desire to conform to any code. We expect, therefore, that every child from time to time will show rebelliousness against being trained, and so will behave in a naughty fashion. Training in social living consists of two concomitant processes which proceed both consciously and unconsciously. The first is the amalgamation of the various partial and often divergent and conflicting erotic instinctual drives into a unified whole in order that their gratification will bring the individual person success and happiness, ensure the perpetuation of the race and the development of the ability to obtain gratification for these amalgamated desires without injuring or interfering too much with the other members of the group—parents, siblings, companions, superiors, peers and subordinates—and their need to obtain their own gratifications. The second process is learning how to obtain the satisfactions mentioned above and at the same time live comfortably in the culture—i. e., the manners, customs and codes—of the society in which the individual lives. Unfortunately we tend often to lay too great emphasis on the latter and seem to forget the importance of the former; e. g., we tend to lay great stress on training a child to select the proper fork instead of training him to eat adequately and in a way that will not be displeasing or disgusting to his fellows. American culture is somewhat restrictive but not too severely so in the matter of sexual gratification—its restrictions do not really interfere with an adequate sexual life. It does bear down more heavily on any attempt to freely exercise aggressive activities, although in any society this is necessary if group life is to be possible. Most of the legal enactments are directed against interpersonal aggressive acts, and even the legal prohibitions against sexuality are not against sexuality itself but against those components that are aggressive and hostile toward other persons.

As we said before, in the ideal situation the parents' and the educator's codes will be the same as the code of the social organization. The child if he wishes to be a member of the group must learn to conform to them. How is this best brought about? The natural answer to this question lies in considering the way in which the child learns to adjust to two situations: toilet training and the Oedipus conflict. In both the child gives up his independent individualism because he loves the parent—in the first because he loves his mother and wishes to please her and in the second because he loves his father and wishes to get along with him happily and peaceably. In neither instance does his giving up prevent him from obtaining satisfaction for his instinctual needs. In the first he can obtain anal gratification through sublimatory activities and in the second he can as an adult live a sexual life with another woman who is not his father's wife.

When the child loves his parents or, more accurately, when they love him, he tries to conform to their code and later to the code of the social organization. At times he finds this difficult and periods of rebellion and naughtiness occur, but they become less and less frequent as he grows older, until in adult life he conforms to the code of his culture automatically and without too much strain. Of course he must be given opportunities that will bring into relief the conflict between his individualism and the social code—e. g., he will never become toilet trained unless he learns that toilet habits are an essential part of civilized life. Is anything more necessary than this general process of training by living together? Admonition and precept of course will occur, for it is natural for the parent to instruct the child verbally. Is it necessary to punish him when he fails to conform? Animals find it necessary to punish their cubs when the cubs decide to rebel against the parents' code, and it would seem that human beings need not be above learning from animals. However, children as a rule require less punishment than do beasts, because their capacity to love and to identify through love is greater than is found among the lower animals.

We have discussed these matters at considerable length because only by an adequate understanding of them is it possible to discuss intelligently persistent and chronic naughtiness in children and what can be done about it. Naughtiness is rebellion and rebellion is an expression of aggressive energy. Therefore we must look for the causes of chronic naughtiness when there are difficulties in dealing with the aggressive urges.

In an earlier chapter we described the various levels of reaction to a frustration. We noted that when a person's desire for gratification was frustrated he experienced a feeling of disappointment to which he reacted by mobilizing his aggressive energy in a rebellion against the frustration. If a child is in a state of constant naughtiness, i. e., of chronic rebellion, we have to ascertain how the child is being frustrated. There are a number of situations where this may occur. Have the instinctual urges of the child been unnecessarily frustrated by the parents in the present or in the past? One mother obstinately determined that her child would not suck her fingers. She used every possible method to prevent it, because the child with great courage and tenacity refused to stop. However the mother's superior strength and ingenuity conquered. The child gave in, but from then on hated the mother with a deep, undying hatred and rebelled in every way possible. The mother succeeded in preventing the child's finger sucking, but at the same time, in ordinary parlance, ruined the child's disposition.

If the battle between this little girl and the mother had remained confined to this one situation the results might not have been so serious, but since the mother represented authority to the child she reacted in the same way to all authority outside her home because she anticipated that any authority would impose on her the unnecessary restrictions her mother did. It may seem strange to the reader that the child should regard finger sucking as so necessary that she could become bitterly antagonistic when the parent required her to stop it. It must be remembered that the parent who objects so obstinately to finger sucking usually objects as rigidly to other manifestations of infantile sensuality so that the child is really deprived of all avenues of obtaining sensual pleasure.

A more important question is why one child reacts by open and bitter hostility to his frustration when another accepts the frustration, represses the hostility, and indulges in the prohibited activity either in secret or in fantasy—in both instances with an intolerable sense of guilt about the wicked behavior. The answer to this question is not clear. Certainly the former shows a much healthier reaction than the latter: it is more practical to attack an enemy than it is to try to appease him through making great personal sacrifices, as the history of the years preceding the present war proves. It may be that these children are innately endowed with more aggressive energy and therefore less inclined to be docile and conforming; or that there is really less parental love for the child, who therefore feels less need to please the parent; or that the parent is less harsh and cruel to manifestations of aggression than he is to manifestations of sexuality; or that the erogenous zones in certain children are more highly sensitized and that therefore their longing for gratification from the particular area exceeds the average and so they must fight to obtain it; or it may be that the child is less impressed by his fears of parental desertion and of punishment at the hands of the parent.

The best treatment for this type of naughtiness is to see that its cause does not occur. Children are entitled to an optimum period of satisfaction for their infantile pleasure needs. They cannot be expected to relinquish them too suddenly, but should be allowed to grow out of them. (By this we mean that they should have the opportunity to find more mature ways of obtaining the same pleasure, and that when they find them they will no longer be interested in the more infantile ways.) If the naughty behavior has only been present a short while it is relatively easy to deal with. The parent should apologize to the child for his unwarranted interference with the child's pleasure pursuits and should encourage him to indulge again if he feels so inclined. As an example of this might be cited a case of stuttering. The father and mother had interfered quite unnecessarily with the child's finger sucking. The child stopped it and immediately began to stutter. The father, recognizing where the fault had been, tried to encourage the child to suck her fingers again, and at the same time, because he realized that his daughter might be ridiculed by her friends if she did too much finger sucking, he laid in a plentiful supply of lollypops, the sucking of which was socially acceptable. Immediately the stuttering ceased.

The naughty behavior should be ignored. If absolute justice were done, punishment would have to be applied to the parent who is the guilty person, and not to the child. If the child is punished in this situation he will regard the punishment as unfair and will react against it with further aggressive behavior (naughtiness). Since such a reaction is usually in turn punished by the parent the child feels more antagonistic and behaves in a worse manner. This secondary vicious circle is the cause of the great difficulty in treating this type of case when the naughty behavior has been present for a period of time. There has been so much battling between parent and child that the original cause is forgotten and both are aware only of the present mutual feeling of hostility. The parent is disgusted with the child and his behavior and the child hates the parent.

For such cases intensive psychotherapy for the child is required, often of the intensity of psychoanalysis. Even during an analysis, if the child lives at home, the constant daily mutual antagonism between child and parents adds fuel to the fire, which can counteract the effects of the treatment and so prolong it unduly or neutralize it entirely. Placement in a foster home is not practical because the child carries his hostile attitude toward the parents over to all persons in authority, which includes the foster parents. Foster parents who can accept into their home a badly behaved child—who may even be a neighborhood nuisance and continue so for some time—and not react with hostility against him are very rare. Practically it seems better to place such a child in an institution such as the Southard School at Topeka, Kansas, or the Children's Department at the Allentown State Hospital where his naughty behavior can be ignored and where intensive psychotherapy can be carried on. The psychotherapeutic problem in these cases is to uncover the anxiety associated with the gratification of infantile sensual needs, allow the child to gratify these needs as much as any child is allowed, and help him from that point to proceed to other more mature forms of gratification of sensual pleasures. We do not believe that the treatment of these more severe cases should be attempted by anyone except a competent psychiatrist.

If the instinctual drives have not been unreasonably or unnecessarily frustrated it is necessary to look deeper into the parent-child relationship because here may lie one of the important causes of a child's bad behavior. Children not only resent the frustration of infantile sensual pleasures but resent more deeply a lack of love, or a decreased amount of love. It is common, for instance, for older children to begin to be mischievous and behave badly about the time a new baby is born in the family. The older child feels that the attention necessarily given to the new baby is an indication that the parents love the latter more than they do him. His wish for love is frustrated and he begins to react antagonistically in order to express his displeasure. If the parents punish him for this reaction he feels more unloved and more antagonistic and behaves worse. Again the vicious circle mentioned before develops. If, however, the parents are wise they will ignore the naughtiness that sometimes heralds the arrival of a new baby and see to it that the older child is helped through his period of frustration in the manner we described in Chapter VI.

This is a simple illustration but it indicates the difficulties that arise when a child feels himself unloved. What of those children who actually are unloved? This is a very serious situation. Theoretically the earliest attitude of the human being toward his environment, human or otherwise, is one of hostility. The overstimulation of the sensory pathways during and after birth is felt by the baby as a painful frustration. Aggressive hostile drives are elicited by pain or by danger—the apprehension of danger being really a special type of pain. Since the infant's first connection with the environment causes him pain he must feel hostile and antagonistic to it. Then he learns to differentiate his mother from himself and begins to realize that she brings him pleasure; it is not till then that his feeling toward her changes from one of hostility to one of longing and desire to re-experience pleasure and comfort from her. This longing is the first budding of a feeling of love. It neutralizes the hostile feelings, causing the child to direct part of them away from the person of the mother and to combine part of them into a new relationship with her—a sado-masochistic one at this stage of development. Before this new relationship comes about, the child's feelings of love are directed entirely onto himself. A moderate degree of this state of affairs is plainly apparent in all young children. They are self-centered and love themselves and their own comforts and pleasures to a much greater extent than they do anyone else. It is even questionable whether anything approaching a real altruistic relationship with other persons is found before puberty. The binding of the feelings of love to the person of the child results in his feeling that he is all important, omniscient and omnipotent, that he really is beyond all physical dangers, and that he must have everything he wants just when he wants it.

When the mother does not love the child she does not care to satisfy his needs for pleasure and comfort. She does what she has to do for him out of a sense of duty and often in a harsh and somewhat painful manner. Thus the child has no reason for changing his hostile attitude toward her or toward anyone else and no incentive for turning his love away from himself to others. He thus tends to remain very much in the same type of emotional rapport with himself and the environment as exists in the very small child, and his personality characteristics are similar to this small child's.

Children who are chronically aggressive because they are unloved show the typical type of personality reactions described above. Their attitude toward others is one of hostility. They behave, in actually dangerous situations, as if they were not afraid (as they are not, since they feel omnipotent). Since they have no feelings of love directed toward any object but themselves, they show no consideration for others and seem totally lacking in respect, sympathy, kindliness, gratitude, and the ordinary niceties of social intercourse. The environment is filled with many things to gratify their wants and needs and they tend to take them where and when they want them without regard to the feelings or needs of others or to the customs we impose on ourselves in order that we may live comfortably together. The presence of any of these traits or reactions, on the other hand, indicates that the child is able to love others, since the decencies in social custom and usage arise from our feelings of affection and love toward the other members of the group. Such capacity has never been developed in the unloved child. The child who is forced to develop in this manner is regarded by ordinary people, whether children or adults, as queer. They do not understand him, and because all their efforts to deal with him in the ways they have found successful in interpersonal relationships—i. e., by kindness and sympathy—elicit only more hostility from him, they in turn become hostile to him. Their hostility calls forth more of his hostile feelings, until he and all members of his social group are in bitter conflict, which lasts as long as the *child* can maintain his hostile attitude and live in society.

In many instances the conflict with the environment ends in victory for the social organization, which either executes the hostile individual or incarcerates him for a longer or shorter period of time. The incarceration usually increases his hostility, with the result that when he is paroled, he emerges with only the determination to keep his part in his hostile acts hidden as much as possible from detection by the authorities. Such is the outcome in many cases. In others the painfulness of the counterhostility of society causes the individual rather suddenly to try to suppress the outward manifestations of his hostile feelings and if possible even his consciousness of them.

A similar attempt may be made by the child if he is moved from a hostile environment to one where there is some attempt to treat him understandingly, kindly and decently. In the first situation nothing has been done to change the structure of the child's personality. It remains unchanged and he has only become *frightened* by the retaliation his hostile behavior produces. In the second, he is beginning to make some attempt to change his personality structure, but his first steps consist only in attempts to inhibit the expression of his hostility. In both instances the change is sudden, and we know from our observations on other phases of child training—e. g., toilet training—that if the child *suddenly* succumbs to the demands of the environment he does not learn to redirect and sublimate the instinctual impulses but suppresses them and keeps them suppressed by feeling and acting exactly in the opposite way; that is, whereas previously he was very dirty, now suddenly he becomes overscrupulously clean, and in this way nullifies any real cultural use of his instincts.

The chronically aggressive child who changes suddenly proceeds on exactly the same pattern: whereas previously he was defiantly rebellious he now becomes defiantly submissive; destructive, now he *never* destroys; previously antisocial and defiantly rebellious against the social organization—now he is asocial and defiantly regards the easy social customs of ordinary society as bad, coarse, vulgar and indecent. He dare not react hostilely to a real injury. Instead he appears not to notice what has happened, or if he notices it he is unaware of any hostile feeling. He puts up with the situation meekly, but on some other occasion begins to feel angry where there is no cause. Thus he splits the emotional reaction from its cause. Since he is unconscious of his hostile feelings when they occur, even in circumstances where a hostile reaction would be valid, he begins to behave as if he had injured someone and tries to make a totally invalid atonement. If he is in a situation where the ordinary person would feel resentment he submits subserviently, but very soon does something that injures himself; thus his aggression which formerly raged against his environment in order to destroy it now rages as fiercely against himself with serious self-destructive tendencies.

In short, from being a chronically aggressive child he has become a compulsive neurotic. There was perhaps some benefit and happiness to himself, though not to society, in his former state. Now, at least, society does not suffer—though it receives no benefits from him—while he loses all benefit to himself and all chances of happiness. No cure has taken place. He has only developed a reaction formation as a defense against his inner feelings. These examples make it evident that any therapeutic measures directed solely toward the suppression of the aggressive reactions, if successful, tend only to destroy the child and his mental health and not to reform him to make him a useful member of society.

There is another group of chronically aggressive children whose condition is worse even than the group just described. In behavior they are the most violent, the most destructive, the most annoying and the most unmanageable. Their life history is a particularly consistent one. The boy has a dominating mother or mother substitute, such as a grandmother. The father is a weak, ineffectual man or is absent from the home all or the greater part of the time. The mother dominates because she resents the fact that she is a woman and not a man. This resentment is unconscious: were she aware of it her lack of femininity would have prevented her ever marrying. Resentful of being a woman she has no desire or use for the great compensation that a woman finds for her femininity—child bearing. She becomes pregnant accidentally. She loathes her state and often makes futile attempts at abortion. When the child is born she does not wish to see him but soon develops feelings of guilt about her rejection of him. She assuages these guilt feelings by developing an overprotective attitude toward her son. Through this protective attitude she crushes every attempt he makes at initiative, independence and masculinity.

In order to avoid the pain of her displeasure the little boy suppresses all his masculine activity and accentuates all his passive attitudes. His attempts to imitate the father also increase his passive attitudes, for if the father is absent he has no man with whom to identify, and if present his weakness and passivity make him a poor model for the boy. As soon as his passive attitudes are well accentuated the mother begins to tease and taunt him for being such a sissy. This hurts his feelings and he tries to prove to her that he is really masculine. In order to do so he has to accentuate his independence which is done best by being defiant and rebellious. Thenceforth every time he feels a passive impulse, which occurs commonly in men and which no one disdains, he suppresses it immediately and behaves in exactly the opposite way.

It is surprising, when one comes to know well such a young hellion who is the neighborhood menace, to find that he really is most interested in playing with dolls or doing housework, but that he keeps these interests to himself lest he be teased. Much of his annoying behavior is directed toward other boys or older men and has its purpose in attracting their attention to his person even though he may suffer pain as a result. Basically, of course, he has a great fear of women and feels more comfortable with men. He also has strong passive desires toward both men and women. When such a child reaches puberty he begins to be aware of his homosexual orientation, which he dreads because he dreads all love relationships. He represses it and gradually develops the classical symptoms of a paranoid state, usually of a schizophrenic type.

This last-mentioned type of chronically aggressive child indicates another source of the difficulty that such unloved children show in making an adjustment. We have mentioned already that one source lies in the fact that never having been loved, they have received no incentive to love others in return and therefore their strivings to love remain attached to their own person while their hostile aggressive strivings are divorced from love and turned toward others. We mentioned also that in order to become socialized it is necessary for the child to fuse his hostility with love, and so neutralize the destructive elements when the fused strivings are directed toward others. In short, one tremendous factor in the etiology of this condition is the child's inability to love. The child learns to redirect and control his aggressive impulses, when he loves his parents, because loving them he wants to be like them. The child who comes from a broken home does not have two parents to love and imitate. The child whose parents hate him has no incentive to love the parents and be like them. Since the identification with the parent is the basis for the formation of the superego and since the function of the superego is to control and redirect the mode of expression of instinctual urges in order that the individual may express them in harmony with the customs and manners of his social organization, these children tend to lack the inner light by which they can view their behavior, and so find pleasure in actions that would overwhelm the ordinary person with feelings of shame, guilt and embarrassment.

There has been some controversy in psychiatric circles as to the status of the superego in these chronically aggressive children and adults. Are they people with little or no moral sense? Have they an overpoweringly severe superego along certain lines and consequently too little along others? Is their superego so severe that no matter how well they behave they are tormented by a sense of guilt and can only assuage it by being punished? We think the controversy is not very valid, for we feel that the naughty children include a number of types of personality structure, all of which tend to produce somewhat the same symptom complexes, just as a variety of different organisms if introduced into the body will all produce fever as a symptom of their presence. It is true that a specific organism may produce a specific type of fever and we feel that etiological factors in a specific combination will produce a specific type of naughtiness, but our powers of observation are not delicate enough to distinguish easily one type of naughtiness from another.

In the first type we mentioned so far (the child whose naughtiness is a rebellion against the unreasonable frustration of his infantile erotic needs) the child suppresses any attempt at gratification of his erotic desires because he must, and later in order to be comfortable represses his awareness of the desire itself. His naughtiness is first an overt rebellion against the parent's restrictions, and eventually a rebellion against his own self-restrictions of which he is only aware as he perceives them in projection, i. e., as if emanating from the social organization instead of from himself. His personality structure therefore is one with an over-severe superego against erotic gratifications and an ego that rebels openly against those restrictions.

In the second type (that in which the child has been unloved and therefore never has learned to love) the personality structure may be formed in one of two ways. In one form the ego has learned through bitter experience that any attempt to love brings pain. Henceforth to avoid pain the ego shuns all love impulses except when directed toward itself. It is not immoral to love, it is painful. Yet there may be actions and feelings which the individual feels it is immoral to do or feel and the awareness of whose presence fills him with shame and guilt—all of which indicates that a superego of a sort is present. It seems to us that this condition arises in children who have not been totally rejected but have received some love. Perhaps the parental attitude toward the child has been one of overprotection rather than open rejection, or perhaps he has known at least a short period of time with some loving person. In the other form, one can find no real evidence of the presence of feelings of shame, guilt or embarrassment about anything—no indication of the presence of a superego. In these cases the child has had no love and therefore has had no incentive to identify with the adult. Such children have no moral sense.

In the third type the ego fears the pain it will suffer if it gives in to passive desires. The superego is severely prohibitive of the homosexual orientation. Here an oversevere superego is definitely present and the ego is timid, weak, and ineffectual.

It is obvious that no treatment can be planned without considering the personality structure of the patient with whom the therapist is dealing. In the first type the treatment must be directed to an amelioration of the prohibitions of the superego against infantile erotic drives. For the two subtypes of the second group the aim of therapy and the methods employed will differ because of the different personality structure. In the first subtype the treatment will be aimed first at removing the dread of loving and second at ameliorating any misdirection or overseverity of the superego that may exist. In the second subtype the aim is to release the ability to love. The more an actual dread of loving is the motivating factor in the child's life the more probable it is that he will be helped best by intensive psychotherapy, especially analysis. The more the motivating factor is not a dread of loving but a lack of opportunity to love, the more the child needs not psychotherapy but an actual twenty-four-hour-a-day experience of being with people who love him.

It is difficult to introduce either subtype into the treatment situation, particularly if the case is severe or the problem of long standing. The attitude of the child usually is hostile and to this hostility is added the hostile reaction engendered by the fear of the strange adult, learned by long and bitter experience. As a result of his feelings of omnipotence the child repudiates any need for help. He has little apprehension about being rebellious and defiant—or if he has he uses it to cover his hostility with a superficial cloak of agreeableness. His defenses against treatment are almost perfect. It is necessary, therefore, before one can begin real treatment of his difficulty to break down his defenses. This can be done in several ways. He can be treated in such a way that he has to change his chronic aggressive reaction to its opposite—a compulsion neurosis—as has been described earlier. He can be allowed such absolute liberty that he breaks down in panic. He can be exposed to painful realities from which the therapist can rescue him. (An example of this in a mild case is the child who steals but has no allowance. The therapist can arrange to have the parents give him an allowance of his very own, one that will be adequate for his needs and that he can spend as he likes without any parental interference.) The purpose of these methods is to get the child to realize that he is not omnipotent, that he is a sick child and really needs help and that the therapist really can help him. When this is accomplished the therapist and the child can work out the problem of the fear of loving. Since in most cases the condition usually has been in existence for a long time, treatment must be intensive and will be lengthy. For reasons we will discuss later the outcome of treatment is not always good even in the hands of the most experienced psychiatrists. Treatment for the third type will follow similar lines.

Therapy for the second subtype consists of placing the child in charge of some adult who can really love him. Such placement is made best in an institution because few foster homes or their neighborhoods can put up with the behavior of such a child. The presence of a person who loves him will call forth an answering love in the deprived child, and he will gradually pass through the same states in the control of his aggression as does the child in the ordinary home. It will not take as long after the initial contact is made, but will take several years. As the process goes on one can watch with interest the development of the child's superego. His course must be watched carefully and if instead of a gradual growth of a superego he shows the development of a compulsion neurosis he should be referred immediately for psychiatric treatment.

There is still a fourth type of naughtiness to be considered. The history is somewhat as follows. The child has been loved, both parents are alive and present but the training has been rather strict. The child's infantile pleasure drives, such as sexual curiosity, destructiveness and masturbation, have been prohibited. The child has conformed because he wants to please the parents. When the child is between four and seven the parents go on a trip, leaving the child with friends or relatives; or the child himself goes on a visit to friends or relatives for several weeks or months. The adults whom he visits are not as strict as the parents, and the child begins to partake of pleasures that previously had been forbidden. When he realizes that the time has come for him to return to the parents, he realizes also that he has to forgo these pleasures in the future lest he get into trouble. He avoids continuing them and tries to put the thought of them and the memory of the pleasures out of his mind. He does this best by beginning to think of his behavior as bad and punishing himself a little by a painful sense of guilt when he thinks about them. Pretty soon, instead of becoming aware of his desire when it is present, he feels only a sense of guilt. This is unpleasant and painful. He has learned from past experience that he always felt uncomfortable when bad and much better after his parents dealt out a sudden punishment such as a spanking. Having this experience at his disposal he proceeds to use it to assuage his painful feeling of guilt. After he arrives home, as soon as this feeling arises he looks around for some rule to break. The naughtiness is perpetrated openly in order that the parents may observe it, which they do, and then they punish him. It should be emphasized that his crime is never the same as that for which he is feeling guilty: during their absence he masturbated; now when he has a feeling of guilt he does not masturbate but may break a dish, spill water on the floor, or steal. As soon as he has been punished he feels better. His guilt feeling is assuaged. He is no longer naughty and seems happier. Obviously from the parents' point of view the punishment has worked. The child has learned not to be naughty.

After a day or two—perhaps more, perhaps less—the guilt feeling reasserts itself. He has now the added experience of the efficacy of a technique that will assuage the feeling of guilt. Again he is naughty, again he is punished and again he feels better. From now on his life is a succession of this pattern—guilt, naughtiness, punishment, and feeling better—and from the observer's point of view it is a succession of episodes of naughty behavior and of the child's never seeming to learn by experience that if he is naughty he will be punished.

It is a human reaction to try to extract pleasure from any situation or behavior. So the child, not satisfied with the negative pleasure of the assuagement of his guilt feeling, begins to get a thrill out of being naughty and to have a thrill superimposed on the pain of being punished. He begins therefore to add a masochistic pleasure to his need for punishment. Now he has two motives in his naughty behavior, and every time his parents punish him they only increase his desire for more punishment. If in desperation they desist from punishment his naughtiness increases until it is almost humanly impossible not to interfere. He begins to react in a similar way outside the home and by the time he has reached adolescence his main aim in life—of which he is unaware—is to receive punishment. Since ordinarily punishment comes less frequently to the adolescent and adult, his naughtiness increases until it becomes real crime and his adult life is a succession of alternating crime and punishment. He becomes a criminal because of a need for punishment.

There is no need to comment on how well the social organization functions in satisfying the need for punishment, because the entire social system is based on the principle that the pain of punishment will reform, whereas with this type of naughtiness the pain of punishment is what the individual desires. It cannot be too strongly emphasized that in the vast majority of instances the individual is unaware of his need for punishment and consciously will ridicule the notion that his naughtiness is deliberately produced in order to get him punished. Occasionally a child will show awareness that he has a need to be punished, for one meets instances where the child will come to the parent and say, "Father, please whip me."

The treatment of the child whose naughtiness arises because he desires punishment will be aimed at discovery both of his sense of guilt and of the memory of the crime about which he feels so guilty. Then the guilt can be relieved. This requires intensive psychotherapy, analysis offering the best chance of cure. At the same time the parents will have to be cautioned along two lines: (1) The child's behavior may become worse from time to time during the period of treatment as he attempts to avoid analyzing his feeling of guilt by using his old method of assuaging it temporarily through punishment. This phenomenon always makes treatment difficult, since the child has so many opportunities for assuaging his guilt through naughty behavior. Too, the social organization may react violently against his behavior, and just at the point when the therapist is really making progress step in and incarcerate the child, discontinuing the treatment. As a consequence, we feel that only the mildest cases of this type should be treated as outpatients, and that the moderate and severe cases should be institutionalized during the period of treatment. (2) The parents or parent substitutes will have to abstain from punishing the child as much as is humanly possible.

It can be seen that the naughty behavior in these cases has a definite beginning and occurs in episodes that suggest that from time to time the child is compelled to be naughty. As we have seen, there is a compulsion that underlies the symptoms. A similar compulsiveness underlies the naughty behavior of the next type. There are certain children who seem to act aggressively without any reason and in fact do not seem to know they are behaving so until the action is almost over. Afterward such a child feels remorseful but that nevertheless he could not help what he did: he did not want to do it, had made up his mind not to, yet here he is doing the very thing he had decided not to do. We saw a good example of this in a nineteen-year-old boy at the induction center. The boy had a history of a number of arrests and short jail sentences for assault and battery. He did not drink. His difficulty lay in the fact that when he got in a crowd or was at a celebration he suddenly found himself getting into fights. He did not know how the fights started. He acted *impulsively* therefore, and so differed from the child who has a *compulsive* need for punishment. The child with a need for punishment has a superego severely prohibitive of a particular form of instinctual desire. If he violates the prohibitions of his superego and gratifies his desire he has to make amends by committing a different act for which he knows he will be punished. The impulsive child has a superego that prohibits a certain type of instinctual expression—often aggression. He gratifies the instinctual desire by circumventing his superego; i. e., he allows himself to be overwhelmed suddenly by his desire, and can propitiate his conscience by denying his responsibility for the act.

The neurologically trained reader may say at this point, "I thought such cases were often closely akin to epilepsy for which there is often an organic basis in some lesion of the cerebral cortex." This brings up a most interesting and complicated question regarding the naughty behavior of children. Does the behavior have a psychological basis or an organic basis, or is it the result of a combination of both? This is not just an academic problem but is important in considering the types of treatment necessary and the prognosis for any kind of treatment.

It is well known that children frequently become naughty after they have suffered from an encephalitis—whether the result of encephalitis lethargica or as a complication of measles, scarlet fever or chickenpox. Naughty behavior also may follow injury to the brain as a result of fracture of the skull or of minute intracerebral hemorrhages produced by whooping cough, electric shock or partial asphyxiation. In adults and older children it has been found that lesions of the brain often produce a change in the personality—a person with a mild, kindly disposition becoming irritable, quarrelsome and hostile. In cats experimental decerebration just above the thalamus, as a result of which cortical control is removed, leaves the animal liable to violent attacks of rage and hostility for which there is no adequate cause. It appears, therefore, that reactions of rage and hostility are mediated through the upper part of the thalamus, but that these reactions are kept in check by the action of the cortex. Some of this cortical control seems to come from the frontal lobes, one function of which is to perceive what may happen in the future as the result of an act or impulse. If the controlling action of the cortex is partially or totally removed the rage reactions appear unmodified. Therefore children who have suffered from a cortical disease or injury, particularly if it involves the pathways from the frontal lobes, are less able to impose and in many cases are incapable of imposing any voluntary control over the expression of hostility, rage and anger. A similar deficiency of cortical control exists in those individuals whose brain physiology is disordered, as in cases of epilepsy.

The problem is exactly the same as in the cases of chronic aggressive reactions due to lack of love, etc., but in the first group the lack of control has a psychological basis, while in this it has an organic one. What can be done about these children? In many instances it is impossible to make any change in the organic dysfunction. Recently there have been reports of improvement by the use of benzedrine sulfate in those cases where the electroencephalogram shows a disturbance in brain physiology. If further work bears out these studies we will be in a better position to deal with these cases. Although treatment for the organic lesion is seldom possible it must be remembered that the lesions usually do not affect the whole cortex, and that it is possible to train parts of the brain that are ordinarily seldom used to take over the function of the destroyed areas. Such retraining cannot be carried on at home or by educators not specially trained in the work. The best treatment is institutionalization in a proper hospital such as the Bradley Home in Providence, Rhode Island, or the Allentown State Hospital.

A second difficulty always arises with such children. Their behavior is annoying and adults tend to react to it with counterhostility, which only increases the hostile feelings and adds an impossible burden to any control mechanism they still possess. It has been found that the aggressive behavior of cases of chronic epidemic encephalitis improves when they are taken from their families and environment and hospitalized in a proper institution. Often they become quite docile and tractable while there, but as soon as they are returned to their families the old behavior reappears. The adults in the institution obviously were able to give such a child more objective, kindly and understanding management than were the parents, and to this treatment the child tried to respond. However, as soon as this type of handling was removed the child felt no need to and perhaps really had no capacity to respond any longer.

The presence of abnormal electroencephalograms in a high percentage of naughty children makes one feel that in most cases there is a combination of organic and psychological causes. Those cases who do well with adequate psychotherapy perhaps have less organic damage, and those who do poorly more. These observations also raise another interesting question. In some cases the history of the hostile resistive behavior goes back through the child's whole life. Mothers of certain of these naughty children state that even at two months of age the child was unmanageable. Are such cases due to a very early brain injury, to a state of rejection practically from birth, to an innate endowment with more aggressive urges than the ordinary child, or to some combination of two or more of these factors? We believe that each of these factors may be causative in certain cases. Cerebral injury either from intracortical hemorrhage or from anoxia during birth is not uncommon. (In fact all children show blood in the cerebrospinal fluid after birth, indicating that a certain amount of hemorrhage has taken place.) In some the hemorrhage may be more severe than in others, and yet not so extensive or so located as to give definite signs of cerebral injury; i. e., the child does not show a true birth palsy. It may be that some of the cases of chronic naughtiness in children are the result of this condition. There is no proof one way or the other for this speculation but it is a theory that should be investigated thoroughly. Many observations have proven that a baby's reactions and disposition are easily influenced by the handling he receives even in the first days of his life, and since this attitude toward him is likely basically to be the same during the succeeding months and years, the rejected child is rejected every day of his life, and it is no wonder that his behavior seems to have existed from birth.

It is possible that some children are born with a greater endowment of aggressive energy. Certainly children differ in the degree of activity even in the uterus and this is probably a constitutional peculiarity. Such an active child can easily become naughty, since often he is more restricted than the average child, and so more frustrated. Adults who desire quietness and peace find it difficult to tolerate his excessive activity and tend to scold and punish him more than is desirable. Social customs involve a great deal of orderly self-restraint and involuntary violations of them on the part of the child provoke counterhostility, which makes the child feel that he is an Ishmael, and having the name might as well have the game too.

As we have already said, hyperactive children need more space for the expression of their physical activities and less rigid demands on them for inactivity, and should either attend a progressive school where constant physical activity is part of the program or else be allowed more freedom of motor action in the ordinary classroom. It is unfortunate to observe how seldom their need for activity is met, and how often parents or educators use their unconscious knowledge of this need to punish them. Often children give a history of being made to sit absolutely still on a chair for several hours as a punishment. Or if their hyperactivity has resulted in wandering away from home they have been tied in the back yard. Such punishment only increases their feeling of tension and makes them feel more resentful and frustrated. There is no way to control the hyperactivity itself, and all that can be done is to provide sufficient outlet for it.

When the resentful, naughty pattern of behavior has arisen as a result of unreasonable interference with the activity of the hyperactive child the treatment will fall into two phases. First, there must be treatment for the child's resentfulness. The aim of this will be to help the child to love instead of resent and to help him to regard his hyperactivity as a useful asset instead of a liability. Second, he must be given opportunity to use his hyperactivity successfully. The intensity of the psychotherapy directed toward the first aim will depend on the degree of the hostility present and on the extent to which it has deformed his ability to adjust socially.

There are many specific complications that arise in the management of a naughty child that do not occur in the management of a child who suffers from conversion symptoms and which must be taken into consideration in approaching its treatment. First, where should the child live during the period of treatment? Although we have discussed this already we want to re-emphasize that in our experience if the degree of naughty behavior is at all serious from a social point of view, treatment does not stand much chance of success if the child remains at home. Foster-home placement in such cases is not desirable. It seems best to place the child in an institution before treatment is started, and usually this is easily done, at least temporarily, because the parents are so disgusted with the child's behavior. When the parent is rejective, however, and particularly if the rejection is unconscious and he suffers from a sense of guilt about his attitude, he often will refuse to allow the child to remain in the institution more than a few weeks. He removes the child—often just as the child is beginning to receive benefit from treatment—because the place is gloomy, the child is with bad children who may corrupt him, or because the child is so unhappy. In these cases it would be well to have some form of legal commitment so that treatment would not be interrupted so inopportunely. It goes without saying that such institutions require a well-trained, carefully selected staff. Psychiatric treatment by well-trained psychiatrists must be available. The staff itself should consist of men and women who have been selected on the basis of an understanding of children and an ability to love. The hours of work should not be too arduous and there should be ample time and opportunity for recreation and social life.

In order to make an adequate prognosis the degree of organic causative factors must be considered and if possible treatment for them given. The introductory steps to treatment are more important in these cases than in any other except delinquency. They should be carefully planned and sufficient time for them allocated. In all cases treatment of the parents should be carried on during the treatment of the child. If this is effective the child may return home after his treatment is completed. If not, or if only partially successful, it is better for the child to go to another home or boarding school. If this is not done the child may develop another neurosis or character disturbance in order to live comfortably with his family.

We realize that we are describing an ideal plan which is usually very difficult to carry out practically. Except in rare instances we lack the type of institution we described, and those that we have are not sufficiently numerous to deal with the number of such children that need them. We lack the trained and selected personnel required, and the salaries are woefully inadequate to attract such persons. This is true both of state institutions and those organized privately. We lack the power necessary to institutionalize and treat these children adequately because democracy has a tendency to lean more toward protecting the liberty of the individual than ensuring the safety and comfort of the group. Even our methods of treatment are in the experimental stage and although they prove adequate in individual cases we cannot lay down such hard and fast rules as we are able to do for the treatment of a case of appendicitis for instance. In the discussion dealing with the complex problems of delinquency that follows, we shall be describing a plan that should really be a function of the state.

DELINQUENCY

The chronic aggressive reaction pattern is really a subdivision of the much wider and more complex problem of delinquency. Etymologically delinquency means "to fall away." A delinquent is a person who in his behavior "falls away" from the customs and mores of the social organization. In this definition the emphasis is laid on the falling away, while the customs and mores are regarded as static. It does not consider the reasons for the falling away, and since legally trained persons consider the problem from the standpoint of this definition they direct their efforts toward making the delinquent individual give up his tendency to fall away. In the past the sociologist has tended to consider the reasons for the individual's falling away, but because he has regarded the customs and mores as static and every delinquent individual as a sick person he has directed his efforts toward making the sick person well, when he no longer will fall away.

The psychiatrist places emphasis on the reasons for the delinquent's not conforming, but in many cases may see these reasons result from the static conditions of the customs and mores. He does not believe that all delinquents are sick people; in fact he feels that certain of them would be sick people if they behaved in an undelinquent manner and at that point would so treat them as to make them delinquent again. His efforts are directed toward curing the illness in those delinquents who are sick and in recommending that other disciplines, such as those of the sociologist, economist, educator, psychologist, etc., use their efforts to change the customs and mores which the culture has outgrown.

These various points of view seem to be contradictory, but the contradictions are more apparent than real. They spring from the fact that each discipline approaches the problem from a different and special angle and from the fact that the problem itself is so complex that it cannot be investigated by any one discipline alone. In fact, any attempt to investigate the facts underlying delinquency must combine the best skills of all the disciplines mentioned. No one discipline can claim the ability to understand delinquency or can offer a panacea for its amelioration. We hope we have made it clear that we realize we are in no position to hand down any dogmatic statements about delinquency, its cause and cure, and that what we have to say is more in the nature of tentative remarks, made largely in the hope of stimulating others to bend greater efforts toward trying to understand the problem.

What are some of the causes of delinquency? The first group of causes might be entitled "delinquency from force of circumstances." A child is hungry for carbohydrates, for instance. His parents have forbidden him to eat candy and give him only a small amount of sugar at meals. Since he cannot get the sugar he needs honestly he has to steal it. In this stealing he has committed an act of delinquency because he has broken the prohibitions imposed by his family. Or an adolescent receives an allowance much smaller than that received by the other boys with whom he associates. The size of his allowance is not the result of his parents' financial stringency but of the fact that they believe the child should not have much spending money. The state law and the parents' opinion both prevent the child's working to supplement his allowance. He has only two courses open to him—to withdraw from his social life (which would be very unpleasant and also very unprofitable for him) or to steal to supplement his allowance. If he steals from his family he has broken their rules; if he steals from the neighborhood he has broken the law. In neither of these instances is the child sick. He dislikes his stealing. He suffers afterward from remorse. The three parts of his personality—id, ego, superego—are functioning together adequately, and one is not developed at the expense of the other. He is a normal, adequate person who is delinquent because circumstances (i. e., his parents' incorrect opinions) are depriving him of necessities. Once he is allowed to have the necessities he no longer is delinquent.

This delinquency from force of circumstances is rather common in childhood, for many parents deal with their children according to their own superstitions which to them seem reasonable ideas. It is also not uncommon in adult life, in a culture that does not permit individuals equal opportunity to satisfy their needs. These needs are not excessive but the cultural or familial restrictions are. Treatment under these circumstances will aim toward liberalizing the attitude of the parents or of the socioeconomic structure, and is a task for the sociologist, economist and educator.

Among any group of delinquents there are always a fairly large percentage who are feeble-minded. Their excursions into delinquency are the result of a combination of causes. The feeble-minded individual has a defective ego which makes him depend a great deal on other people. Hence he is easily led. His defective reasoning power—a function of the ego—makes him relatively incapable of distinguishing clearly in the matter of property ownership or the consequences of his acts. His ego defect makes it difficult for him to develop an adequate superego. The defect in the superego is increased by the fact that the mentally defective child as a rule does not receive as much real love and understanding from his family or companions as does the intelligent child, and he is more likely to develop some degree of a chronic aggressive reaction pattern. Furthermore, his mental defect makes it more difficult for him to learn to control his primitive reactions. If he falls into association with delinquents he rather readily follows in their footsteps, and is often used to pull their chestnuts out of the fire, so to speak. If anyone gets caught it will be he, and not the other, more intelligent members of the gang. Similarly a mentally defective girl is more liable than an intelligent one to be free with sexual favors for a slight recompense. The delinquency of the mental defective is a problem for the educator. Above all he needs training and supervision.

A certain number of delinquents are psychotic, whose delinquency really would be correct behavior if their delusional world were the real one. The paranoid person who kills an imagined persecutor or the paretic who issues worthless checks for purchases he cannot afford under the delusion he is a millionaire would both be behaving in a nondelinquent fashion if the first was really being hounded to death and the second was very wealthy. Psychotic delinquency is not observed often in children.

We have already discussed neurotic delinquency—the individual who is delinquent in order to satisfy a need for punishment. His treatment is obviously a task for the psychiatrist.

A child reared in the culture of one of the tribes of New Guinea, for instance, will learn to observe the customs and taboos of his tribe even though they may include ritual murder. If he does not conform to them he is a delinquent. If he were transported suddenly to the United States, however, his obedience to the culture of New Guinea would be regarded as delinquency. Similarly, if a well-behaved American boy were suddenly transplanted to New Guinea his behavior would be regarded there as delinquency. In both cases the child has a normal superego—an adequate sense of guilt and of right and wrong—but the mores to which he has learned to react are different; i. e., his superego functions normally but its structure in New Guinea is different from its structure in America.

There are certain parents in America who bring their children up according to their own mores which are different from those of organized society. Such cases flourish in certain areas in large cities—the so-called delinquency areas—and in isolated backward communities such as those where killing in feuds is regarded as a virtue instead of a crime. The child is a normal child. He has a normal superego, but through his identification with the parents the mores incorporated in his superego are different from those of the social organization. Therefore in the eyes of the social organization he is a delinquent.

It is more important to place emphasis on preventing the occurrence of such a type of delinquency than on correcting it once it has arisen, and the sociologist and the educator are responsible for curing the social situation that is producing it. When a child has become delinquent through being raised in a delinquent environment his treatment cannot be successful as long as he lives in the delinquent environment and family. He must be removed to a situation where he can be induced to love a person who has a code closer to that of the culture. As a result of the relationship the child will change the character of his superego. The younger the child is the more easily this can be accomplished. The older he gets the less likely will it be for such a change to take place. This is a large problem that will face the United Nations after the war. The very young children who have imbibed the Nazi philosophy, i. e., who are developing the Nazi type of superego, can be helped. The longer the child has lived under the Nazi ideology the more difficult it will be to change him. Perhaps it will be impossible in many cases and therefore we can be grateful to the Russians for their systematic elimination of the Hitler youth.

The last two types of delinquents are the same as that of the child who is chronically aggressive because of lack of love. In some cases the delinquency is the result of a fear of loving and in others of the absence of a superego. Their management has already been discussed.

Since we are so lacking in real knowledge as to the causes, types, treatment and prognosis for delinquents, it seems to us that the following scheme for the management of delinquents might be adopted as a means of helping the individual delinquent, and at the same time furthering our knowledge. The scheme is ideal and has never been put into practice.

When the delinquent is arrested he should receive a trial to determine his guilt or innocence of the criminal act. In our Anglo-Saxon culture this is always done for adults, but not always for children. A child who is an onlooker may be picked up by the police even though he has no share in the crime. His protestations of innocence are not believed because all children tend to lie when accused, and he is treated as a delinquent. If the individual is found guilty the task of the judge and jury is finished regardless of the nature of the crime. He is sent to a clearing institution. Here are studied thoroughly his personal history, his physical, intellectual and emotional status. His family and environment are investigated thoroughly by sociologists and economists. Finally all the results from these various studies are compiled and reviewed by a board that might consist of a criminologist, a lawyer, a physician, a psychiatrist, a psychologist and a sociologist. This review is directed toward making a diagnosis as to the type of delinquency. If the data is insufficient to make such a working diagnosis the delinquent is remanded for further study.

This working diagnosis forms the basis for determining what shall be done with him. If his delinquent act is the result of force of circumstances only, he can be released immediately provided he can be returned to an environment where circumstances will not be so adverse. If he is feeble-minded he will be referred to a school for the feeble-minded, where if he is tractable and educable he can be trained. If he is untrainable he will be referred to an institution for the custodial care of the feeble-minded. If he has a psychosis he will be referred to a hospital for psychiatric treatment. If he recovers he can be discharged; if not he must remain under custodial care. If he is delinquent from a sense of guilt he is referred to a special hospital for the treatment of neurotic delinquency. Here he is offered the opportunity for treatment. If he accepts and it is successful he can be discharged. If he refuses or if it is not successful he will be transferred to a special custodial institution, the purpose of which will be discussed later. If his delinquency is the result of a delinquent superego he will be sent to an institution or a foster home where he can establish a relationship with substitute parents whose superegos are more in accord with the culture. If he does not improve he is transferred to the special custodial institution. Individuals whose delinquency is the result of lack of love are sent to a reformatory where they will meet a highly select staff who are able to love them and whom they in turn may learn to love. If a compulsion neurosis develops the patient is transferred to the institution for neurotic delinquents where he will receive psychiatric treatment. If the reformatory does not help, the individual will be transferred to the special custodial institution. The special custodial institution is for those cases that so far have not responded to treatment. On admission the whole case would be reviewed again.

This plan will offer a chance for experimental methods to be used and their efficacy proved, and for finer methods of classification to be developed. Those whom no methods of treatment seem to help would be detained for the remainder of their lives regardless of the nature of the original crime. As can be seen this plan requires the assistance of a highly select and trained personnel and therefore would be expensive, but it seems to us that if some state would try it out for a period of five or ten years so much could be learned, and our ability to cope with and understand the problem of delinquency so increased that it would be worth the expense. Further, the increase of our knowledge would lead to a more permanent and a less expensive plan for the future.

BIBLIOGRAPHY FOR CHAPTER IX

Caílle, Ruth Kennedy, *Resistant Behavior of Preschool Children,* Teachers College, Columbia University, 1939.

Cook, Stewart W., "A Survey of Methods Used to Produce Experimental Neurosis," *American Journal of Psychiatry* 96, 1939, 1259.

Darwin, Charles, *The Expression of Emotions in Men and Animals,* Appleton, 1890.

Dunbar, Flanders H., Wolff, Theodore P., Traber, Edward S., and Bursh, Louise A., "The Psychic Component of the Disease Processes (including Convalescence) in Cardiac, Diabetic, and Fracture Patients," *American Journal of Psychiatry* 95, 1939, 1319.

Levin, Paul M., "Restlessness in Children," *Archives of Neurology and Psychiatry* 39, 1938, 784.

Levy, David M., "Resistant Behavior of Children," *American Journal of Psychiatry* 4, 1925, 503.

Orton, Samuel T., *Reading, Writing and Speech Problems in Children,* Norton, 1937.

Pearson, Gerald H. J., "The Inverted Position in Children's Drawings," *Journal of Nervous and Mental Diseases* 88, 1928, 449.

Sayers, R. R., "Major Studies on Fatigue," *War Medicine* 2, 1942, 786.

Schilder, Paul, "The Concept of Hysteria," *American Journal of Psychiatry* 95, 1939, 1389.

Schilder, Paul, "Psychic Disturbances after Head Injuries," *American Journal of Psychiatry* 91, 1934, 155.

Chapter X

DEVELOPMENT OF PERSONALITY DURING PUBERTY AND ADOLESCENCE

THE PHENOMENON of puberty takes place at the onset of the activity of the sexual glands and continues for the next two or three years. Psychiatrists and psychologists of European countries tend to use the word puberty to cover the whole period from the onset of sexual glandular activity to adulthood. However, in this country puberty and adolescence are usually spoken of separately.

PUBERTY

The age at which the onset of puberty occurs differs in different climates and in different races. In America it usually begins at the age of twelve and carries over to the age of fifteen, merging into adolescence. In the female, puberty is marked by changes in body contour, widening of the hips, enlargement of the breasts, growth of pubic and axillary hair and the onset of menstruation. At least several months, and sometimes years, are required for the regularity of menstruation to become stabilized in the female. While this process is going on psychological reverberations occur within her. A great many of these are caused by the unfortunate reactions to the growing-up process to which we have alluded in previous chapters and also by the fact that children are not adequately prepared or educated for the various phenomena of life, particularly those concerning sexual functioning. In spite of a growing public awareness of the need for sex education and sex understanding we still have a poor acceptance of sexuality itself.

Menstruation

It is generally accepted that the capacity for sexuality has begun by the time the child reaches puberty. Both the girl and the boy have within them a great many feelings of shame and uneasiness at this period. Menstruation is one of the most obvious signs of this change in the female, and it is superfluous to say that we do not have a wholesome attitude toward menstruation and that many taboos surround it. These taboos go back thousands of years into the beliefs of primitive man, some of which are difficult to trace; attempts to explain others are made through theories of anthropologists who have uncovered primitive beliefs of ancient tribes and who have tried to explain such behavior by gathering together much of the ancient folklore and superstitions.

Most primitive people seem to have felt a need to explain menstruation to themselves in one way or another. Some believed the phenomenon was brought about because the woman had been bitten by a snake or a wild animal. Some believed that she had had sexual relations with a god. No matter what the reason, all ancient tribes seem to have believed that the phenomenon made the woman dangerous to the men and that men should not come in contact with her during the time. Consequently many tribes have various cruel taboos for the newly menstruating woman. For days, and sometimes for months, she is isolated in a hut without light and without company. Food is brought to her by older women, who themselves have to remain secluded until some of the supposed evil in them has disappeared. Even those tribes who do not carry out so stringent a rite as the foregoing, nevertheless have rather strict taboos about the menstruating period each month. The man is not supposed to touch either the woman, her bed, or her clothing for a period of six to eight days after the menstruation has stopped, and then only after she has bathed in running water.

These stringent taboos of primitive people are still existent and little changed in various areas today, indicating that after thousands of years we are still under the influence of the beliefs of our primitive ancestors. Women are prohibited in some regions from canning while they are menstruating, the belief being that they will cause the canned goods to spoil. They are not supposed to plant seed, or tend flowers, or cut flowers, because it is assumed the flowers will wither and the seeds will not grow. They are not supposed to come in contact with pregnant animals on the farm because it is believed that the animals will abort.

This tendency in society to seclude and exclude the female while she is menstruating is still followed in the twentieth century by thousands of mothers who believe their daughters should go to bed and stay there for two or three days while menstruation is going on. If a mother does not insist that the girl go to bed, she feels she must prohibit her from going about socially, and even if she does not openly prohibit social life, she is still likely to discourage the girl from participating in it. If asked why she feels this way, the mother probably would not have any definite reason to offer. If pressed, however, for an answer we would very likely find that she feels menstruating women to be offensive in some way, and that men feel a repulsion toward or their esthetic sense is revolted by mentruating women.

Another idea that mothers have is that the girl is in an unhealthy state during this period and so should not take part in ordinary social activities lest she do herself harm. Menstruation is a perfectly normal physiological phenomenon; it is not debilitating; and the loss of blood is trivial and soon made up. There is no reason at all why women should greatly disturb their existence because of menstruation. In spite of this, the fact remains that the effectuality and peace of mind of many women are spoiled by these old wives' tales, and by the implication that menstruation is a great misfortune, an illness, a shameful phenomenon, in some vague way disgusting and harmful to others.

Some readers may feel these ideas to be fantastic and that if they occur at all do so only occasionally. However, if the reader cannot accept these facts at this point, we hope that by the time he has reached the end of the book he will agree in part at least that modern man is only one step ahead of the cave man in his thinking and that civilization has not enabled man to advance much beyond those ancestors who believed that the menstruating woman had been bitten by a snake or injured by an animal.

Children invariably come to know that the mother is menstruating without having been informed about it. Like everything else connected with sex, children build up their own theories and may quite naturally develop the theory that since the mother bleeds she must be ill, that she has been injured, or that some peculiar sickness has taken hold of her. If this idea is coupled with the tendency on the part of the mother to be irritable or depressed or to take to her bed during the monthly period, then it makes the girl feel she also is bound to be incapacitated by menstruation during her lifetime. These impressions and ideas about menstruation which are laid down in the child's mind during the childhood stay with her a long time and are difficult to shake off. Just as we have not shaken off some of our primitive beliefs of many hundreds of years ago, so the individual does not shake off the beliefs that he has acquired ten or twenty years previously.

If the castration problem was not solved during the genital period, the girl continues to be distressed because she does not have a male genital organ. She may maintain the belief until puberty that she is neither a woman exactly nor a castrated individual. However the true nature of her anatomy becomes more definite with the onset of menstruation. Women must accept the fact of their womanhood and must, by puberty at least, give up the hope of being like the male, if that has been the tendency of their thinking in their earlier life. Girls who have not accepted the fact of womanhood may be extremely disturbed by menstruation. Without any previous instruction, they are in no way prepared for the phenomenon when it occurs, nor prepared for the fact that their breasts must enlarge, nor for the other changes in body contour. The female child particularly should have some explanation of her anatomy and physiology and the role she should play in life. If she has not had the instruction before puberty, certainly she should have it at this critical time. But all too frequently we may find this phase of life going by with neither the father nor the mother—certainly this role belongs to the mother—talking to the daughter, neither telling her anything about the meaning of menstruation nor explaining the role she is going to play as a woman. When the child is six or eight the mother believes firmly that she will discuss the matter at puberty. When puberty arrives and the daughter starts menstruating, the mother thinks, "She is still a child. Why should I spoil her innocence?" So the girl is left to draw her own conclusions and struggle alone with the process of menstruating.

Menstruation is often distressing to women because of the nature of the discharge: they have a flow of blood from their bodies that lasts three or four days—more or less—and they cannot stop it. Women become psychologically disturbed because menstruation reminds them of the difficulty they had during the toilet-training period when they were made to feel shame and chagrin during the process of learning control of bowels and bladder. Much of the distress and uneasiness about menstruation that exists in the minds of women could be prevented if mothers would only come forward at this period and say, "You do not have to be worried about it. Menstruation is a normal phenomenon. It has the function of preparing the uterus for pregnancy and is part of the whole process of preparation for childbirth. It happens to all women. I am not distressed about it; I never have been; you should not be."

Even ten minutes of wise explanation would be extremely reassuring to daughters if mothers only had enough mental equilibrium to discuss the phenomenon. Medical students have said to us after hearing the explanations of body phenomena that they suddenly realized that they, themselves, had never had adequate sex instruction but had picked up bits of information here and there. Studies of college women show that they also have not had any instruction about sex or even any instruction about menstruation. The importance of imparting this information to women should be stressed because they do not stumble upon the correct facts by themselves.

Doctors are in a good position to instruct mothers in the importance of these things, because in the lay mind physicians are supposed to know everything about the human body and its physiological and psychological functions. Women will accept information from the family physician; in fact, there is no other authority to whom they can turn, no other person whose explanations they will accept as valid. They get more from him than from reading two or three books, for people are often more skeptical about what they read than about what they hear, though there are some who take the written word more seriously than the spoken word.

Some girls grow up looking forward to menstruation with anticipation, as if it were a badge of womanhood, and expect their mothers to look upon it in the same way. But when puberty comes they are disappointed: the mother ignores the phenomenon and implies, thereby, that they should keep the matter to themselves. So girls think about it alone and manage it to the best of their limited ability.

Many women suffer from extreme symptoms during menstruation and relate them directly to the menstrual period: like fatigue, backache, headache, irritability, depression of spirits. We know of a woman who went to bed for two weeks each month. She had the theory that all the food she ate turned sour in her stomach because some poison invaded her body during the process of menstruation. This was not a delusion but only a slight exaggeration of current thought. She felt that menstruation was a toxic and poisonous process. When talking with her, one was impressed by the extravagance of her beliefs about the menstruating woman.

In the course of practice, doctors hear many strange fantasies and beliefs surrounding sexuality and menstruation. They should reassure such a woman by telling her they have heard these tales before. When she feels that the doctor is receptive to her feelings and ideas of menstruation, he will be in a position—after he has listened to her—to tell her it is her fear that is making her sick and keeping her in bed and not the glandular activity or the flow of blood.

The Awkward Age

Puberty is marked by a rather rapid phase of growth and change in body contour in both sexes, which results in their having a little difficulty in handling themselves and is the reason for giving the name "awkward age" to the period. The awkwardness is due in part to the need young people have to getting used to their growth changes and in part to the self-consciousness or anxiety that is caused by the changes. During this rapid growth boys and girls feel they are being looked at by others. A change in contour of the larynx due to rapid growth causes the boy to have difficulty in controlling the pitch of his voice and sometimes results in embarrassment. In him, as well as in the girl, there is growth of pubic and axillary hair. The boy has some accelerated growth of the sexual organs and the onset of nocturnal emissions.

Nocturnal Emissions

The loss of seminal fluid during sleep, sometimes accompanied by an erotic dream, can be a source of great worry and concern to boys. Those boys who have had no adequate instruction or who have been allowed to be anxious about their body organs or about matters pertaining to sex have particular concern about it. They feel that the loss of seminal fluid is devitalizing to them, or that it represents a disease or illness, or that it is the outgrowth of too much preoccupation with the subject of sex. Though they worry about it they do not dare ask the father or mother or friend of the family about it lest the person question them too closely or lest they be accused of masturbating. Often they struggle on alone, worrying a great deal about these emissions of seminal fluid. Like menstruation in the girl, seminal emission is a normal phenomenon in the boy and takes place from the age of puberty onward. It merely denotes the activity of the sexual glands and that sperm cells and spermatic fluid are being manufactured. Occasional release of·fluids during sleep is of no pathological significance and should cause no concern.

All in all, boys probably worry less about seminal emissions than do girls about menstruation. Boys have the advantage of being able to talk more freely among themselves and of having more sources of information than girls. The majority of boys tend to accept the phenomenon rather philosophically. A few are concerned, and for these sexual instruction by the father or mother when they were younger would have prevented their worry and enabled them to accept the phenomenon. If these facts in relation to the body and its functions were better understood, the anxiety, uneasiness and social awkwardness that children have at this age would be relieved considerably.

Social Adjustment

During the transition period boys and girls do not know whether they are children or adolescents. Even the adults are not very clear about it, nor about the role they expect the young ones to play. Adults arrange dances and parties. They dress the children in the newest fashion and then push them into social situations without giving them an inkling of what it is all about. Obviously boys and girls have to get used to each other; they have to acquire some ability to get along with each other. Often a child is offered a social opportunity but he is not told its meaning in a sufficiently distinct way to enable him to understand its significance and importance and enjoy it. In his mind he is made to feel uncomfortable and to waste his time gratifying a whim of his parents instead of being made aware that he is getting practice in social enjoyment useful for all time.

During puberty (as is the case during the genital period) an increased tendency toward masturbation takes place due to the extra impetus of the sexual glands upon the already existing personality. For the future welfare of the child the relationship between him and the parents should be friendly at this time, just as at other times, thus sparing him concern about the moral issues of the phenomenon. If the parents have not been on good terms with the child and have not explained sexual functions to him, then, of course, guilt about the behavior may be quite marked. The developing individual is not likely to go to the parents to discuss a sexual problem at this period if a great deal of anxiety has been associated with masturbation previously.

Nightmares

Excessive anxiety over sexual matters may take the form of nightmares. Sometimes the anxiety troubles the young person during the day as well, and may take the form of his believing himself to be the victim of a disease. At puberty children may go through a mild or even severe phobia, the content of which is that they have tuberculosis, cancer, heart disease, or possibly that they are going insane. If the anxiety manifests itself at night, it is prone to come automatically in a nightmare. The girl may dream of being pursued by a man, of being chased by an animal, of being run over by a horse or automobile. Both sexes often dream of being on top of a tall building or precipice from which they are about to fall. Nightmares grow out of a distortion of ideas relating to instinctual impulses and are usually concerned with the sexual or the aggressive impulses with which the young person is struggling at this period.

If at this time nightmares occur frequently, or the girl or boy has a fear of disease, the young person should be given particular attention by parents or doctor, because these manifestations are danger signals and not just phenomena of growing up, to be taken lightly or ignored. It may be true that when the pubertal period comes to a close the anxiety in many cases does seem to disappear, but actually if the problem has not been talked over with the young person and solved it has not been absorbed but repressed, only to reappear in a more disturbing way later, possibly during the excitement of courtship or, for the female, at the time of the birth of her first child. It is a wise plan to deal with these evidences of anxiety at the time they arise. In a vulnerable child they arise early, and if not evident before can usually be seen during puberty when the activity of the sexual glands increases and menstruation begins.

It is often pointed out proudly by people who do not want to be bothered to think specifically about these things that many people got along adequately without sexual education or a wholesome sharing of information between parent and child. They may even point to themselves and say, "I never had any help with sex questions and I got along all right." First, such a person may not be the paragon he thinks he is and, second, it should be clear to any thinking person that with the high divorce rate and the great difficulties in human understanding in every walk of life no opportunity for close friendship such as is afforded through better education should be overlooked. One woman said, "When I first heard of telling children about sex, I just thought it couldn't be done. But the more I thought of it, the easier it seemed. I discovered that I didn't need to talk about sex at all but only about love and procreation." This wholesome change in attitude shows how much sex is thought of as dirty, deceitful, dishonorable, an act done in the dark and thought about darkly. If we are to have a healthier attitude about loving and about reproducing ourselves, we must remove the shame, filth and dishonor that still cling in the minds of many to the word sex.

ADOLESCENCE

Adolescence. is a period of life that is poorly understood and greatly neglected by adults, though the reasons are not readily apparent. Everyone is aware of the fact that a great many misunderstandings arise between parents and their adolescent children. It is perhaps easy to understand why parents do not perceive the forces at work during the first year of life or even early childhood, but adult life follows adolescence so closely that one would expect parents to remember better how they felt in their teens and so be more understanding of the adolescent's problems.

From fourteen to twenty-one the adolescent must (1) decide upon a vocation and do some work in preparation for it, (2) effect on emancipation from his parents and family, (3) bring about a satisfactory relation with the opposite sex and at least begin to make some solution of his love life, and (4) effect an integration in his personality for mature responsibility. If the personality development has progressed fairly well thus far, these four aims should not be too difficult of achievement, and the adolescent should derive intense pleasure in their accomplishment and his family gain considerable satisfaction from helping him to do so. Actually a great many instances of unhappiness, friction and misunderstanding are precipitated between the adolescent and his parent while the adolescent is attempting to solve these problems, causing the adolescent years to be so extremely stormy and even making some adolescents emerge from the period in a rather disorganized state of mind.

To some degree the adolescent is still a tractable, suggestible, modifiable personality, subject to change and to help, yet this possibility for change has its limit. Some overly optimistic people think that the right environment and good advice can change any adolescent, no matter how maladjusted, and enable him to become an amiable and worth-while citizen. We should be cautious about being too sure of our ability to change the adolescent, even though his personality is not completely molded. However, our personalities are never wholly set at any age, nor should they be; we should always try to keep growing, no matter how old we are.

The law makes us responsible at the age of twenty-one, which inclines us to think we are then the finished product of maturity. This is not so, though on the other hand we must not conceive of the adolescent as being so modifiable that we can push him to and fro or change him overmuch. The adolescent should be a fairly well-integrated personality by the time he enters his teens. He will have ways of reacting, which he will use rather consistently, and we may be limited in what we can do to change his pattern. For instance, if the development of the child has been good, he comes to adolescence with a healthy, confident way of meeting reality, of taking hold of situations and doing something constructive with them.

In another child the opposite reaction pattern of escape may have been built, and this adolescent enters the period with an anxious, shy personality and with a tendency to retreat, to isolate himself and to try to avoid as much social intercourse and responsibility as possible. Naturally such an adolescent misses some of the most pleasant and strengthening influences of life. If nothing is done about it, he will emerge at twenty-one supposedly prepared to meet life, yet actually feeling cheated, afraid and dissatisfied, unprepared either for social adjustment, work adjustment or marriage, with the result that he does not succeed in the environment or fails to keep jobs, friends, or his marital partner.

Adolescence is usually the last period of dependence and the last period when environmental forces alone can help the individual. For example, a great many human beings enter the period as anxious, shy, timid individuals, unused to associating with others and without having had sufficient responsibilities. However, they may be fortunate in the school selected, or in the friends they make, or fortunate in attracting the interest of an older person—teacher, uncle, aunt, or friend of the family —and so develop remarkably well during this period. A certain amount of cure of a potential neurosis can take place as a result of a chance happening in the environment. High schools, colleges, sororities, fraternities, dormitory life and societies of one kind or another do a great deal to help the development of the personality during adolescence.

Luckily a great many adolescents are caught hold of by life and helped to grow outward and expand in spite of themselves. A few, however, even though placed in the best of circumstances, cannot utilize the opportunities that are available. They are still too shy and anxious, too fearful to risk the competition or exposure that is inherent in the situation. They stay by themselves and lead a sterile existence, and in spite of our best efforts to help we may not be able to succeed with them because they cannot use our help and friendship. Their experiences and associations during the first years of life were of such poor quality that they cannot understand what their friends are trying to do for them. Actually they cannot utilize friends because they have no mental pictures of friendship to respond with.

In terms of years the adolescent may be having his last chance of catching the attention of a person or group that will help him. After adolescence his chances grow slimmer because he is supposed to be a grown-up individual and take care of himself. From then on the environment is not so likely to be interested in him.

Choice of Vocation

It is important that adolescents of both sexes prepare to do some specific kind of work. Some young people go through adolescence having a marvelous vacation. They expose themselves to the classroom but do not catch any ideas. They do not look into the future and see themselves as playing any active, useful role in life. This unfortunate attitude is often fostered by the American parent who sometimes has a strange pride in the thought that his children won't have to work. Such a thought is, of course, a great compliment to the father's success and to the idea that he has so much income and has arranged his estate in such a manner that he can take care of his family indefinitely. The financial crash of 1929 did a great deal to dispel this illusion in the minds of the American people and to break up their feeling of omnipotence that through great wealth a man can take care of all members of his family for generations without the necessity of any of them working. In the last twenty years the American people have become a little more realistic about work—but only a little.

In some groups it is considered a joke to ask the adolescent what he is planning to do. The impression is given that the possibilities on the American scene are so limitless and the intellectual, emotional and economic possibilities of the adolescent so limitless that absolutely no thought or planning is necessary. Like the delusion of the happy marriage that every American is going to have by right of his very existence on this earth, there may be a feeling in the adolescent that a happy wedding is bound to take place between his potential worth and American society, and all will be happy ever after.

Plans for vocation should be made with some consideration for the economic resources of the family. It is true that opportunities to work one's way through school have been quite plentiful in this country, and that many institutions and organizations help the deserving student. At the same time, a too ambitious educational program may take up time that should be spent in recreation, and so draw upon the young person's emotional and physical resources as to make it impossible for him ever to be able to enjoy the fruits of his sacrifice, and so leave him with a feeling of bitterness.

Many parents still have a feeling that work is a disgrace, especially for a daughter. Others feel there is time enough to think about a vocation "later" and that the whole matter will take care of itself. Unfortunately, this is not true. About ten years ago business and professional men were complaining that the colleges were turning out too many students not well enough equipped to take responsibility. The difficulty in most of these cases lay in the parents, who did no concrete thinking about the specific role the student would play once he had obtained a college degree. They thought that sending the boy or girl to high school or college was sufficient, that when he graduated, desirable employers would be stretching out their arms to him. One mother expressed her disillusionment when she exclaimed, "I have discovered that four years of college have equipped my daughter to sell dishmops in the basement of a five-and-ten-cent store!"

The biggest work problems come in families where the idea that work is not important is introduced subtly and insidiously. In the case of the girl the bad effects are more profound than in the case of the boy. Even though the mother and father do not think their boy should have to work, he may be smart enough to see that he ought to do something and get ready for life in spite of the parents. Because girls have a more dependent position, it is harder for them to insist on vocational choice or on breaking away from home to follow their choice.

During adolescence the girl should consider whether she is going to have a career or whether she is going to marry. The reader might ask how she is going to know what her chances are in either case. Nothing can be guaranteed, of course, but she will have a better chance to get what she wants if she makes a choice and prepares for it and does not leave the matter entirely in the hands of fate. In fact, it is probably an excellent idea for girls to be prepared for *both* marriage and a career. Certainly if a girl plans for a home of her own, a husband and sex life and children, she is much more likely to achieve these goals through the aid of inner thought and preparation. Also, she will not be harmed by preparing herself to do some outside work, since in the interim between school and marriage, holding a job, perhaps living in a home of her own and taking care of it, and being dependent upon her own income make excellent training for later life problems: such as the loss of the husband by death, or providing for herself in a crisis such as war, which has forced many women to take care of themselves financially and even of a child or two. Also, such a woman does not feel so frightened or helpless about obtaining and holding a job again in later life when the children have grown up and she needs the income or the added interest of outside employment.

One of the most important ways of feeling worth while in this world is to be able to make a contribution to the social order through work. The deficiency of this feeling is illustrated by the case of a young man of nineteen who was failing in his college work. He was worried and gaining little satisfaction either in his social life or in his work. He was an only child who from early childhood was shielded and protected from unpleasant realities. Whenever he asked questions, his parents said, "Wait until you are older." Whenever he wished to undertake a piece of work his parents asked, "Do you think you are strong enough?" When he began to discuss the matter of vocation, they said, "There is time enough. Just go to school." The only hobby he was allowed to take up was golf, the one hobby in which his father indulged. When he went to college, he asked, "What am I going for?" His parents said, "We can decide later." Actually they had a career in mind for him but they were keeping it secret because they wanted to make sure he was obedient and subservient.

However, he got tired of all this. The day came—as it always does for children who are too thoroughly repressed—when he said, "I am getting discouraged. I do not know where I am going. I do not seem to have any part in decisions. When I ask questions, I get no answer, and even if I come upon my parents when they are talking, they suddenly shut up. I have not been getting much fun out of life for the past two or three years. I am getting too worried about my health. I think things are going badly with me." That boy needed help to free himself from a neurotic pattern. One of the outstanding features of his case was the unrealistic attitude he had toward a vocation. His parents could not seem to cope with the idea that he had to go out in the world to occupy a certain place and that in order to do so he needed the opportunity to project himself through the imagination and freedom to think about being and working on his own.

The four tasks of adolescence merge one into the other to some degree. Some parents are afraid to emancipate their children, to allow them to think independently, to permit them to plan their own lives because of the great urge—much of which is unconscious—to master and control them and to have them dependent upon themselves. Other parents seem to have a need to live emotionally in the child in a kind of parasitic way, instead of getting satisfaction from seeing to it that he lives his own life and makes his own contribution to society. Instead of willingly helping the child to gain independence, they unconsciously try to hinder his progress. In practically every family the adolescent fights a war of independence. The parents fight to retain authority and prestige in the eyes of the child, and the child, we hope in spite of this, fights for his liberty.

If this situation must bring such conflict, at least the war between parent and child ought to be friendly. But in many cases it is actually hostile. The parent fights with frowns, black looks, reproaches, scolding, forbidding rules and taboos. The child fights with sullenness, reticent determination, secret rendezvous, disobedience and, in many cases, open defiance, sometimes even leaving home.

Going away to school is a specific problem in the child's fight for emancipation from the parents. Sometimes young people want to go away to school from a desire for a particular type of education, but more often they want to go anywhere that will take them away from mother and father. Parents may reproach their children for expressing a desire to go away. Frequently they tell the child he will be lonely and not be able to bear being away from home for a three- or four-month period. Unconsciously, the parents are talking about themselves. In reality, it is *they* who contemplate the separation with dread, they who will be lonely. Sometimes, when a child gives up his plans for going away, he becomes angry and may perhaps never forgive the parents for forcing him to take the decision. It may result in his carrying a feeling of being cheated throughout his life and, later, be an important factor in a depression of spirits. Some parents are afraid to be without their children because they fear they will be lonely themselves; others fear the children will fall into bad company, will learn to smoke, to drink, to pet, and thereby come to some bad end and bring disgrace upon them as parents.

A great many of the parents' fears of the emancipation of the adolescent are ill founded. Challenge one of these parents as to whether he could actually prevent the child from smoking or drinking and he would have to admit that the child goes to many places where he could smoke or drink, without the parent's presence to supervise. Parents have fifteen or twenty years in which to instruct their sons or daughters in proper conduct. If they have not succeeded in that time, they might as well let matters take their course or seek specialized help. Repeated quarreling between parent and child is more likely to make matters worse rather than better.

In the first twelve years of life a great deal of time is spent by parents in teaching children the kind of behavior expected of them. Children learn their parents' wishes very well—parents can be sure of that! If the parents have gained the love and respect of their children, they need have no fear that the children will get into any too serious difficulty or deviate very much from the pattern they have laid down.

Paradoxically, some parents approve of independence as the end result but seem unable to approve of the inevitable intermediate steps. Ask a mother if she wants her child to be a capable, useful, happy individual, and she will undoubtedly respond, "Of course!" Yet in the next breath she will forbid her daughter to go on a harmless enough picnic with a few girls, giving the excuse that her daughter is too young or that she will not know when to come home. It would be well for parents to maintain a future perspective and to think of their children in relation to that future; then they would see that an end desire must have intermediate steps. The wise parent realizes that a child must take responsibility for a time to prove to his parents and the community that he can take care of himself and that he is not such a weak person as to overindulge himself, misbehave, disgrace his family or fail to be a responsible member of society.

So doctors, teachers, friends may have to be on the side of the adolescent who is seeking emancipation through undertaking some new project. For instance, parents often wonder if the child is old enough to be a junior counselor at camp, or to go away to a resort with a chum, or to work as an errand boy. Children must begin some time to live their own lives. Adolescence is the logical time. In other words, parents should pay more attention to the positive values inherent in adolescent responsibility and give less attention to the adolescent's need for overprotection and to the supposed dangers that can overtake him; they should have less fear about his coming to harm. At the same time that parents are worrying about their adolescent children, they are often destructive in their thinking about them. Parents often think the worst of an adolescent child, and seem to expect the worst from him. It is not a salutary way on which to pattern their ways of thinking. When the worst is expected of an adolescent, he may well deliver the worst. A fairly safe procedure is to expect the best, for then the adolescent is likely to respond with the best. Adults should remember that the adolescent is just one step from maturity, and that he needs their help in a positive way to prepare him for functioning when he reaches maturity.

A girl of eighteen who wanted to go to a seashore resort to work as a waitress presented an interesting problem involving emancipation. She was the oldest of a family of six. Her father was not earning enough money for her to have the same kind of clothes her friends wore, so she wanted to work to provide them for herself and prepared herself to do so. We had known her for six years and had found her reliable and trustworthy. Her father was most insistent that she not go to the shore. During our talk he became rather confidential about the real reason for his objection. "You know how it is, doctor," he said. "Men come in the restaurant, they like a girl's looks, they leave a large tip, then they ask her to go out with them the next time. That is the beginning of a girl's ruin. It ends in sexual promiscuity." We said, "Why do you think this?" and he answered, "I have good reason to know. I used to do this myself." He was judging the situation in the light of his own experience. We told him we would be willing to trust his daughter, and that if it would help him we would share the anxiety and responsibility connected with her going. He seemed relieved and let her go. Nothing unfortunate happened. From then on the girl was free to work every summer.

A great many fathers and mothers imagine a young person, male or female, being carried away by sexual impulses. They feel the danger but can say nothing to the children about it. Had these parents been close to their children during the years preceding adolescence, and had they known what the children were thinking, they would not be so distrustful. An element of distrust has a bad influence. Adolescents should be trusted more and we should expect the best from them. Girls and boys should be helped in their fight for emancipation from their parents as an extremely important factor in gaining maturity.

Adjustment to the Opposite Sex

Courtship, marriage, marriage adjustment, parenthood and responsibility in community life lie just ahead of adolescents. An important preparation for these responsibilities is the necessity for both sexes to become accustomed to each other through association in work and play in order that they may learn to know each other and give each other the benefit of their emotional resources. A great deal of practice in living is needed to enable the individual to live a satisfactory and successful life and should be encouraged during adolescence. Ordinarily adolescents get this practice through a mutual participation in parties, dances, movies, concerts, theaters, hikes, picnics and the like. This association tends to lead to the physical expression of hand holding, kissing, embracing and fondling, which are normal manifestations of human beings who are functioning in a normal manner and who are preparing for future responsibilities. Adolescence is one of the last opportunities for having a good time with a minimum of responsibility, and should be shared by both sexes. This seems to be so obvious that the point hardly needs elaboration or defense. However, as everyone knows, in their efforts to adjust to each other and to develop a love life adolescents are often thwarted by adults.

Various problems arise because parents object to any free mingling of the sexes. They regard the girl or boy as having too much interest in the opposite sex and fear the young person will "lose his good name" or get a "bad reputation" running around too much. This terrible thing called "running around too much" is, of course, only an increased desire to be in association with the opposite sex. However, parents feel it can have bad consequences and they take this point of view without thinking through the factors involved. They are afraid that if young people come in too frequent contact with each other, they will be prone to marry too young and thus require a longer period of financial support, instead of being a source of support to the parents. Parents also fear that a young person may marry unwisely, or marry the wrong person, or someone beneath him—whatever that may mean to the particular family. Moreover, they fear that there is a real danger of sexual indulgence before marriage and that this friendly proximity is going to be a temptation to sexual intercourse with the resultant danger of illegitimate pregnancy or disease and the consequent disgrace.

Parents also have an unrecognized and unconscious jealousy that their offspring will have good times that they themselves missed. Consciously parents would not be that selfish but unconscious jealousy is quite an important factor in each generation. Up to now members of each succeeding generation have had opportunity for more freedom and to mingle and enjoy themselves more freely together; thus each generation of parents, having had less, is jealous of its children and at the same time fears their promiscuous sexual behavior.

Much of the difficulty in understanding between parents and adolescents in this regard comes from the fact that the parents become frightened by newspaper reports or rumors about young people having illicit sexual relations. They fear the possibility that such activities will become universal, forgetting that if a child has been taught a sense of fair play, of consideration for others, and of social responsibility, and that if they as parents have been sufficiently considerate of the child, when they ask him to give his consideration to their wishes in the matter of sexual behavior during adolescence, things will generally go all right.

All too many parents do not give their children any sexual information, are not on a frank footing with them or close to them in sexual matters. Instead, a great mutual distrust exists between them. The parents focus fear and anxiety on the problem and become restrictive. They develop anxiety in the child's presence, do not have any frank discussion about the matter, and do not make any appeal for a sensible control of sexual impulses. Parent-child relations are in a sad state when a parent, hearing of a sexual indiscretion in some adolescent, is overcome by fear for her own child, and at the same time has to admit to herself, "I never really told my child how I want her to conduct herself with boys. She has heard my opinion on a multitude of things and yet not on that important one."

If parents paid less attention to accounts of promiscuity they read or hear about and concentrated instead on their own relationships with their children, they would have little reason to worry about their children's sexual behavior. If they would encourage the sexes to mix, to play and to dance with each other with confidence, the young people would finally find themselves in marriage without disgrace and without harm to their character, and without having indulged in years of frustrated petting. We feel it is unnecessary to think that as a race of human beings we have to be always standing in fear of our sexual impulses. Surely we can figure out a way of controlling sexuality rather than having it control us and distort so much of our social life by sexual taboos and inhibitions which deprive people emotionally and which lead to so many unhappy marriages, divorces and neuroses.

Doctors are in a position to reassure parents about this matter of wholesome social life for adolescents and to see that young people have the opportunity to go about and to live out their desire to mix with each other without shame and anxiety.

Some parents, during adolescence, discourage friendships between boys and girls of the type called "going steady together." They feel that a serious emotional investment of a young person in one of the opposite sex may lead to too severe disappointment should the friendship have to terminate. It should be pointed out that whether adolescents "go steady" or not, they *are* in contact with one another and are having the necessary emotional experience, and this is what is most important. If and when separation comes, it may be an unpleasant disappointment but we believe adolescence is a time for gaining experience in the emotions felt toward the opposite sex. If short and superficial relationships are encouraged during adolescence, the deeper relationships later may be interfered with. Furthermore, though a disappointment in love during adolescence may be an unhappy matter, much may be learned from it— and the parents are on hand to give their emotional support should it happen. It is important that young people come together close enough to learn how to evaluate each other in terms of compatibility, for in this way many of the disappointments of married life, which are much more significant, especially if the family has been started, can be averted. Hence we repeat that adolescence is the time for getting some practice in the matter of one's feelings toward the opposite sex.

Doctors can also speak about jealousy to the parents and point out that they cannot expect the child of today to live by the same rules they did and grow up a happy and satisfied person. Life changes too much for that. Young people always have to live more or less in harmony with current standards. Any parent who tries to bring up a child today on the standards of twenty-five years ago is likely to run into grief, and he can console himself with the thought that the same will probably be true twenty-five years hence. Some parents are prone to object to a free mingling of the sexes for fear that it will precipitate an early marriage. We are not assuming that closer association between the sexes influences young people to marry at twenty-three, for instance, instead of at twenty-seven or twenty-eight, but for those who do desire an early marriage the matter can be worked out satisfactorily if the parents of the young people co-operate and help financially. Society should strive for early marriages. It is better for people to have children while they are young and still remember how they felt as children and adolescents, while they have more interests in common. Also, children are less likely to lose parents through death or partially lose them through chronic illness. Early marriage is not a bad idea from the emotional standpoint, yet it is looked upon by society in general as a luxury of questionable value rather than as a potential social asset.

We are a nation in which a great deal of prestige is given to unaided individual effort. If a man works hard to be a success and make a lot of money, if a woman works hard to keep her house spic and span and bring up the children, both may reach old age feeling that they have nothing behind them and not knowing what to do with themselves when their job is done. In America being a success brings a certain prestige. If a man is caught taking an afternoon off, his colleagues will kid him, saying, "Made your pile already, have you?" the implication being that he is a little immoral or is destined to ruin if he does not keep his nose to the grindstone all the time. In other words, we have to remold some of our ideas about work and acquire more recreational pursuits and hobbies in order to make more rounded personalities. To do this is not a luxury but very much a necessity. Likewise, for young people to desire and work for an early marriage is not a luxury but a sensible plan and one that can possibly be classed as a necessity. Certainly the trend toward later marriages on the part of men and women brings with it more and more anxiety and, because of selfish habits formed in living alone, less buoyancy and generosity to put into marriage.

Perhaps the parents' greatest concern is over the matter of actual sexual relations with the possibility of pregnancy and venereal disease. There is no doubt that here and there sexual activity is participated in by young people before they can arrange marriage. However, we think a great deal of it would decrease if young people had a decent sexual education in the first place, for a great many of them are drawn into sexual relations early from intense curiosity rather than from any desire to participate in a sexual relationship. If parents have not succeeded in educating the young person by the time he or she has reached the age of eighteen or nineteen, they had better let him use his own judgment and avoid the arguments, hostility and restrictions that can grow out of a battle of whether he is going to lead an active social life or not. When these battles occur, the young person has hard feelings, to say the least. Often he leaves home for good, or returns only at infrequent intervals for as long as the parents live.

Such a problem was caused by a mother who believed her only course lay in keeping the subject of sex from her daughter. She brought the girl up strictly and told her nothing about sex. The daughter did not have a date until she was eighteen, and in the succeeding two years every date was supervised by the mother. When the girl went shopping by herself, the mother warned her about men who cruised around in cars ready to pull her in and abduct her into white slavery. In the mother's mind not only was sex everywhere and very dangerous but her own daughter had dangerous sex impulses. The mother made the remark that if she could frighten the girl enough to get her through high school safely, she would be greatly relieved. She succeeded so well with her plan that when the girl reached the age of twenty-one she was getting so little out of life and was so afraid to go out alone that she could not travel anywhere unless accompanied by someone. Moreover, she developed headache and sick stomach until a doctor had to be consulted who in turn suggested she see a psychiatrist. The fear ideas and emotions that the mother had instilled in the girl trying to keep her "safe" had finally resulted in making her so sick that it took a long time to make her well.

Integration of Personality

Even if the individual adjusts to work, chooses a mate and becomes emancipated from his parents, he is still not completely whole. He must be helped to see the necessity for participation in the life of the community, the nation, and even of the world, and thus become a part of the world in which he lives. After all, society does not function entirely for John Citizen. John Citizen must function in relation to society as a whole or society will soon break down. Once this fact is put into words, it becomes obvious, yet a great many families do not teach the child to perform any public service or to be any part of the larger world.

As an adolescent is growing up he needs not only to be taught to think of himself and his own perfection but to be tolerant of people individually, tolerant of their foibles, to refrain from being too critical and too aloof and to have a willingness to take part in community life. As people become more successful and well to do, they tend to build their houses farther and farther apart, and each family tends to live as a separate unit. Friendly neighborliness decreases. This is not as it should be at all, as is well illustrated in Huxley's *Point Counter Point,* in which a man and a woman are struggling to understand each other. The girl has a well-to-do background; the boy has not. He points out to her that her wealth has enabled her to live aloof from people, to have servants and to feel complete. He says, "In the part of the world where I come from, that would have been impossible. We lived very close together in every sense of the word. Not only were our houses close, but when we had illness or trouble, we had to have the neighbors come in and help us out. We had to be close to and depend upon each other or we could not have survived at all." People everywhere need to get a feeling of greater willingness to help each other in order to achieve a better feeling of social unity, for only in unity will we have real strength.

BIBLIOGRAPHY FOR CHAPTER X

Chadwick, Mary, *Psychological Effects of Menstruation,* Nervous and Mental Disease Monographs, 1934.

Elliott, Grace Louckes, *Understanding the Adolescent Girl,* Holt, 1930.

Howard, E. McC., "An Analysis of Adolescent Adjustment Problems," *Mental Hygiene* **25**, July, 1941, pp. 363–391.

Huxley, Aldous, *Point Counter Point,* Modern Library.

Zachry, Caroline, *Emotions and Conduct in Adolescence,* Appleton, 1940.

Chapter XI

EMOTIONAL DISTURBANCES THAT OCCUR DURING PUBERTY AND ADOLESCENCE

THE CHILD who has made a satisfactory adjustment in his infancy and childhood will nevertheless have some difficulties of adjustment in adolescence because the development of his ego is still far from complete and his superego may be still too much a simple reflection of the parents' attitude during childhood and not yet sufficiently modified by the influence of the social organization. The child who already has shown serious incapacities in adjustment because his superego is too severe and his ego capacity proportionately too weak will be liable to suffer an increase of symptoms during adolescence. The child who has not made an adequate solution in the latent period cannot be expected to make a more adequate adjustment in adolescence. The child who seems to have made a solution in the latent period may find that the new upsurging of the sexual life in adolescence proves that his adjustment was a pretense and not a reality. The emotional illnesses that develop in adolescence are the same as those that develop during the latent period, for the phenomena of adolescence in themselves do not produce any serious maladjustments. A description of the symptom complexes of the emotional illnesses of adolescence would be simply a recapitulation of what we have said before.

Adolescent neuroses, however, tend to have two peculiarities. The illness is either very stormy and the disorganization of the personality great—so that often there is difficulty in deciding whether the illness is a neurosis or a psychosis—or it tends to attack the character so that the symptoms appear in the social and vocational spheres. The reasons for this lie in the resurgence of the sexual drives. If the resurging sexuality is very powerful or the governing forces of the ego too weak, the adolescent neurosis will run a stormy course which may cause the illness to resemble a psychosis, since there is a real danger that the inner drives will overwhelm the controlling mechanisms. If the forces of the superego are proportionately too strong the ego will have to deform itself more and more as the resurging sexuality appears. Here the clinical picture will be a progressively severe character disturbance.

The relative weakness of the ego makes psychotherapy of a neurosis in an adolescent extremely difficult, and often after a short period of therapy he stops treatment. Several years later when he has entered into late adolescence or young adult life he will get in touch with the therapist again with the statement, "Doctor, we started treatment years ago but we never finished it, and I think it is time we got it finished now." The usual story is that at the time of the first break the patient was about to confess some of his sexual experiences—usually his masturbation—but was too frightened to do so. This weakness of the ego in the adolescent neurotic produces another type of difficulty. One day he gives in to his feelings of ego weakness and is clinging and dependent, wanting concrete help with situations that he is perfectly capable of dealing with, and the next he compensates for this feeling by protesting that he is more capable and knows more than any adult and therefore needs help from no one. Both attitudes and particularly their rapid alternation make it difficult for therapist and patient to establish a basis for mutual understanding.

On account of these weaknesses of the ego there is always considerable difficulty in determining the type of treatment most desirable for the neurotic adolescent. Shall we engage in intensive psychotherapy—the only treatment that in the majority of cases will really be of value—realizing that the patient's ego may be too weak to tolerate the unconscious ideas and feelings and that treatment may be inopportunely interrupted? Would it be better to adjust the environment as much as possible and wait until he has reached late adolescence or early adult life when he will have more experience to help him in the difficulties of intensive treatment? In many instances we feel that the latter is perhaps the best course, for the patient then will come to treatment with greater realization of his need for it and with more ability to undergo it. Since the attitudes of the neurotic adolescent are the product of traumatic experiences he suffered as a small child—frequently due to adverse parental attitudes—it is unlikely that they will have changed when he becomes adolescent. In fact they are likely to be more firmly fixed. In many cases it is perhaps better to deal with the problem by changing the residence of the patient—usually by placing him in boarding school. The school authorities will not have an easy time with him, but if he can be tolerated, he may be helped to grow up until it seems timely to undertake intensive psychotherapy.

Educational Difficulties

There is one type of adolescent maladjustment that we wish to discuss specifically because it is a common one and extremely difficult to handle. It is a well-known fact that the beginning of adolescence has a definite though temporary effect on the learning capacity of most children. A child who has made good progress in school in the early grades often shows deterioration in the quality of his schoolwork when he reaches the seventh or eighth grade and for a year or so does not do so well; then his efficiency comes back to its old level again. In some children this phenomenon is very marked; in others it occurs only to a slight degree. Its explanation seems to lie in two directions—the acceleration in the growth of the central nervous system that occurs about this time (this growth is mainly in the associational tracts, and the learning difficulty results from the bewilderment that is produced by the number of these new associations) and the increased sensitization of the sensory organs by the resurging sexual life (this makes the child keener in his perception but temporarily overwhelms him with new sensations).

There are adolescents, however, who do not recover from this setback. Instead of making a comeback the schoolwork becomes gradually worse. In the classroom such a child is inattentive: he daydreams or annoys his neighbors. Frequently he forgets to bring the right textbook, or he has it open at the wrong place. When the teacher reprimands him he becomes sullen or attempts to justify his actions. Often his attempts at self-justification are couched in such a way as to provoke the mirth of the class. The reprimand does not improve the behavior, for after a few minutes he is acting in the same way again. His homework is neglected. He forgets to bring home the proper books. He has a dozen important pursuits—radio programs to be listened to, newspapers to be read, phone calls to be made, etc.—before he sits down to study. When he does sit down he turns the radio on. As bedtime approaches he becomes somewhat panicky because his exercises are not done, and he asks his parents to help. Since the hour is late they tend to do his work for him rather than just help him. If they refuse to co-operate he takes his unfinished work to school where he either neglects to hand it in or presents it with a great variety of excuses. In schools that use the Dalton plan this type of child gets far behind with his particular project. Laboratory notebooks are neglected and there is a mad scramble at the end of the time limit to get the work done. It seldom is completed.

The teacher, disturbed by the child's failure, calls in the parents for a consultation. The parents in turn are disturbed and begin to insist that the child devote specified hours to his homework. The child is usually engaged in some activity or other when homework time comes and gets started only after much parental nagging. By this time the parent is quite irritated and often sits with the child so he will not dawdle. The parent may try to help him with the work, but since by this time there is great mutual discord the session ends in violent quarreling. Of course the less work the child does, the farther behind he gets, until he reaches the point where to bring himself up to date, even with his required written work, would require two or three weeks' solid concentration. Even if he wanted to he could not get this extra work done and the term ends as a dismal failure.

Only infrequently does the child fail on his examinations, since he does know much of the work. His failure is based on his day-to-day productions. When the parents talk to him about his work he blames his difficulties on the unreasonableness of the teachers, on the type of school he attends, on the annoying behavior of his classmates, or he becomes sullen and angry. He expresses a desire to change schools, to leave school and go to work, or to leave home and go to boarding school. (The last solution emanates more commonly from the parents than from the child. They usually feel that he needs discipline and believe he can get that in a good—i. e. a strict—military school.) Often in these cases the teacher and the psychiatrist who see the case feel that the child must have a low level of intelligence and that the work is beyond him. A psychometric rating, however, usually shows him to be better than average. In fact it is not uncommon to find that these children have intelligence quotients of 130 to 150.

The passage of time does not improve the difficulty—neither does the scolding and punishment by teacher or parents. In fact the more the parents scold the less work he does. He is inclined to react to attempts at discipline in the school by absenting himself from classes—which makes matters worse. It is often painful for the adults who are interested in the child to see this bright and potentially able person making no use of his capabilities and heading with apparent recklessness toward making a complete wreck of his future. This is so painful that both teachers and parents resort to extreme degrees of nagging in order to force the child to avoid his fate. They feel that he is lacking in character, that he has no sense of responsibility and is incapable of self-discipline, and as a result use every measure they can think of to get him to discipline himself and to take responsibility. They often deal with the latter in a curious way. Because the child has no sense of responsibility they take on all his responsibility for him. If he dawdles in the morning they nag him in order to get him to school on time; if he dawdles over his home-work they do the same. In both instances they forget that a sense of responsibility comes from taking one's own responsibility and that the best discipline comes from practical reality—e. g., in letting the child learn the unpleasantness of being late through being tardy rather than through admonition. There is no question that both parents and teach-ers are correct in their evaluation of the situation. The child has no sense of responsibility and no self-discipline. But these are symptoms, just as his school behavior is a symptom, of an unconscious neurotic conflict, and until this conflict is understood and treated to a successful solution the symptoms will continue.

What is this conflict? The first point that strikes everyone about these children is that they act as if they had no ambition to learn and be suc-cessful in their present and future life, to be grown up and take responsi-bility for their daily lives and to be self-confident. In fact they act not as if they had no ambition but as if their ambition was to do the oppo-site. It is not that they do not have ambition but that their ambition is directed toward doing poorly rather than doing well. As one child said to us, "I see the better and do the worse." They seem to have placed an inhibition on their ability successfully to accomplish the ambitions of the ordinary American adolescent and to have directed their ambitional energy to accomplish successfully the opposite. Although they try as hard as they can *not* to be successful their intellectual capacity often is so great that it nullifies part of their efforts. Through this procedure they are able to gratify two impulses of which they usually are unconscious: to express their spite at their mother's (and sometimes their father's) nagging, and to attract their mother's punitive attention to themselves.

In some instances these two desires are kept unconscious simply be-cause the child has displaced the spite and the desire for attention from the mother onto the teacher. As one boy said, "If the teachers criticize me I will refuse to do any work for them." Here the spite element was conscious but since the teachers really were not critical of him, by his behavior he was able to remain unconscious of the fact that his mother was the critical person. Another boy remarked that he would do no work for the teacher because she favored the other pupils. Therefore he was aware of his desire for her attention, but by thinking as he did he was able to be unaware that it was his mother's attention he craved. This desire for attention really is directed toward the mother, as is also the spiteful reaction. The latter is an expression of rage at her. (Usually the child is unaware of his rage at his mother, but the awareness is so close to consciousness that it does not take much time or skill to bring it to consciousness.) He may feel enraged at her because of her constant and irritating nagging or because he recognizes that she does not love him, and often he is correct in his judgment. We have found in our cases that the mother either has rejected the boy—or the father the girl—or has overprotected him because she has felt guilty about her dislike for him. In many of these cases the child had had a prolonged serious illness or a period during which he had in quick succession a number of less serious illnesses. During these illnesses his mother gave him a great deal of attention, often of a physical type, which he enjoyed very much. When he recovered she ceased her attentions because in reality they were no longer necessary. The child resented this behavior and became enraged at her. He may act as if he felt rage but this rage really is an expression of a sadistic form of love—the type of love that finds gratification *only* if the loved object is hurt.

In all of these instances the child does not love his mother with the mature tenderness of the adolescent. Instead his love is either extremely ambivalent, as in the first three instances cited, or has regressed to the type of love natural to the anal-sadistic period of development because he has become frightened or guilty about it, as in the last-mentioned instance. His active love relationship with his mother is either ambivalent or sadistic. If he is to be successful in carrying out the ambitions of the adult he must be an active person. If he is active he will hurt or destroy the mother whom he loves. If he does this he will feel very guilty. In order to avoid this sense of guilt it is better for him to inhibit all his activity. Therefore he has to inhibit his ambitions to be successful in school.

It is plain that he desires his mother's attention since he deliberately does the very things he knows will produce her anger and scolding; i. e., he tries to establish a passive receptive relationship with her. In this relationship he receives attention, coupled with her anger and the pain inflicted by her. Ordinarily we would expect that the pain and her anger would cause him to change his behavior, but they do not. Indeed often he provokes a critical reaction from other adults, particularly his teachers, and although he complains similarly about their attitude he does nothing to change his own behavior which has produced it. He desires the attention so much that he is willing to put up with associated painful feelings. The pain still is painful, so in order to avoid the pain he endeavors to extract pleasure from it. He is able to do this by enhancing the masochistic attitude that brought him gratification during his anal-sadistic phase of development. Although he is conscious of his wish to be placed in a military school where firm discipline would correct the faults he sees in his character, he revolts consciously against any awareness of his masochistic attitude because it hurts his pride. It appears in his behavior but his conscious mind repudiates the idea that his actions have this meaning. His ambition therefore becomes directed toward the gratification of his passive receptive desires, with the result that he can no longer be successful actively. His school progress ceases and he does not take responsibility for his daily life.

The history of these children is interesting. During the latent period they do creditable schoolwork but are tormented day and night by anxieties and phobias. They lie awake at night in terror of the skeleton that will come out of the closet, of the bear under the bed, of the ghost that will ascend the stairs. These symptoms, which they keep to themselves except when they become very disturbing, continue throughout the latent period until the beginning of adolescence. Then they stop, either suddenly, due to an effort of will, or gradually for no apparent reason. As the anxiety symptoms cease or lessen the schoolwork becomes poorer and poorer. The character defects of which the parents and teachers complain therefore are symptoms that have developed to replace the anxieties.

The underlying conflict in these cases of school difficulty therefore is the same as that which underlies a phobia. We have noted that the preadolescent solution for the problem was a phobia. During the phobia the child's school progress was good. When the phobia came to an end the educational difficulty developed. In the cases we have seen the conflict resulted from an undue attachment to the parent of the opposite sex and an inability to solve adequately the resultant ambivalence to the parent of the same sex. In many of these cases the parent of the same sex is either overly proud and foolishly fond of the child or is indifferent and withdrawn, either as a result of the occupation followed or because of some emotional difficulty of his own. As a consequence the child has great difficulty in allowing himself to feel hostile toward this parent, who is either very kindly or very unimportant, and so has to repress his hostility, developing a strong sense of guilt in order to keep it repressed. As long as the child can project the problem—i. e., as long as the phobic objects carry his conflicting feelings—he feels relatively safe from his problem. When the phobic mechanism fails because his ego dislikes the pain of the constant feelings of anxiety he has to adopt a new method of defense against the unsolved problem of the conflicting love and hate for the parent of the same sex.

To grow up, to develop skills that later will make for vocational success, to be ambitious and work toward vocational fulfillment, is to utilize aggressive desires about which the child feels guilty. Therefore it is better to inhibit them. This is done by changing the ambitions and the skills needful to accomplish them into their opposite, i. e., into an apparent absence of ambition and an incapacity for accomplishment. More basically this requires that all activity be changed into its opposite—passivity. To please the parent of the opposite sex is equivalent to an expression of love. This must not be expressed as such. The attitude, instead, must be one of *apparent* hostility—then there will be no feeling of guilt about the love. This apparent hostility, however, can only be maintained by partially repressing the love. The repressed love joins with the tendency to be passive rather than active and appears as a masochistic attitude which assuages the sense of guilt. The impression that the entire difficulty lies in the relationship with the parent of the opposite sex skillfully masks the true problem—the relationship with the parent of the same sex. So skillfully is this done that the child is really unconscious that such a problem exists.

We have tried to make clear that the renunciation of the phobic mechanism causes the ego to recoil from the problem which it feels too weak to solve. As a result of the recoil a regression takes place and a slow and insidious deformation of character results (which could not occur if the phobic mechanism were retained). This deformation affects directly the main acts of the individual's life—in the adolescent appearing most markedly in the school life. (In the adult it appears in the vocation.) Once the ego has adopted the mechanisms of defense which deform the character the process does not remain stationary but continues with more and more distortions.

The purpose of education is to train the ego in skills that will enable it to deal with the realities of life. The more complex the culture, the more skills and the more training for each skill are required. In our culture we tend to regard the struggle for personal existence as of utmost importance and spend years training the child in methods of earning a living. We have to do so because the degree of knowledge required for any particular occupation is great, and if the individual is to be successful he must acquire as much of this knowledge as possible. He must also know a great deal about society—its social organization, present structure and historical background. On the other hand we seem to feel that the individual should be able without much help to acquire knowledge of his own inner life and impulses, to understand them and to learn to use them automatically. In fact we act as if we preferred that the individual think and learn about the former group of skills to the exclusion of the latter.

One of us recently had the opportunity to listen to a sermon given to college students. The preacher encouraged his audience to set up ideals for themselves and to try to attain them. These ideals were a positive appeal to follow courses of action whose tendency would be toward self-control and self-denial. The speaker recognized that anyone following his advice would be very saintly and admitted that there was something unnatural about saintliness, but he extricated himself from the dilemma by endeavoring to prove that it was possible to be saintly and at the same time natural. In short his thesis was that his audience must learn to restrict and to frustrate their inner impulses in daily life. He made no attempt to urge his hearers to learn about the nature of these impulses or how they might be gratified through socially acceptable methods of expression. Instead he encouraged them not even to think about them but rather to pay attention to other things, saying there would be rewards and benefits to be received from following his advice.

Though the sermon was of a religious nature, the point of view is found in all education. Glover says education tells the child, "We want you to think about this group of concepts and concern yourself with performing this group of actions." We encourage him to follow our advice, but implied in the advice is the statement, though we do not add it explicitly, "We do *not* want you to think about this other group of concepts or to concern yourself with performing this other group of actions." We say to the adolescent, "You must think hard and work hard in learning your schoolwork." This statement really implies, "You must *not* think hard or work hard in learning how to get along with people of the opposite sex or how to lead an adequate sexual life." Osler makes such a definite statement. He says that the medical student and the young doctor should put their emotions on ice, for a young man married is a young man marred.

Children understand that this implication exists in their parents' and teachers' emphasis upon education and often make use of it as a repressive measure against their inner impulses. One boy, after being punished for some childish sexual curiosity, decided that he never again could allow himself to have any physical feelings—such as had produced trouble for him. Instead he would approach every situation through the use of his intelligence, i. e., through the development of his intellectual skills. An adolescent girl who feared to compete with her sister (who had many boy friends and was not overly interested in educational matters) decided that she would solve the jealousy situation by giving up any interest in boys and devote herself entirely to her education, in short, by behavior exactly the opposite of her sister's. These children therefore fell back on the dichotomy, which is found in education, between learning and the gratification of inner needs and decided to make it even greater than it is in our culture, in order to protect themselves from the dangers they perceived in being human beings. Unfortunately the plan does not work. The dangers that they perceive might occur if they try to satisfy their inner desires now become displaced onto the opposite (i. e., the educational process) and they do poorly in their schoolwork and in the use of their intellectual faculties.

Without treatment the prognosis in these cases is extremely poor, for each step in character deformation serves as a temporary level of adjustment which produces a relief of tension for the time being only to break down under its own strain—which breakdown is dealt with again by a further character deformity. These temporary reliefs lull to sleep the individual's perception of his danger (i. e., they reduce his anxiety) and perhaps it is only as he approaches middle age that he perceives that his life has not produced the same degree of happiness and success as has his peers'. In the face of this knowledge he becomes depressed and discouraged, and rightly so, because his rehabilitation at this time is extremely difficult, and even if it is successful he has little real future to look forward to. This type of educational disability is a grave condition and should not be treated lightly nor subjected to half measures. Psychoanalysis is called for.

We have discussed this type of educational disability first because it is a type to which not enough attention has been paid in the literature available to most physicians and teachers, and because it furnishes such a baffling problem even to the experienced psychiatrist. Although we have delineated it from the standpoint of one symptom—the scholastic progress—its psychopathology is closely allied to those of certain other types of "bad" characters one sees in adolescents.

Educational Problems Associated with Intellectual Capacity

There are a number of types of educational disabilities that occur in adolescence but are not peculiar to it. We need not do more than mention that a frequent cause of school difficulty is due to the fact that the child is not graded according to his intellectual capacity. If his level of intelligence is different from that of the class—whether it be higher or lower is immaterial—he does not have the pleasure of success resulting from his efforts, or the pleasure of having to put effort into attaining success. As a result he works less and less hard; he becomes annoyed because to him other children receive preferential treatment, i. e., they get higher grades, and this annoyance causes a feeling of hostility toward them and the teachers, which in some instances reaches the height of feeling that he is being persecuted. He expresses his hostile feeling in his behavior, which then gets him into trouble and often results in a real feeling of dislike on the part of the other children and the teachers. This makes him more hostile and the vicious circle of hostility and counter-hostility develops.

Instead of becoming openly hostile he may try to get away from the irritating situation by truancy. If he goes by himself he gets into trouble with the school authorities and with his parents, to whom the school complains. If he goes with other children the same results occur, but in addition he may become associated with a gang of delinquents and himself become one. (This result obtains more frequently in children with a low intelligence level. We discussed this problem earlier under the caption "delinquency because of intellectual retardation"; see page 265.) If he does not withdraw himself physically he may do so psychically, i. e., sit in the classroom and daydream instead of attending to his work. From the psychiatric standpoint this last-mentioned reaction is more likely to result in serious maladjustment than the other two, in which the maladjustment is an open conflict between the individual and society.

The treatment for these cases is a proper regrading. In the ordinary school setup this would mean that the child would be placed with much younger or much older children, where he would feel a difference in physical size and be treated differently by the other children than if he were with his peers. What he needs is to be placed in a special class or in a school where there are no actual grades—i. e., a good progressive school.

In our opinion entrance to school should be preceded not only by a thorough physical examination but also by an estimation of the intellectual capacity, and ideally of the emotional status, of the child. If his intellectual level is considerably less than the average he should be placed in a special class for backward children. The children in this class should have a careful estimation of all their intellectual capabilities and assets made, and their educational life planned on the results of this estimation. Children whose intellectual capacity is much above the average should be placed either in a special class for intellectually advanced children or in a good progressive school.

In either situation more attention should be given to helping the child in his social and emotional adjustments and in his physical and manual development than to the process of scholastic achievement. Ordinarily a child with a very high intelligence level tends to progress through school too fast. He may even graduate from high school at the age of fourteen or fifteen, which is too young to enter college, where he will be unwelcome in the social and recreational activities. With the school program adjusted to his total needs—physical, social, recreational and emotional as well as intellectual—these unnecessary and painful difficulties of adjustment could be avoided. (It was to avoid the tendency to have bright children put all their efforts into intellectual accomplishments that Cecil Rhodes wisely laid down the requirements he did for selecting Rhodes scholars.)

If the child is gifted, and also exceptionally gifted along one particular line such as music, an added difficulty arises, for the parents and other interested adults often desire that the exceptional skill be highly developed and forget the other needs of the child. This is perhaps the reason why so many great musicians and other artists are so often emotionally maladjusted individuals. It should be the care of those who are entrusted with the education of a genius to see that all his needs are met, and not just those of his talent. Sometimes we feel that not only should the life of such a child be planned carefully to ensure a well-rounded development of his ego and superego, but that as part of his training he should have a period of psychoanalysis as a really preventive measure against personality unbalance.

Educational Problems Due to Physical Ill Health

Another reason for educational difficulties lies in poor physical health. A child who has uncorrected defective vision or hearing, pain and discomfort due to chronic illness, weakness and lethargy due to avitaminosis, anemia, chronic fatigue or endocrine disorders, or disturbed metabolism cannot perform his school tasks efficiently. In the last 25 years educators and parents have become increasingly aware of this fact and frequent checkups are now the rule rather than the exception. However, the results of the examination of draftees in the Selective Service program indicate that more attention still needs to be paid to the physical health of children.

Educational Problems Due to Parental Attitudes

There are certain parents who deify scholastic achievement as a goal for their children. No other interest or activity of the child meets with their approval, and when he wishes to take part in something else they regard this desire as a sign that he is neglecting his schoolwork. Homework must be completed before he can have recreation. They forget that he has attended school all day, is somewhat fatigued, and that he would do better work if he were allowed a respite until after dinner, particularly since his friends usually have to stay in the house in the evenings. They frown and scold if his school reports are not super excellent, although he really may be contributing much to the social and recreational life of the school. In short, they forget the old adage that all work and no play makes Jack a dull boy. The child, weary from the unreasonable need to use his intelligence and resentful because so many of his other needs are being frustrated, balks. His schoolwork becomes poorer, the parents become more stringent in their desires and a conflict between child and parents develops. This conflict upsets him and makes him less capable than he was before. Here it is the parents and their attitude toward the child and his education that need treatment rather than the child. If their attitude cannot be made more reasonable, it is often a good solution to send the child to boarding school.

Educational Problems Due to Worry

Every human being realizes that he cannot do good work if he is worried or unhappy. It is true that some people plunge into work in order to avoid their worries, but unless the actual working is able to remove the cause of the worry, the work output is usually deficient. Children usually have two sources of worry: sexual matters and the family situation.

If a child—particularly an adolescent—begins rather rapidly to slow up in his school progress, it is advisable to try to find out whether he is worried about his sexual life, i. e., about the harm he may be doing himself by some sexual practice such as masturbation. If he can be relieved of this worry—as he should be—his schoolwork will improve. Or he may be worried and frightened about what he has heard about the facts of sexuality. For example, a girl either in the latent period or in adolescence may have heard a particularly gory description of the process of childbirth. She believes what she has heard and, having a girl's wish to bear children, is frightened and disturbed at the prospect ahead of her. She sits in the classroom ruminating over the problem and has neither eyes nor ears for her work. In her case the schoolwork will improve when the worry has been removed.

It must be mentioned that we do not mean that the adult should come to the child and say, "Your school report is the result of your being worried about sexual matters. Tell me and I will straighten the matter out for you," or, "Sit down and I'll give you some sex instruction." We mean that when the child shows a poor school record it should be borne in mind by the adult who is investigating the causes that such worries may be responsible and recommend that the child might profit by a series of sessions with a psychiatrist.

We have seen many children whose poor school progress was the result of worries about the family situation. We have known cases where it was impossible for the child even to sit in school because he was so disturbed by the problem as to whether when he got home from school he would find that his parents had separated and that one or the other had left permanently. Even though the child may not be so upset that he has to stay away from school—this, by the way, is a not uncommon cause of truancy—he cannot attend to his schoolwork with any degree of efficiency when his mind is so engrossed in the trouble at home. One girl went into an examination, suddenly had the thought "my father has killed my mother," and had to go home and reassure herself. A little girl who was devoted to her father heard that he had enlisted, and from that time on her schoolwork became poor because she spent her time grieving over his departure. It would have been better had she grieved openly, but her parents had tried to hide the facts about the father's military service lest it disturb her, and since she had heard a secret she could not admit openly that she felt grief. Too, when the cause of a child's worry is discord between the parents or difficulties between the parents and the other siblings the child dare not give open evidence of worry because in such homes direct and honest statements about facts are received with disfavor. Worry due to this cause affects the schoolwork of children in the latent period to a much greater degree than it does that of adolescents because the former are more helpless and really need adults to care for them more than do the latter. The older the adolescent the less power do these influences have.

Educational Problems Due to Nostalgia

Another cause of poor schoolwork among adolescents, particularly in America, is a result of admission to boarding school. Often when a child first enters boarding school his schoolwork is poor. He seems rather confused and in a daze about it. (There have been reports recently of a similar condition arising among men in the armed forces.) When questioned they state that they do not feel lonely away from home, that they like the place where they are and are interested in what is going on, giving the examiner the impression of having adjusted excellently to the change from home. When questioned more intensively, however, it is found that they are preoccupied by thoughts of home, but have made themselves unaware of the feelings attached to these thoughts. In short, these children are homesick but are not aware of it. When they are made aware of the difficulty and allow themselves to feel and express their homesickness their work improves. This condition is known technically as cryptic nostalgia.

The School's Responsibility

For the sake of completeness we mention again the fact that the poor schoolwork done by some children is the result of the antagonistic attitude of the teacher. Treatment must be applied to the teacher's attitude or the children must be changed to a new and more sympathetic teacher.

We are of the opinion that when a child shows an educational difficulty the attitude of his teacher, his physical condition, his intellectual status, the attitudes and emotional conditions within his home, and his total personality should be investigated. It is only on the results of such an investigation that a valid diagnosis can be made and treatment instituted. We believe that all public- and private-school systems should have the opportunity to consult with physicians, psychologists and psychiatrists about the problems shown by their pupils. In fact we would go so far as to say that all school systems should have on their permanent staff a team composed of one or more physicians, psychologists and psychiatrists as an essential part of the educational setup. The school system *cannot* function efficiently if one or more of these disciplines is omitted. This applies to all schools, from the nursery school up to the university and professional school. The considered judgment of this team should be adhered to regardless of the opinion of some educator who after all is a layman in these professional fields.

BIBLIOGRAPHY FOR CHAPTER XI

Glover, Edward, "The Unconscious Function of Education," *International Journal of Psychoanalysis* 18, 1937, 190.

Chapter XII

WORK AND MARRIAGE

The Place of Work in Emotional Satisfaction

A GREAT many people go to work at the end of adolescence or early in their twenties and undergo a varying amount of anxiety in their effort to adjust to the new routine. The job may take them away from home and they become homesick, which is an anxiety condition. They may be poor mixers and get on badly with their fellow workers. The people they have to work with do not seem to be as kind as the family atmosphere or as the neighborhood they grew up in, and they sense a hostility and lack of acceptance in the new environment. When that test comes, the individual is in the position of the new boy in school whose classmates tease him to find out whether or not he is a good sport. If the boy meets the test, he is taken into the group; if he does not, his schoolmates make life rather difficult for him.

The same thing usually occurs to the individual at twenty-one as occurred to him at four or five when he went to school. A newcomer in the office or factory has to prove himself. Some people are aware of the fact that they are on trial and are so nicely balanced that they can meet people with a smile, co-operate on the first request, show friendliness and goodwill and fit in. Such personalities are taken in right away. Other people, a little more sensitive and a little more suspicious, on the second, third or fourth day will sense that they are being tested and will have to take flight from it. They just do not have any personality tools with which to meet the test that the environment makes and they withdraw. They are too serious. They cannot laugh when a joke is played upon them. Those in the group sense that such a person is not "one of them." They tend to exclude him and he tends to exclude himself and does not like the place. He wakes up in the morning thinking, "Have I got to go down there again where they do not like me, where they may find fault with me?" Even if such a person succeeds tolerably well with co-workers, he may find it difficult to take orders from the boss or superintendent. He feels resentful toward him and a kind of battle springs up between him and his superior.

These restrictions and rigidities in the personality stir up anxiety and often result in a person's going from job to job, trying to find something he likes. He becomes a floater, one who never makes good anywhere, who never stays long enough to find himself, to do himself or the organization any good. Or he stays on the job, in which case the anxiety upsets his stomach, or he has palpitation of the heart, or colitis, or some symptom or combination of symptoms that necessitates medical attention. (The history of a person's illness should include these environmental considerations.) Leaving the parental roof and going to work are more of a strain than some individuals can bear and are enough to make them ill. The vulnerability of people in this regard varies. One who breaks down on his first job is more vulnerable than another who does so after working ten years, for instance, when some crisis upsets his emotional equilibrium. It is useless to think that "others can stand it, why shouldn't he?" The point is he is *not* standing it. Doctors should recognize the possibility of vulnerability to work adjustment in order to be in the best position to help a patient who falls neurotically sick at this time.

A young man of twenty-two entered the hospital for severe headaches for which no organic cause could be found. When he was studied psychologically it was found that he was an only child who lived a great deal by himself both during grade school and high school. He had only one good friend, who had recently moved to a distant city. After leaving high school, he took a course in radio manufacture; just as he was about to go to work, his father died. This left him to be the support of his mother. He had never had any friendships of any length or depth with the opposite sex, never having been encouraged to do so by his parents. When he went to work he seemed unable to make friends with his fellow workers. He remained aloof, found his work monotonous and had no social life in the evening, and finally became quite bored with his activities. It was in this setting that his headaches began, which seemed to symbolize the commonly heard statement, "This job is a headache."

Just as the events in the early life period add to personality development and cause it to expand, so middle adult life can have a similar effect upon the individual's makeup. Young people may feel that all the excitement of living occurs in youth. However, middle life can be both an exciting and critical period. Some people conduct their lives in such a way as to make life richer and more meaningful all the time; while others follow a procedure of living that tends to impoverish them emotionally, ideationally and even economically.

Adjustment to Work

Adjustment to work is one of the important practical problems of adult life. Many people fail, or at least undergo a decline, in their careers in middle life because they lack the aggression with which to make decisions and meet responsibilities or are illogical in their approach to their work. Some people have an intuitive feeling for saying the right thing at the right time on the job and for taking advantage of opportunities, while others seem to lack this astute intuition and thereby miss being successful, even though they are regarded as charming persons by their friends. An illustration of this is the case of a thirty-nine-year-old man who became discouraged over his progress, began to feel tired, was sleeping poorly and instead of advancing in his business suffered two minor emotional depressions in a period of four years. He had been sent by an indulgent father to the best schools but had never been required to take any responsibility in his early life. His father was a capable man who ran everything himself, never giving the son any practice in managing a situation or allowing him to share any responsibilities. As a result when the son had to assume responsibility he was anxious about it and did not do well. One of his colleagues said, "X is a very fine fellow. He endears himself to everyone with whom he comes in contact but when he is given a responsibility and has to make a decision he drives us all crazy. Recently X had to decide whether to add a necessary piece of machinery to our plant. It was important to make the decision right away yet X let it drag on for two weeks while he paced the office, smoked cigarettes and slept poorly at night; finally we had to get together and make the decision for him. Right now he has three opportunities pending where he ought to get in touch with clients. He puts it off from day to day on a flimsy excuse. If he does not improve we will have to ease him out of the business. We like him but we cannot stand this degree of inefficiency indefinitely."

A man who behaves himself thus in regard to his work has suffered many of the crises of life which we have been discussing in previous chapters. Some of the anxiety felt by this man goes back to early childhood and even at the age of thirty-nine he could not feel important; his

ego was still so weak that he feared whatever he said or d
criticized, and he could not stand criticism. Moreover, he co be
ture himself as a person taking responsibility, leading and c-
others, even people who were willing to be led and directed. g
sonality weaknesses such as these that contribute to the so-called r
breakdowns that come on during middle life to those in various
of life.

Women as well as men suffer in this way. Such was the case o
woman of forty who came for treatment because life had ceased to hav
much meaning for her. She was an unmarried professional woman who
had done good work, who was well-thought-of in her profession but who
had grown discouraged and had begun to question whether life was
worth living. She was one of a family of five whose mother had subtly
engendered the idea that they were better than anyone else. By criticizing the foibles of people outside the home, pointing out their selfishness,
pettiness, and minor aggressions—neglecting to note that these same
people probably had strengths and virtues as well—she implied, "We
are better than that. We would not do that." At the same time that she
played up the vices of others, she played up the virtues of her own family, so that our patient felt intolerant of others and rarely accepting
of them. This influenced her ideas about marriage. She had opportunities to marry, but no man seemed good enough and she let the opportunities pass, apparently hoping that some paragon of virtue and ability
would appear some day to claim her. He never did. As she neared forty
she was without husband or children, had practically no friends, and
was looking ahead to an empty future. Unwittingly she had deprived
herself, and through re-education had to learn what was wrong with
her thinking and feeling.

Satisfactions from Wifehood

The mind might be compared to a provision storehouse where the
stock becomes depleted if it is not replenished. When people do not
give thought to conducting themselves in such a way as to gain prestige
and satisfaction from work and from everyday social life, they very
often reach a point in middle life where they find themselves impoverished. This impoverishment manifests itself by depression of spirits or
in body symptoms (see Chapter XIII for a discussion of neurosis) and
can come to married women as well as to single women because while

...ge has many potentialities for happiness and satisfaction, not ...ne can get out of it what is potentially there—not everyone has ...ersonality equipment to do so.

...ch was the case of a woman who had been brought up in a well-...do family with excellent educational opportunities. The father was a ...sy, important person in the world of finance and the mother was busy ...ith a great many social interests—she was a patron of art and music and had left the training of her children in the hands of governesses and nurses and did not even supervise the quality of the persons she employed for the job. Consequently, this woman had an unhappy childhood and a barren adolescence. At puberty she appeared awkward and the family made fun of her. Apparently none of them expected very much from her socially or otherwise. She did not have a happy social life during adolescence and early in her twenties she married at the first opportunity, hoping through marriage to solve her difficulties. The man she married was a popular and capable person who turned out to be very much like her parents in that his interest went to his work and hobbies, again leaving her deprived. She had three children and a lovely home; she entertained a great deal, but with it all she grew tremendously unhappy, and at thirty-five considered her life a total failure in spite of all the assets she had to make a life with. Her unhappiness was due to the fact that she could never seem to feel wanted or accepted by anyone; nothing she did seemed important to anyone. Neither her children nor her husband appreciated her—the latter lacked warmth, tenderness and affection.

These three examples illustrate how subtly people may fail in middle life, while all the while we may be assuming that things are going well with them. The pictures we create of life and people are not always correct. For instance, we usually believe that children are happy. Many a public speaker has commented upon the happy, smiling faces of children and their gay laughter, of the patter of little feet in the home as though childhood were a universally joyous experience. Of course, some children are happy, but a great many are not. Often the tension in the home from day to day between mother and children is great indeed.

We must not assume that because a man has a job with a large income or because a woman comes from a socially acceptable section of town and has a beautiful home and attractive children that they are necessarily happy, for they may be extremely anxious and unhappy. Middle life provides many occasions for stress and strain which may bring people to the point where they are overwhelmed with discouragement or body symptoms, for when people are unhappy or maladjusted there is often some kind of symptomatology present.

Courtship and Preparation for Marriage

Courtship is to some an emotional strain. Fortunately, it does not affect all people adversely. The dates of adolescence carry little responsibility but the dates of courtship in the twenties or later bring both persons involved closer to marriage and its implications: namely, greater responsibility, the actual beginning of sexual experience and, for the woman, pregnancy and motherhood. If people have not had an opportunity to think these matters over, if they have drifted along with no thought as to the responsibilities of marriage, as they reach the twenties the prospect is frightening and causes anxiety. Men question whether they can earn enough to support a wife and family. Women question whether they can be happily adjusted to living with a man in a sexual relationship, whether they can go through a pregnancy, whether they are able to bring up a child. Even before they get to marriage, courtship brings the realities of marriage close enough to make people anxious rather than happy at this time. Anxiety may cause them to put off setting a date for the marriage, or to postpone the date, or to break the engagement, or it may cause the engaged person to fall ill in a way that will conveniently impede the natural progress into matrimony. Young people who have symptoms in relation to an engagement are already poorly equipped to cope with marriage. Part of the medicine a doctor needs to give them will be in the form of preparation for marriage. Marriage counsel clinics with a staff equipped to lecture on the question of preparation for marriage are established in many cities in the United States, where the responsibilities of marriage, matters of sexual adjustment and contraception are discussed in an effort to help young people understand themselves and the source of the anxiety and problems that often occur in courtship, marriage and parenthood.

Every physician should be well informed and able to give premarital advice and instruction both in the physical and emotional sides of marriage. He *is* such a counselor when he has acquainted himself with the problems of growth and maturity and is willing to see whether the person about to enter marriage has done likewise. He surely can make a physical examination, and many young people today wish to have such an examination. They want to know that they are healthy and to have some ideas as to whether they can function sexually. The woman may want assurance that her physique is one that will readily be able to bear children.

Any concern about sexual functioning can be elicited by asking the man some such questions as: Have you any question about your sexual potency? Has contact with women produced erection? Does the idea of intercourse with a woman cause your erection to disappear? Do you ever feel that masturbation might harm your sexual or procreative power? Such questions frankly and easily put by the doctor should make the prospective bridegroom feel free to discuss any doubts or anxieties that he has. Another question might be: Are you concerned about your technique as a satisfactory lover for your wife-to-be? If so, then it can be explained to him that his desire to kiss, embrace and fondle the woman, culminating in his insertion of the penis into her vagina, is shared by her and that if he can remember this and proceed with it, her anxieties, if she has any, will be greatly helped by his confidence. Two good works on sexual adjustment in marriage may be suggested: *Marriage and Sexual Harmony,* by Oliver M. Butterfield, and *Sane Sex Life and Sane Sex Living,* by H. W. Long.

Women often want assurance that they are genitally "normal"— that they can have intercourse satisfactorily. They have probably heard more or less about the hymen and wonder about its presence or absence, and the implication of either state. The hymen is a fold of mucous membrane just inside the vagina opening, which extends from the sides toward a middle opening of varying size. This mucous membrane may in some cases be thin and easily destroyed and little of it present at the time of marriage. In others, however, it is thicker and tougher, and may persist until marriage and offer some impediment to the entry of the penis. If the physician feels that with gentle but firm pressure it will not yield at the onset of attempted intercourse, he should tell the woman so and suggest manual or instrumental stretching or cutting with scissors in the office. Depending upon the condition of the hymen, there may or may not be bleeding with the first intercourse. Few husbands insist any more upon bleeding with the first intercourse as an evidence of virginity, but of course any attempt before marriage to prepare for avoidance of some of the anxieties and frustrations of sexual adjustments should keep in mind the possible attitudes of both parties.

As in the case of the man, the woman also can be asked certain questions, around which some healthy thinking is necessary in order to dispel those false notions that threaten sexual harmony: Do you fear pain with intercourse? Do you feel that intercourse is in any way humiliating and degrading? Do you feel ashamed of being exposed so intimately with a man? Do you feel ashamed to assume the necessary position for intercourse with your legs apart and your knees flexed? Are you afraid that either you will or that you will not have orgasm? Are you afraid your husband will think you a "bad woman" if you participate too actively either physically or emotionally in the sex act?

These questions and others help the woman to see what attitudes might hinder their enjoying their sexual relations and by the very asking of them, even without the reassurance he can give, the physician is helping her greatly by being able to discuss a natural everyday matter naturally and wholesomely. A doctor who counsels in marriage can in an hour's time save a married couple hours of worry and unhappiness by giving information and dispelling anxieties.

The woman, and oftentimes both parties, is interested in spacing the children properly in order to preserve the wife's health and that of the children, and in order to be in a position economically to give the children the proper advantages. Every doctor should be familiar with contraceptive procedures and be able to discuss them with his patient whether he uses them or not. The time has come when contraception has a high degree of safety and simplicity, and the proper use of contraceptives is a matter of the highest importance for physical and mental health. Hence any physician has the obligation to his profession and to humanity to know the subject of contraception and to present its possibilities to his patients whether his religion allows its application by him or not.

These are some of the more important points in regard to preparation for marriage. Marriage and child rearing are two of the most important fields of human relations, and yet up to the present time they are the least prepared-for human activities. Less is said about them in the home, in the school, in the university, than about any other subject of half their importance—and all because of shame and prudery. We will never have a much better world until we have happier marriages, happier homes, happier and more emotionally stable children. The doctor of today has a contribution to make to social health as well as to individual personal health.

Adjustment in Marriage

Human adjustment in marriage often causes great difficulty. The choice of a mate and adjustment to marriage are a test of maturity which a great many people cannot meet. In some marriages one or the other of the marital partners is an unusually long-suffering person and the marriage continues with a surface smoothness, with little of the underneath difficulty seen or noticed by the outsider. Such a marriage does not break up, nor is it known as a faulty marriage, but it is one in which one party has to endure a great deal. There are some married people who seem to manage tolerably well but who are actually not mature people; their adjustment causes a great deal of strain upon the children, who suffer as a result of their immaturity and neurotic attitudes which are worked out on the children. We should not just deplore our high divorce rate and damn people who cannot stay in marriage. We believe that the whole question of marriage needs closer scrutiny and that divorce and separation are symptoms of personality disturbance in our social life and, therefore, that we need to investigate why people cannot live together in marriage instead of merely taking a condemnatory or moralistic attitude toward it.

People should come to marriage with a knowledge of human nature, having successfully lived through some of the crises that occur in the various phases of personality development, and with a decent sexual education because sexual adjustment is important to marital happiness. However, sexual adjustment is not a part of living standing entirely by itself, since a mature person usually is able to adapt sexually to another person. It is not a matter of pure accident that people find a compatible sexual adjustment in marriage; good sexual adjustment is related to their total personality growth. People should come to marriage with a realistic attitude rather than a sophisticated one which they have gleaned from the movies. Everyday life cannot be lived constantly the way Myrna Loy and William Powell live it in their gracefully acted screen comedies.

It is better for young people to realize that two cannot live as cheaply as one, that groceries and clothes cost money, and that the rent has to be paid. If they intend to have children, they should realize that pregnancy takes nine months, in spite of the fact that many other things in this world have speeded up, and that during that time her figure will be changed and some of their mutual activities will have to be curtailed, especially toward the end of the pregnancy. They should realize that babies cry and need a great deal of attention. From the time a young couple starts raising a family until the children are independent, they will have to devote considerable time and attention to their development.

Until married people are emotionally ready to give their interest to this responsibility they should learn about contraception and practice it, rather than bring children into the world to be neglected, abused, grudgingly given love and education and raised to adulthood and sent out into the world with hatred, feelings of inferiority, dependency upon others, unequipped to be of any use to themselves or others. If adolescents were helped to more wholesome contacts, instead of adjured to stay away from each other, they would have more "good times" and thus be more willing to have their children early in marriage and grow up with them. Marriage is a reality and contains day-to-day problems which should be considered by young people before they marry. It is useless for a couple to think they can be avoided.

It is wrong for any two mature young people to enter marriage feeling they are going to live together indefinitely like two peanuts in a shell and pay no attention to the rest of the world. No matter how interested they are in each other, they will eventually tire of each other's company somewhat and will have to live with the rest of the world—and they should be willing and able to do so without jealousy. Marriage is a great test of whether the human being can love someone other than himself; that is, whether he can be considerate of another person. If marriage is going to be successful at all, it must be an arrangement whereby each member plans to contribute something to the development of the other.

Some men seem to marry with the idea of having a permanent, cheap housekeeper with whom they can occasionally have sexual relations. Though any intelligent woman of spirit will resent this attitude, yet there are many who though aware of such an attitude on the part of the man during the courtship days do not believe what they see and hear. Many people of both sexes are a little more in love with love and romance than they are with the person they want to marry, so that when in their contact with the betrothed they see and hear attitudes, mannerisms and opinions which they dislike, nevertheless close their eyes and ears or imagine the unpleasant side of the person will disappear magically after they have appeared before the clergyman. If it does, a minor miracle has occurred. Some women marry in order to have free board and room for the rest of their lives. With that attitude a woman cannot contribute much to the man or to the children who result from the union.

Attitudes such as these in men and women are bound to result in complaints, friction, dissatisfaction and strife which may lead directly to separation or divorce or, if the marriage continues, to unhappiness, alcoholism or neurotic symptoms or even to actual mental disease. A bad marriage does not often produce mental disease but it can be a contributing cause. Marriage should be an enriching experience for both partners and both should enter it with the idea of contributing to the other person's development. If such is not a strong trend in the minds of both people and the marriage turns out to be a success, they are just lucky young people.

When considering marriage, men and women should have certain goals which they are able to discuss and define and of which they are clearly aware. They should be interested in each other's work, feel respect for each other's contribution to the marriage, and be in full agreement upon the matter of children and whether or not they will have them at all. For when these matters are not discussed and plans not made and when those around them are planning more wisely, the comparison can be a cause of friction and strife. Therefore, young people who are entering marriage should have a rough plan at least, and in spite of occasional accidents, conception can usually be regulated these days. People say that life cannot be planned, that life is too uncertain and that one must drift along from one thing to another. We think that life *can* be planned and *should* be planned, and that most of the people who are successful *do* make plans, even though a few who do not do so get along after a fashion. A great many of these nonplanners are afraid to plan because they fear interference with their plans and they could not stand the blow that fate might give them. They like to be in a position to be able to say, "Well, I did not have my heart set on it. I am not disappointed." They use that attitude as a kind of sedative. People should have more courage than that and frankly discuss plans for marriage.

Married couples should both work together and play together. They may not work in the same factory or in the same office, but each should have his or her work, and each should take an interest in and have respect for the work of the other person. Generally the man expects respect and gets it because, in his masculine pride, he relates his exploits to the little woman in the home and expects her to listen. She knows she had better do so if she is going to keep him in good humor. Yet when she tries to talk about *her* work, or the baby's progress, or a conversation with a neighbor, he grows impatient and frowns and says, "Why do I have to listen to that?"

The male reader who is disconcerted by the fact that there are women who want to leave the home, who do not want to have children and be housewives, can find a great part of the cause in the traditional attitude of the male toward the job of homemaking. If men accorded more prestige and honor to woman's work in the home and gave more appreciation to the efforts that are expended in the care of children, in washing dishes and making beds, women would be more willing to stay home, more willing to consider marriage and child rearing seriously, and not be in such haste to go into the office or factory. Just as most women know that they need to be interested in the man's work, so men need to understand that they should be interested in the woman's work. The work has to be done, and women do it even when they regard it as tedious and monotonous. Wives would look upon homemaking differently if their husbands regarded it more highly. People often follow a monotonous job because the job has a certain prestige attached to it. The job of homemaking can be idealized, and it is up to the man to help the woman do this by taking more interest in her work in the home.

Both men and women need encouragement from each other. Some of the most serious difficulties in marriage are caused by the fact that the wife or husband has forgotten to give encouragement or appreciation to the other and has reached the point where he takes the other for granted. Now, no one likes to be taken for granted indefinitely. Everyone wants to be noticed. A man *is* usually noticed in the shop, factory, business, or professional world, so he in turn should make sure his wife receives attention if he wants to keep her happy and continue thinking that he is a remarkable fellow.

Husbands and wives should play together and not let their common interests wane. When two people marry who do not have common interests in the field of recreation, it is important that they create some; otherwise they will tend to grow apart and lack interest in each other. And it should be pointed out that their recreations should be of a kind they can afford.

Sexual Adjustment in Marriage

The sexual relation in marriage is one of the rewards of maturity. This activity should be a pleasure to both sexes and should be so regarded frankly by each. Much has been said on the art of love and lovemaking. The average human being who has been allowed to think freely on the question of sex, to read and assimilate in his imagination what he has read and to integrate the material with the sensory experiences he has already had in his life, should have no difficulty in lovemaking. If he has failed to accomplish these things, he can, if he encounters difficulty, again seek enlightenment by reading specially written treatises on the subject of sexual adjustment in marriage.

Problems in marriage do not necessarily arise over whether sexual intercourse takes place two or three times a week or once in two weeks, because people's rhythms vary greatly in this sphere. Neither is pleasure in intercourse a question of duration, because some men and women gain satisfaction in two or three minutes, while others require fifteen. The main point is whether sexual relations between husband and wife are mutually satisfying, a process of pleasurable excitement followed by relaxation shared by both. If this does not take place after a period of two or three months, the couple should consult a physician or a psychiatrist or a marriage counselor. If sexual compatibility is possible at all, it is important that it should be achieved as early as possible; otherwise, unfortunate attributes spring up because the longer the difficulty exists, the harder it is to treat. Men and women are almost universally modest and anxious about their sexuality and their ability to gain sexual satisfaction, and therefore reluctant to confess the lack to each other. (We sometimes think this is more true of women than of men.) Each is afraid he will hurt the other's feelings. Thus a woman who does not get satisfaction may pretend she does and make no complaint, feeling it would be immodest to do so. She may go on for some time and not realize her dissatisfaction with this state of affairs. She thinks she is enduring it, but it finds its way into unhappiness or criticism of the husband on some entirely different score. She becomes nagging about something else, dissatisfied with the home or with the marriage because a part of the marriage has disappointed her, and she is bound to feel this dissatisfaction. Thus also a man who does not get satisfaction may keep his feelings to himself and even, after a time, become unfaithful, instead of talking over the problem with his wife or taking it to someone who can help.

Consideration of the partner's interests and a satisfactory sexual adjustment seem to be the greatest difficulties in marriage, and of about equal importance. It is sometimes said that most marriages break up because two people are not sexually mated. We do not think that is true. A great many marriages are unsuccessful and unhappy because the man or the woman cannot be considerate of the partner in dozens of ways besides the sexual relationship, yet these considerations are always related to sexual feeling.

Let us take the example of a couple who visited us. The man came first, complaining about his married life. He told us that his wife was cold, disinterested in his work, stubborn and unsociable. One gained the picture of a very disagreeable woman. Without making any comment we asked to see her because it is never wise for a doctor to commit himself on a marital problem until he has talked to both parties.

We found the wife to be a highly attractive and intelligent woman. She said, "I dare say I am all of those things that my husband says, but let me tell you some things about him and how he appears to me. When we married I had a position and did work in which I was given respect. After marriage my husband was intent on bossing me around, taking me all over the country to follow him in his work, deciding everything without consulting me. I did not want to fight about everything, yet I cannot be happily married if I have to be dominated and pushed and pulled around over this country like a child."

He was a man whose business took him from city to city. He would come home and announce, "We are going to move to Buffalo next week." The wife was supposed to pack everything, arrange for transportation and, when they got to the new town, make friends and see to social engagements. He could never be consulted about anything because he was too busy. He hardly ever took time off or attended social functions. She would arrange bridge games, only to have him call up at the last minute and say he could not get home. He had not been able to put himself in this woman's place and see her struggle, and he gave no cooperation, only complained over her attitude. His own opinion of himself was that he was a very busy, efficient man who managed everything without help. So, surprisingly enough, even though he was the first to seek advice and had said, "Doctor, if anything is wrong with me I want you to tell me," he did not take to criticism kindly at first. Eventually, in the fourth or fifth interview, he began to see the point and to understand better the co-operation necessary to make a well-rounded marriage. He became more amiable and friendly and a more sharing husband.

As with this couple, so there are many others who do not see their blind spots, or who do not make plans before they marry, or who have no goals in marriage but just drift into it, at the same time each expecting too much from the partner. The matter of consideration is more important in a successful marriage and marriage adjustment than the sexual relationship itself, even though we grant that sexual adjustment is extremely important indeed. (For a more detailed discussion of sexual adjustment the reader is referred to Chapter XIV, to the section on Impotence and Frigidity.)

BIBLIOGRAPHY FOR CHAPTER XII

Butterfield, Oliver M., *Marriage and Sexual Harmony*, Emerson, 1938.
Himes, Norman E., *Your Marriage*, Farrar and Rinehart, 1940.
Levy, John, and Munroe, Ruth, *The Happy Family*, Knopf, 1938.
Menninger, Karl A., *Love against Hate*, Harcourt, 1943.
Popenoe, Paul, *Preparing for Marriage*, Institute of Family Relations, 1938.
Suggestions for Planning Budgets, U.S. Dept. of Agriculture, Bureau of General Reading List, Pamphlets.

Chapter XIII

NEUROSES

Up to this point we have been discussing the great number of instinctual impulses for which the human being demands gratification—impulses that are impossible to satisfy in a world that is not at all adapted to their complete gratification and that result in compromises and frustrations as he constantly strives to make adjustment between them and the world around him.

Put in another way, growing up and adapting to life are a difficult process even under the best of circumstances, and some failures in making a satisfactory adjustment are bound to occur. A group of conditions called psychoneuroses represents some of the failures of a satisfactory adjustment between the needs and demands of the human personality and those of the environment, or what we call life itself. These failures in life adaptation are divided into four large groups: (1) psychoneurosis, (2) criminality or delinquency, (3) psychosis, and (4) the so-called neurotic personality (often termed the psychopathic personality) or the fate or destiny neurosis. This latter group of neurotic personalities is not always distinct from the other three; that is, one of these neurotic personalities may be similar to a psychoneurosis, another be close to insanity, or another be in trouble with the law. However, for purposes of classification and study, there is a greater tendency to put these so-called fate-neurosis or neurotic characters together because they form a large group. In common parlance, they are sometimes called misfits in our society.

The psychoneurosis has four subgroups: (a) conversion hysteria, (b) anxiety hysteria, (c) neurasthenia, and (d) compulsion neurosis. As the human being goes through life and meets circumstances that cause him to be afraid or to feel frustrated and angry, an emotion is generated called anxiety. This anxiety acts through the autonomic nervous system and causes dysfunction of certain organs or groups of organs. Everyone is aware that when he is unduly apprehensive he may have palpitation of the heart, sweating, digestive disturbances or, possibly, urinary disturbances. One or more of these phenomena are common to everyone at some time or other, at least in a mild degree, and are the result of anxiety exerting its force through the autonomic nervous system. They have been well described and known to us for a long time through the work of various experimental physiologists.

CONVERSION HYSTERIA

Instead of experiencing the phenomenon of anxiety in any great quantity at any one time, psychoneurotic people may react through the phenomenon of *regression*. When a human being has to face a situation that is difficult, painful or distressing, he tends to regress to a mode of behavior he has known before. There are also occasions when the adult human being wants to return to childhood and does so in periods of relaxation, such as in games, play, and lovemaking, and it is right for him to have these outlets. However, a great many people sometimes feel a strong impulse toward childish behavior quite aside from recreation or play, in which case symptoms arise in which the body as a whole, or as a part, behaves as it did in childhood.

We will illustrate this reaction by a discussion of a case of conversion hysteria. (The symptoms of conversion hysteria can occur in any one of five different spheres—that of motor activity, sensory activity, vasomotor activity, visceral activity or psychic activity.) A girl of twenty-two working as a domestic was at her place of employment one day. Her husband entered and demanded that she give him some money. She demurred, whereupon he struck her upon the right side of the face. She still refused and then he struck her again on the other side. She fell down in a heap and was unable to get up. He walked out and left her. Her employer came home and found her lying on the floor, sobbing convulsively and unable to stand and support herself. She was taken home where she remained in this state for more than five weeks when psychiatric treatment was begun. During this time she wept and sobbed convulsively, slept poorly, had little appetite and had to be helped to feed herself. When she finally sought psychiatric treatment she had to be brought in a taxicab and carried by two people. The following history was elicited from the patient and her stepmother.

She had been a healthy baby whose mother died when she was six months old, when she passed into the care of an aunt who seemed in no way interested in her and who actually beat her on many occasions for trivial offenses. The result was that she cried a great deal and because of this was very unpopular with her brothers and sisters who teased her and called her crybaby. As might be expected, when she began school she did not do well. She was afraid of the teacher and of the other children, who found her an excellent butt for their teasing. She seemed to have been saved from complete emotional failure in school by the fact that she was attractive in appearance and paid a great deal of attention to her clothes, for which reasons her classmates tended to forgive her and find her acceptable to some degree. Often when asked to recite she would "seem too paralyzed to do anything." At the age of seven her father married again. She found her stepmother a satisfactory though never a completely understanding person. She took good care of the home and the children in physical ways, and the cruelties that had been practiced by the aunt ceased.

Because the girl paid so much attention to her appearance, implications were made by her older sisters and her relatives that she would probably turn out to be a prostitute. Only her father occasionally stood up for her and called her his "nice girl." She managed to finish high school and then went into domestic service. The family's implications that she would probably end up a sexual delinquent made her suppress her sexual curiosity and feelings, and after a few years of service she accepted the first offer of marriage that came her way. The husband proved to be a rather immature person with little understanding of the meaning of home and family formation. He wanted to dress well, to have a new automobile frequently and to spend his time in drinking at parties. She, on the other hand, wanted a home, children and a quiet life. With these differences in their outlook there were frequent arguments. She tried to save her money, and he insisted upon spending it. A point was reached when the thought of his coming home made her feel "bad all over." She said, "I used to dread meeting him or having him come around, so I used to stay at my work more and more and go home less and less. When I knew I had to meet him I got all tight inside."

Her capacity for sexual pleasure had been weak in the beginning of the marriage and had finally ended in complete frigidity. In marrying him she had brought upon herself some of the same cruelty and lack of consideration that had been so much a part of her childhood. On the day that he beat her she regressed into the same state of sobbing, crying and physical weakness that had characterized her childhood existence with her aunt. (This sudden onset of a rather dramatic symptom picture is characteristic of conversion hysteria.) She remained in this state while in her own home, where she was overcome by memories of the past as well as memories of her recent life with her cruel husband.

When she came for treatment we showed her the relation between the experience and the symptoms. We pointed out that she could energize her limbs and that she could gain control of her convulsive sobbing if she could cease to feel so much enveloped in this aura of unkindness and danger of punishment. We told her that unpleasant emotions can cause various parts of the body to function perversely and that we had communicated with her husband and would see that he did not reappear to treat her in this manner again. We encouraged her to try to walk so that she could go back to her work where she was fond of her employer and the family. She was willing to make some attempt, which we appreciated highly, and after the second visit she was able to come for treatment on the trolley car accompanied by a younger sister. We encouraged her to talk about her unhappy childhood and thus ventilate some of the emotions connected with her unhappy experiences of that time. We opened up the question of whether she might have to seek separation or divorce from this husband with whom she seemed so completely incompatible. By opening up possibilities of escape from the unpleasant stimuli that had brought on her illness, the patient improved steadily and in two weeks' time was completely symptom free and back again on the job.

In this case both voluntary and involuntary musculature were involved. In some cases numbness of the skin may be present, blindness, deafness or difficulty in speech. Severe gastrointestinal upsets with either vomiting or diarrhea or both may be hysterial in origin. A very common form of conversion hysteria is amnesia. Fainting is likewise a vasomotor phenomenon and is a way of meeting an unpleasant situation, such as an accident, unpleasant odors or an unpleasant event. The autonomic nervous system responds to this particular shock by concentrating blood in the splanchnic area and withdrawing it from the peripheral areas such as the brain, resulting in unconsciousness. While unconscious the fainting person escapes from the unpleasant situation and does not have to deal with it. This is a special way of being anesthetic to it, just as a patient may develop anesthesia of one-half of the body or one-half of the limbs. Through fainting he becomes anesthetic all over and escapes completely for the time being. Fainting is a dramatic kind of escape and calls people's attention to the person. When he regains consciousness he is treated well, and usually he does not have to return to the unpleasant situation that caused the fainting.

Amnesia is a fairly common hysterical phenomenon. Hardly a day goes by in any large city when at least one amnesic victim does not come to the police station stating that he does not know who he is or where he comes from or what he has been doing. In amnesia, the victim is able to dissociate the events within a certain period of time from the rest of his mind. He is able to segregate a certain number of ideas and emotions from the rest of his mind and for the time being the remainder of his mind cannot control the split-off ideas or feelings. He forgets who he is and what he has been doing for a variable period of time, which may be a few hours or several days or weeks or even months.

In the psychic sphere we have the hysterical phenomena of the dual personality and the multiple personality, which are less common than amnesia. Multiple personalities are so rare that they seldom occur except in literature. Dr. Jekyll and Mr. Hyde provide the well-known fictional example of the dual personality. The dual personality shows a complete change from time to time. As in Dr. Jekyll the individual may be one personality during the day and another at night, or he may show one personality for a period of weeks and then change and be completely different and completely out of touch with his other characteristics.

A truck driver came to the hospital suffering from amnesia. He lived two hundred miles away where he had had an accident. A suit had been brought against him, and in spite of the fact that he was driving for a corporation, he lost because of some technicality and a large proportion of his wages was to be taken from his pay over a long period of time. This situation occurred just at the time he was having trouble with his wife who was demanding more money from him. He saw that the results of the suit were only going to make matters worse, and that he was going to be censored when he got home because of his reduced income. He remembered walking out of the courthouse and down the steps. From there on he lost his memory for two days. The next thing he knew he was in the hospital not knowing what had occurred in those two days. It was some time before he was able to recall the events that led up to the amnesic period.

This kind of amnesia is called circumscribed amnesia. Another type is called retrograde amnesia, in which the individual is unable to remember anything up to a certain date of his whole previous life. For instance, if he cannot remember anything that happened previous to, say, six months ago, it is called retrograde amnesia; if, on the other hand, he does not remember anything in the past six months, it is called circumscribed amnesia, which is the most common type.

Another case was a young man of about twenty who had been shipping from England on merchant boats. He was a minor kind of black sheep in a good English family. Though he had a fiancée in England he fell violently in love with a girl in New York and could not make up his mind which one he wanted to marry. The pressure of his dilemma became so great that he confessed his engagement to the girl in New York. The fiancée seemed to be a practical sort of person and insisted he choose between the two. To make the decision seemed to be too much for him. When he left her house he went out on the street and remembered nothing more until he was picked up in New York and brought to the hospital. With a certain amount of effort his past life was reconstructed and he eventually remembered what had caused the conflict, and then he was able to go back to his work.

The person who develops hysteria is generally a pleasing personality with imagination, considerable feeling and sensitivity. Most of them are agreeable people, although they may have alternating moods and be more or less ambivalent in their reactions. The hysterical person makes friends easily and makes a ready appeal to those with whom he comes in contact. Put another way, our imagination and interest are drawn to the hysterical personality because he is a more interesting individual and we feel more inclined to want to do more for him than for some of the other neurotic types. In terms of personality development, the hysterical person fared rather well in his first year of life—in the so-called oral stage of development; also he fared rather well during his anal stage of development; he has not been treated too harshly and has not had too much pressure put upon him to be a conformist. The traumatic occurrences of his life took place during his genital period of development— during that period when the child's erotic life is in a predominant phase of development (between three and six years). These children are easily disappointed in love, rather easily frustrated, and have not been hardened to deal with the shocks of fate with as much flexibility as the ordinary individual. Being loved and treated well mean a great deal to them, and the energy for normal body functions can be quickly withdrawn from certain areas when they are disappointed or frightened. A great many symptoms of conversion hysteria occur around a current love or an erotic situation—certainly to a greater degree than in other neuroses.

Treatment of Conversion Hysteria

A discussion of the treatment of conversion hysteria can apply to some degree to the treatment of all the neuroses. If symptoms are due to an emotional conflict and the body is healthy, then it is obvious the physician must treat the personality and let the body alone. Of course, the doctor must first take a good history and make a thorough and complete examination even when, from the appearance, manner and history of the patient, he thoroughly expects the symptoms to be hysterical. It should include, also, laboratory and X-ray studies, if indicated, because hysteria can simulate any disease condition. In other words we have to be careful not to confuse hysteria with some organic disease condition. However, once the examination and tests have ruled out organic disease and the physician realizes he is dealing with a personality problem, then he must treat the personality and not try to treat a personality disturbance with drugs, operations, or medications of one kind or another.

During the taking of the history the physician comes to see the background in which the patient grew up and the circumstances in which he lives. He finds out whether there are any stresses acting as toxic agents, so to speak, in his environment. The history should also reveal the way the patient has reacted previously to difficult circumstances and whether he has ever had symptoms associated with anxiety. When all the data are collected, the physician can say to the patient, "I do not find that you have any sign of disease in the region where you have symptoms. Therefore, I think that your symptoms are the result of your emotional distress. I am sure they will disappear if you can adjust yourself to the thing in your environment that is hurting you. This hurt in your body and the distress symptoms you are complaining of are representations of the emotional distress within you and will disappear if you adjust yourself to the circumstances."

When a doctor attempts to put across ideas like these he meets with a certain amount of resistance in the average patient. People do not like to be regarded as nervous or weak; they feel it is shameful, and that it is much more respectable for their bodies to have a real disease and to take real medicine. They do not like to think that they have broken down and have symptoms of a so-called nervous origin. The physician must tell them that nervous symptoms are common, which is true. He can say, "You know a great many people have symptoms because they are sensitive and because the environmental circumstances exert an unpleasant pressure upon them. You need not be ashamed of this. It just happens to be so. If you want to be well you have to consider the cause and effect a different relationship between you and the environment. If you will work on yourself with these ideas in mind, you will get well."

Some people respond to a little discussion like this extremely well. As a matter of fact, hysteria is the easiest emotional illness to cure. Imagination helps the hysterical patient to get well because his mind is better prepared to catch the point the doctor is trying to make. He usually knows something of what the doctor is talking about because experience has told him that he gets symptoms whenever he feels upset and he is, to some degree, ready to respond. Patients will often bring up the question, "Do you think, doctor, this is *only* in my imagination?" The doctor can say, "It is *not only* in your imagination. You have real distress. You have pain [if it happens to be pain]. You have been uncomfortable. Let's not conclude because we used the word imagination that I am merely suggesting that you think you have pain. You are suffering in another way. Think of the suffering that takes place between you and your job, or between you and your husband. Let's treat that suffering. I know the suffering in your body is merely an end result of the suffering in your mind."

When the physician makes a serious appeal on that assumption, nine out of ten patients will respond, the percentage being higher in hysteria than in the other neuroses. Most hysterical people go along with the physician if the cause of their symptoms is explained and they are asked to turn their attention from their body to the conflict in their lives and to try with the physician to solve the problem. Even the hysterical person has to be asked to return more than once because the doctor wants to watch him and to keep his attention directed in the right path. There is a great tendency for a human being with any kind of neurotic symptoms to focus his attention on his body, to forget what the doctor has said about the conflicts in his situation and to come back the second or third time offering his symptoms instead of some solution of his conflict. So when he comes in the second time the physician must notice how the patient feels, whether he starts talking about his indigestion or headache, or whether he talks about the problem that was discussed on his last visit. If he does not discuss the problem but keeps to the topic of his symptoms, the physician must draw his attention away from his body toward his life problem.

The above description of the management of conversion hysteria makes it seem easy—which it is in most cases. Many years ago Freud predicted that there would be a decrease in conversion hysteria as some of the more easily understandable conflicts of mankind became better understood. Thousands of cases of hysterical conversion symptoms are treated each day by physicians through the suggestive effect of drug or physical therapy. Many such symptoms appear and disappear in the lives of people without their ever consulting a physician. They know that if they are worried or under tension they will be physically uncomfortable, and they have their own means of relief. For the more intractable cases we refer the reader to Chapter XVI on "Treatment."

ANXIETY HYSTERIA

A married woman of twenty-nine was brought to the doctor in a car by her husband and accompanied by her sister into the doctor's office. She said that she had been nervous for eight years and that her nervousness had come on in the form of spells in which she felt faint and thought she might die before the spell was over. She had gone to a doctor after her first attack, had been told she had had a nervous spell, was given some bromides, and sent home. She was all right until two weeks later when another spell occurred. These spells continued to come two or three times a month, and with each succeeding one the patient felt less and less like doing her work or going about by herself. Finally it became possible for her to function only when she had her husband, her sister, or her mother with her. Without them she feared a spell would come on. Since these spells were so uncomfortable and frightening that she could not manage by herself, she consulted another physician who also told her that her trouble was "nervous"; he gave her some injections of iron and some vitamin preparation. Still no change occurred in her nervousness. Other physicians suspected and treated her for thyroid disease and heart disease in turn, without benefit. At the end of eight years she was practically a slave to fear that a spell would come on and that the sensation accompanying the spell would either be too much for her to bear or that she would actually get into some difficulty before it passed.

Going back in her life we learned that she was the younger of two sisters, the sister being two years older. The father was a machinist, a steady worker, and a quiet, reserved man who paid little attention to his daughters. He liked hunting, fishing and playing cards, and indulged in them occasionally. He felt that he had done his duty to his family when he supported them materially. The mother was a quiet, kind woman, not regarded as nervous, who, when first married, accompanied her husband around the country in the course of job changes and lived in two or three different cities before the family finally settled down. The patient, incidentally, thought her mother was very courageous in making these moves and did not see how she herself could do the same thing.

The patient had some kind of indigestion during the first year of life and her mother had trouble in getting her to eat. She recalled that she was regarded as rather sickly up to the time she entered school. She never liked school, never looked forward with anticipation to any day at school either during grade or high school. She had no special difficulty either with her classmates or her teachers but she had a certain timidity and dread all during her school years. Her life in high school was unspectacular. She received moderate grades and took no part in any extracurricular activities.

Menstruation began at the age of eleven. About that time a fairly critical event occurred. One day while coming home from school with a school chum the chum told her about the "facts of life," i. e., sexual intercourse and the dangers involved. This imparting of knowledge arose over the discussion of a girl in the neighborhood who had supposedly been attacked by a man. The school friend emphasized the dangers of sexual contact, although she was not at all clear in describing what took place in sexual relations. However, she did a great deal to frighten the patient about sex relations and venereal disease.

For several nights after this discussion the patient slept poorly. She did not feel her sister could enlighten her because the sister was only two years older, and she did not feel close enough to her mother in a matter of this kind to question or discuss it with her. So she carried these thoughts alone through her whole adolescence. This made her social contacts very difficult for her. She never knew how she should conduct herself with the opposite sex or how free she should be in her comings and goings socially. Consequently, she usually chose to stay away from school functions, rather than go and be considered bold or get into what she considered dangerous situations.

After high school she stayed around the house doing very little, and at the age of twenty-one she married. At no time during either child-hood or adolescence was she or her sister enlightened by the mother in regard to sexuality, courtship or social relations. On the day of her marriage, her mother called her aside and said, "You had better not become pregnant because you would probably die." This, of course, terrified her so much that she felt a great deal of anxiety during her early married life. She knew nothing about the means of contraception, and even though her husband used a contraceptive measure she still feared pregnancy and was frigid throughout her married life. Because of her illness she and her husband lived in her parents' home, where she needed to be constantly in the presence of mother, sister or husband. Medical and neurological examinations were negative. She was a well-nourished, healthy woman whose simple complaint was that if she had to be by herself, she would feel "terrible."

What is the diagnosis of such an incapacity? *The manner of living* described in this woman's history leads to anxiety. Anxiety is, first, an emotion that has an unpleasant affect. Besides the unpleasant affect, it produces a motor discharge through the nervous system into every part of the body. Therefore, anxiety is an unpleasant affect with somatic reverberations.

A person can have *real anxiety* which comes about as a result of a definite threatened danger, or he may have *neurotic anxiety* brought about by instinctual demands that threaten as a danger from within himself. The stimulus of real anxiety comes from without; the stimulus of neurotic anxiety comes from within the individual. The person with neurotic anxiety can be thrown into as great a state of panic—with undesirable, somatic manifestations—as he would be if, for instance, he were frightened by a truck bearing down upon him or held up by a gunman.

At the present time this symptom picture of anxiety is extremely confusing to patient and doctor alike because it is not yet well recognized that the instinctual forces within the body can be as threatening as in the patient just described. Such a person has just as much potential force for constructive aggressive behavior and for pleasurable sexual activity as anyone else, but being untutored and uninstructed about these forces, and having no help in their management and direction, finds them pressing forward from the unconscious as dangers and bringing forth unpleasant sensations in the body to result in disease or discomfort.

In discussing the various phases of development of personality, we learned that the newborn child has instinctual needs and drives and that they have to be met by the mother, that during the anal stage these impulses have to be disciplined and that during the genital stage the child's curiosity about sexuality comes forward and his interest in masturbation increases in intensity, and that at the same time he is coping with all these instinctual urges he is also struggling hard to maintain the good opinion and to have the goodwill of the adults around him. Many parents fear it is dangerous to give too much goodwill to the child when he exhibits curiosity or any aggressive urges. The child is, therefore, left to deal with them himself. These instinctual impulses can be too much for a human being to handle unless they are recognized and trained and disciplined with the parents' interest and goodwill.

Such training and co-operation are exactly what our patient did not have. In some homes the parents are actually cruel to the child, make definite threats against him, and a great deal of anxiety arises as a consequence. In other homes the parents are gentle enough but nevertheless unconsciously do a great deal of harm to the personality development of the child by simply ignoring any questions relating to sexual and aggressive impulses; thus the child's ego is not strengthened either to recognize or control these instinctual needs.

Our patient felt she had good parents, and in many ways they *were* good. They were not entirely friendly, however, and they certainly were not far-sighted or understanding about life; otherwise they would have let the child express herself, would have told her the facts of life, would have specifically and definitely planned with her how she could do some work and how she might so handle her social and romantic life as to lead to a satisfactory marriage. When good parents ignore these important activities, the child feels that these interests must be wrong, bad and undesirable and should be kept out of sight—repressed, we call it. Our patient kept all her sexual desires and romantic interests repressed not only during childhood but during adolescence as well, so that she entered into marriage at twenty, a very "nice" girl but also an empty and weak one, completely unable to be a useful or happy person.

Her symptoms of anxiety were coincident with responsibility and sexual activity. She had been nervous for eight years; she had been married for eight years. At home under the protection of her parents and without any responsibilities, her anxiety did not produce symptoms; with marriage and the beginning of sexual activity, the anxiety became so intense as to upset the action of the heart, throw out a stream of motor impulses into various parts of the body, make her feel uncomfortable, disturb the equilibrium of the circulation, and cause her to think she was going to faint and even die. This is the way that the anxiety existing in an individual can come to incapacitate him when he is forced to take on responsibility.

Anxiety manifests itself early in life. Young children have fears about being alone, about the dark, and about animals. Let us ask ourselves what fear of the dark means. It means that the relationship between child and mother has not been good enough to enable him to retain a mental picture of the feeling of her kindness, goodness and protection as he goes in the dark room. There has been too little *incorporation* of the parent, or parents. The human being must get a great part of his feeling of security in the first, second and third years of life. The older he becomes, the more his habits of feeling and thinking are built up and, therefore, the harder it is to give him that sense of security. Also, the older he grows the harder the parent will have to work to make him feel secure. When a child shows his anxiety by not wanting to go to school, it means that he cannot take with him a mental picture or a memory and an accompanying feeling that the kindness, goodness and acceptance of his parents are going there with him. If these feelings do go with him, he transfers them to his teachers and to the other children, and he comes to feel as secure as if he were at home.

Anxiety manifests itself during childhood and may be exaggerated at puberty through the form of nightmares. A nightmare is a nocturnal anxiety attack and is the product of the memory of a frightening event reactivated within the mind. Probably no one escapes occasional nightmares, at least during childhood and adolescence. There is probably no one whose aggressive and sexual impulses are so nicely balanced at all times as not to be stimulated in a way sufficient to produce anxiety in some form. When nightmares become too frequent they are a signal that the child is being forced to cope with too many frightening stimuli, and the parents or the doctor should inquire into the reason for them— the content of the dream will very often give the clue to the difficulty. They may be accompanied by sleepwalking during puberty or at any time when the child is under stress.

Nightmares are a sign that the child needs help with the problems of his love relations or the problem of his hostility toward someone in his environment. For instance, during the so-called Oedipus period (between three and six) when a boy's erotic feeling for his mother takes on a too romantic coloring and when his relationship with his father is not good, he may have dreams in which a man is doing some injury to him or in which he is being chased by an animal. We do not have to stretch our imaginations very far to see that the animal represents the father in disguise. Human beings are often symbolized in dreams by animals. When we speak of the animal nature of man we are usually referring either to his unrestrained sexual impulses or to his violence or aggression.

The cases just described are ones of anxiety hysteria. Many of them progress to a state where they have phobias. A phobia is a kind of protective behavior through reduction in activity which aims to prevent the individual from coming in contact with the situation that produces his anxiety. The person having anxiety attacks soon learns that if he avoids certain places he does not have these "terrible attacks," or that if he takes someone to accompany him he does not have the attacks. The person who goes with him acts as a protecting agent, a kind of substitute for his conscience or superego, as if he were to say, "I might do something violent, wicked or sexually improper, but this person with me will prevent such an occurrence. So long as I have him with me I do not need to worry so much, for if I have any improper impulses, I will be restrained by him."

The ego formation in such a person is weak because the parents have either never taken the trouble or dared to discuss the instinctual impulses of the human being with him. In the case of our patient, if as she was growing up the mother had talked to her about her violent impulses and sexual impulses, the girl could have thought, "My mother has set the limits. She has told me what life is like and how people behave. She has told me what I may do and may not do. Therefore I can go about in the world more comfortably because I have the facts and because I have some rules of conduct." Having no facts and no rules or opinions of the parents about how to behave, such a person becomes a slave to her instinctual impulses, which eventually results in the condition we call anxiety hysteria. It is a common condition and one not easily cured. People suffering from it have regressed to a state of helplessness in which they behave like very young children. Our patient is now much more helpless than she was as a child in grade school, when she was able to go by herself and did a job fairly well. Today she says, "I am a frightened child. I cannot do anything by myself. Help me." In her childishness she enjoys some of the privileges of being a child. She has the contacts and attention of her family and husband, but she pays a high price for these privileges because she is not only ashamed of herself but is missing all the advantages and pleasures that go with more mature behavior. In order to get well and to get over being a child, she must learn from the doctor that it is safe to go around by herself; she must be reassured that she will not misbehave when she is by herself. It takes much patience and a long time to put such a conviction into the mind of a person when it has been neglected so long. It is as if the person were to say, "Doctor, what you say sounds reasonable but it cannot be true or my good father or mother would have told me so." Children have great faith in their parents even when they have been let down. They think that father and mother do what is right. Therefore, if it was right for mother to have been so quiet and aloof, to have left sexual questions untouched and without discussion, then that behavior is normal or natural. When the doctor tells such a person otherwise, a great deal of distrust comes to the surface. He appears willing to be treated and to wish to be better, but he also wants to remain as he was—he fears the truth of what the physician says and gets a certain pleasure from being helpless and childish.

The tendency to regress is in all of us. While hysterical people are usually attractive people and seem to be essentially sincere, they have a very hard time following directions. When the doctor tests out their feelings of responsibility, they do not seem to be able to respond and be as dependable and useful as they would like to think they are. The doctor has to hold them to the new behavior pattern very strongly, insist that they behave logically, accept the security he offers and use it. There is no medicine for anxiety hysteria. Medicine will only do the patient harm because the doctor merely postpones the day of treatment of the real cause, and fixes in the patient's mind the idea that he has organic disease. The physician might just as well begin to treat the personality weakness in the beginning and in that way he will get the best results. His interest in the patient, his understanding of the patient's personality defect and his ability to get the patient to understand himself, and as a result become willing and able to act more maturely—*these are the medicine.*

NEURASTHENIA

The concept of neurasthenia was formed around the first attempt to describe neurosis. When medical observers first recognized an emotional or psychological element in disease they listed over a hundred symptoms that were a part of this syndrome, which Beard in 1869 called neurasthenia. With the passing of time and with increasing attention paid to these conditions, the entities of conversion hysteria, anxiety hysteria and compulsion neurosis have been split from their original concept, and what is left is still called neurasthenia. As a result of its history and of the fact that emotional conflict can produce so many types of disturbance in the body, neurasthenia was a vague and not well-defined entity, and so it remains to this day.

However, we must define as well as we can this remaining group of psychoneurotic people in terms of symptoms. The symptoms that form the core of neurasthenia are a triad of fatigue, distress of the gastrointestinal tract, and what we are going to call a reduced capacity for the joy of living. This third part of the triad has often been referred to as depression of spirits, but diminution in the joy of living seems more appropriate because the neurasthenic individual not only has some depression of spirits but he also has a lack of enthusiasm and ambition and a general disgruntlement with life, which is different from the depressive phase of manic-depressive psychosis. Moreover, "diminution in the joy of living" seems more descriptive than just "depression" alone, and actually, "depression" should be broken down into its elements.

The person with neurasthenia is quite a problem to himself and to those around him because, due to his lack of interest in living, he tends to become gradually preoccupied with his body and the way it functions. He has often been called a hypochondriac, which word does not enlighten us very much since it is not descriptive of what takes place in the neurasthenic individual by way of symptoms. Actually neurasthenia is a better term because it means lack of nerve strength. At first it was presumed that this lack of nerve strength was inherited or was a pathology acquired in the nerve cells. With time, however, this has not proved to be true. If we use a popular concept of "nerves"—meaning a personality weakness which makes the person unable to meet the responsibilities of life—and think thereafter of neurasthenia as a lack of emotional strength, the term itself still gives a fair description of what seems apparent in the condition.

Neurasthenia contains certain features of other psychiatric entities: a little of depression, a little of the schizophrenic personality, a little of the compulsive neurotic personality and, possibly at times, a little of the element of paranoia. With the passing of time it is possible that we will do away with the concept of neurasthenia, but in order to help us in our thinking at present we have to try to understand as well as we can this rather large group of neuroses which does not fit into any of the other classifications.

Possibly neurasthenia can best be described by relating a typical case. The patient was a single man twenty-five years of age, the youngest of five children. His father was a salesman, a rather detached kind of man, little interested in his family, concerned only with his ability as a salesman and looking at life and measuring it in quite materialistic terms. His mother was a tight-lipped, severe woman who was proud of her religious convictions and who had brought her family up with a great sense of duty. The parents had not wanted this fifth child—he came after they thought their family was complete. Under such circumstances he became a problem as an infant. He cried a great deal and was a feeding problem. It was difficult to get him to eat and keep his food down. Throughout his childhood he was sensitive and fussy. He had few playmates during his preschool years and fewer still after. He did not like either grade school or high school. He was, as he described himself, a "lone wolf" who did not mix much and who read a great deal. His grades in high school were mediocre. After leaving high school he had five jobs in about seventeen months, none of which he liked any better than he had liked school.

It was during his fifth job that he began to feel tired, to have a poor appetite, to worry about his strength and ability to carry on. One day he had a severe, cramplike pain in his abdomen and from then on complained of what he called a "churning" sensation in his lower bowel. He began to visit doctors to find out what was the matter with him. One doctor told him he had "lymphatic glands" and that they were the cause of his disturbance, another told him his tonsils needed to be removed, another sent him to have his eyes examined, another said he had chronic appendicitis, and finally one said he had acute appendicitis and that he ought to have his appendix out. He went to an excellent surgeon who, after an examination, said he did not have any disease of the appendix and that he would not remove it. However, as with many neurotic people who like the idea of surgical removal, he persisted until he found a surgeon who was willing to remove it. After the operation he was better for about six weeks. Then when he returned to work his distress recurred as before—with fatigue, poor appetite, abdominal distress and occasional diarrhea.

This boy had always been quite limited in his ability to enjoy life as can be seen from his history. We saw him about a month before he went to the surgeon. On taking his history and watching his reactions, we felt he was suffering from a neurosis, and told him we felt his distress was due to his lack of enthusiasm for his work and an actual fear of going to work and meeting the people he had to deal with, as well as to the fact that his home life was pretty unfriendly and colorless and that he had no outside interests, sports or hobbies to relieve the monotony of his work. However, he did not seem to understand this very well and was not able to use what we pointed out to him. He would talk on and on about his symptoms and advance theories about what he thought was wrong, so that we were glad when the surgeons proved unwilling to remove his appendix because we thought an operation might only lead to a greater fixation on his symptoms. We told him this, but he was in no mood to listen and he had his appendix removed anyway.

While resting in the hospital—and removed from his unfriendly home environment—he found life and the attention he received there interesting. He felt better and believed he *was* better. He took the attitude toward the psychiatrist, "You did not know what was wrong with me all the time." However, even though his symptoms returned, he still believed that he must have some organic condition in his gastrointestinal tract, which had not been properly diagnosed and dealt with. He so completely ignored our endeavors to help him that we felt he was possibly in the hypochondriacal stage of schizophrenia. He would go on talking about his body and ignore the outside world, feeling persecuted by his bowel just as the mentally sick person may feel persecuted by the devil. We wrote to his family doctor saying that the patient seemed to be going in the direction of a frank mental disease and that since he would not listen we thought it advisable to refer him to the Psychopathic Hospital, hoping that finding himself in the psychopathic ward would give him a realization that he was thinking along dangerous lines.

This did not prove to be necessary because the doctor handed the letter to the family. The mother, being a practical person, said to the boy, "Look here, the doctor thinks you are going crazy and you ought to go to a hospital." That startled him. He came back to us and for the first time began to pay attention. He said, "I did not realize you thought I was that bad." We pointed out we had been talking to him about himself, telling the truth as we saw it, with the wish to help him get well, and that after all he must have some capacity to see that paying attention to his symptoms themselves over a period of months had not been helping him. We pleaded with him to pay attention to himself and to the way he was reacting to people. We emphasized how he had come to us for advice and yet had ignored what we had been talking about to him. He said, "I will tell you why that is. I have always been that way. I have never been able to pay attention to people because my father and mother always told me what to do. If I ever protested and wanted to do anything else, they never listened. I think I got in the habit of being stubborn, saying nothing, but going my own way."

After this particular talk, he became willing to stop thinking of his stomach and the function of his bowels and worrying about his fatigue. He started being interested in the world around him. He had always regretted that he did not have more friends and particularly regretted that he was not popular with the opposite sex. He took the suggestion that he learn to dance, began to enjoy going to dances, got himself a girl, in fact several girl friends, all of which gave him a great boost in morale. He became more interested in trying to make friends with the people with whom he worked. We told him, "Try to see if you can make a new friend a day. Try to impress a little bit of yourself on one new individual." He took the challenge, tried it, and had a fair degree of success.

In the beginning we saw him once a week, then once in two weeks, finally once a month. Now we have not seen him for about six months, except for occasional visits when he relapsed a little. He has been working and doing tolerably well. He remains a vulnerable individual, however, and we do not know how he is going to keep going in future years. If he marries, we do not know how he will react to the responsibilities of marriage and parenthood. He might have a return of symptoms. However, having come to understand himself better, he is able to work more effectively and enjoy life more and as a result of these efforts has lost his overwhelming fatigue, and his gastrointestinal tract functions well enough. This man was suffering not from a lack of *nerve strength* but from a lack of *ego strength*. His lack of enthusiasm and interest in his friends and work and the world around him was due to the fact that his parents had never had any enthusiasm or interest in him. He had never had these feelings in relation to himself and he did not know the joy of expressing them.

Recall that when we were discussing the first year of life we said it was important for the parents, especially the mother or whoever takes care of the child, to be able to find an interest in the child himself. We have an increasing amount of evidence that the function of the gastrointestinal tract can operate well only when the environment is one of friendliness and that if that combination of forces gets off to a good start in infancy the human being is not likely to have stomach upsets. He is not frightened by his environment and does not get the indigestion and gastrointestinal distress that many people get under stress or in a situation with which they feel inadequate to cope. To our mind every case of neurasthenia is the result of a bad start in the first year of life: a lack of parental interest, the child left too much to himself, too little effort made to cultivate happiness in the baby. In these cases an inertia seems to develop, and it is only with great difficulty that the neurasthenic is helped to be awakened to feelings of happiness and altruism.

Fatigue

Many think that fatigue, especially extreme fatigue, is due to organic causes. This is not necessarily so, although a great many organic diseases such as leukemia, tuberculosis and many other serious diseases can cause fatigue. Severe fatigue can occur in a neurosis and especially in neurasthenia. Studies on fatigue are contained in a symposium on the subject in the journal *Psychosomatic Medicine,* July, 1943. These studies emphasize the difficulty of measuring and studying fatigue but they make quite clear that fatigue can be a result of emotional conflict. Ordinarily it is thought that fatigue is the result of physical exercise such as in sports or in work, but it can also come about as a result of a lack of interest. People are fatigued who are unenthusiastic and uninspired about their work. Uninspired people are the ones who are always talking about being "tired of the job" or of life, which expressions grow out of the fact that they actually suffer a sensation of fatigue along with their lack of interest.

The neurasthenic is a most uninspired human being. He looks and acts as if he wanted someone to inspire him and give him something that will make him strong and alive. The neurasthenic person has more complaints than any other neurotic and makes them in a more fretful, demanding way. It is hard for the doctor to see what the neurasthenic patient wants and needs (and this applies to the patient as well) because what he has missed goes so far back in life that it is difficult to recognize and can be sensed only by a use of the imagination. In thinking about what takes place between child and mother and reliving that experience we can get some idea. Children can miss a great deal of happiness and inspiration in the first year of life and a connection is established between emotions and the gastrointestinal function which can produce great instability and dysfunction in that organ system.

The traumas that cause conversion hysteria and that produce its symptoms usually occur after the first year of life. It is different in the case of neurasthenia. As a rule nothing very critical happened in the neurasthenic's life. He is usually a droopy, unalert-looking individual, dependent in attitude. And it is the dependent attitude of the neurotic that has done so much to make psychoneurosis unpopular in the past and that inclines physicians to say, "The damn neurotic!" or, "I always get mad when I see a neurotic coming into my office."

The neurasthenic has missed so much as an infant that later he wants from the doctor more than is given the ordinary office patient. But what he wants is so obscure and so vaguely defined that he is baffling to himself and to his physician. We often get annoyed at what we cannot understand. Not being understood, the neurasthenic has been scolded; he has made the doctor angry and has been put out of the office; he has been given lectures; sometimes he has been given electric shocks. Because neurotics have not been sympathetically dealt with, many have gone to cultists who understand their emotional makeup better and are therefore able to obtain better results than the general practitioner.

As in any other neurosis, the doctor takes the history and makes a thorough and complete examination to make sure he is not dealing with organic disease. When tests indicate no organic disease, the physician should not give medicine or treat the case of neurasthenia as he would grippe or typhoid fever just because the patient has aches or pains or is so tired he hurts. The appropriate treatment for muscular pains of grippe would not help the neurasthenic. Just because diet will help certain organic conditions of the gastrointestinal tract does not mean it will help a neurosis. What needs to be treated in neurasthenia is the personality, the patient's failure to adapt, his lack of inspiration. If the doctor treats with medicine, it may result in the patient's getting temporary relief—but soon his symptoms return; he loses faith in the physician who, in turn, feels somewhat touchy about any criticism, and they part bad friends. It is much better to tell the patient the truth, to try to understand him, and to tell him the nature of his condition, even though he may seem discouraged and not impressed.

This character disturbance is so severe that we feel if the patient can afford the time and money he should have intensive psychiatric treatment in the nature of psychoanalysis, which means as often as four or five days a week over a period of many months. This seems like a great deal in the way of treatment but some cases are so stubborn that they will not yield to anything else. Ideally the neurasthenic patient we described should have had more intensive personality re-education than we were able to give. However, he was helped greatly, and by keeping in contact with us throughout life he may continue to function fairly adequately. When the cure is complete, the individual becomes more effectual and efficient, a more satisfactory employee or employer, a more satisfactory husband and father.

COMPULSION NEUROSIS

A single woman of thirty came to her physician complaining of "nervousness." She said, "I have been a wreck for five years. I am ridden by fears. I fear everything. I'm afraid to eat food that anyone else has touched. I have to have my own dishes, my own loaf of bread. I'm afraid I'll get dirt inside me. I have to have everything so clean. I wash and scrub for hours on something I should get clean in a couple of minutes. I'm such a burden to everyone. I'm so depressed about myself I cry and deplore the way I seem, but I can't seem to do better."

As a girl she was attractive, dressed neatly, seductively, and with great care in regard to detail, in spite of her misery. Her history revealed that she was the youngest of a large, religious family. The father had been a teacher and was temperamental, high strung, irritable and meticulous. She said, "He had to have everything just so, and when I was a child he was always scolding even when I tried to please him. I was fond of him but he never paid any attention to me, so I gave up." He died when the patient was fourteen. The mother was a quiet, undemonstrative woman who saw that the children were given food, and thought her duty ended there. As a child the patient was aggressive and demanding, flew into rages, was destructive, careless of her appearance and a "dirty little tomboy." She never liked school and was an indifferent student. At puberty she changed somewhat and became neat and meticulous. About a year after her father died she began to go out with boys. She had an insatiable longing for fun and excitement. The mother and sisters disapproved, but they could do nothing with her. She broke off her religious affiliations with the church and spent her nights in night clubs, drinking to excess and having a good time. During the first part of the evening she would be shy, but after a few drinks she would become bold, free in her speech and behavior and the life of the party.

For three years she was courted by a man who wanted to marry her if she would control her drinking. But she would not, and he gave her up. This grieved her tremendously. The family was not well-to-do and she continued working at an uncongenial job for several years. Then she met a second man who was married. An attachment grew up between them and she was the means of breaking up his marriage. About this time, however, she began to have fears, "a terrible fear that something would happen to me. I didn't know what. I wanted to be with people, but I still could not feel right. I began to worry about eating something that would be bad for me. I began to have all these rituals about food. I became obsessed with the idea of dirt. I always liked to have things neat and clean, but in the last few years this is about all I think of. I'm not only worried about the effect of dirt upon me, but I'm also worried about its effect upon others. Please help me to enjoy life again. I've returned to church and pray and try hard but nothing seems to help."

Let us see what the material of the previous chapters has given us to help in the understanding of this case. This youngest child was partly neglected and partly overindulged by a materialistic and ineffectual mother, to whom food for the body was important but food for the spirit was not, and who stood helplessly by during the girl's teens and allowed her to run wild, attempting to restrain her with only a few weak protests. The continued rage outbreaks in childhood indicate lack of love and lack of discipline. These, combined with her dirtiness as a tomboy, are evidences of what we call a poor superego formation. Turning to her father for love interest, friendship and inspiration, she finds him busy, cranky and disinterested—again a denial of the factors that build strong ego and superego functions. Shortly after his death she enters upon a long, ten-year period of rampant instinctual indulgence. What conscience she had developed as a child was dissociated for the time being. While the father's method of control was harsh and unkind, it is possible that had he lived he would have held her behavior in check, but with him gone and with a limited love bond between her and the mother and the rest of the family, she ignored them all and indulged herself to the limit.

In the first love affair of three years' duration she was with a man who was steadfastly devoted to her and who begged her to stop drinking and behaving so badly and marry him. She ignored him completely. Had a more positive normal Oedipus relation been present between her and her father she might have loved this man more sincerely and been guided by him. But never having known love in the beginning she could not appreciate what loyalty and co-operation with him could do for her in a positive way. When she finally fell in love with a second man and he with her, and she had broken up his home, she began at last to be in conflict. She wanted to become "good." She returned to church, prayed, and it is interesting that the "bad" of her sexual behavior became displaced to food. This displacement commonly happens, however, and the fact that she was of a religious family made it even more possible. The symbolic significance of communion is that the "goodness" of the host is taken in and nourishes the mind and spirit—infuses one with better feelings and intentions. Hence that "bad" feelings and intentions also can be displaced onto food is readily understandable. So in trying to avoid dirt she is ritualistically trying to lead a better life. In compulsive cleaning she is trying to atone for her sins, to clean up her past, so to speak, and at the same time trying to become the clean little girl which she was not during the anal and latent periods.

Apropos of the Oedipus complex, it is noteworthy that she does not fall in love with a young man her own age but with an older man already married—and has an outbreak of her illness upon taking him from the other woman—the mother substitute. She thought she could be cured by marrying him, but this would, of course, not be possible. To be well she would have to understand the meaning of her symptoms and come to terms with her distorted human relations and come to a solution of them. She would have to grow up through hard self-discipline, after learning to understand—gradually through interviews—the causes of her fear. She was still the selfish, demanding little girl wanting as much indulgence as ever. Only now the parts of her personality were at war within her. Her conscience (superego) which had been thrown aside (dissociated) for ten years had started functioning again. Why? Probably because at twenty-five it dawned upon her that irresponsible youth had had its fling and that she should be a more responsible human being. Why did she not go on, a ruthless coquette? Because she was a member of a responsible family. The others were doing well, indicating that she could not have avoided absorbing at least enough of their moral, responsible attitude to make it unlikely that she would ever entirely dispense with it. One might say that she was a weak, childish personality, disintegrated at fifteen and behaving in an irresponsible, selfish way for ten years, and that she became reintegrated at twenty-five, but with a neurosis as the solution rather than any constructive reform—a conversion if we use the word in a religious sense.

To cure this girl, it would be necessary for her to relate herself to a psychiatrist for a long period of time during which she would be (a) repeatedly shown the structure of her neurosis as outlined above, and the connection made between her present behavior and her childhood and past social adjustment, and (b) made to renounce her ritualistic morality of avoiding "dirt" and repetitive cleaning and made to function responsibly toward society as a useful, loyal and unselfish individual. When this technique is followed, using the Freudian concepts of personality formation, a cure can be brought about in most compulsion neuroses if they are treated before too late in life. Some become so fixed in pattern and get so much enjoyment from ritualistic thinking and acting that they remain neurotic in spite of their own efforts and those of the doctor to effect a cure.

In some families there is a tendency to make the children very afraid of their instinctual impulses quite early in life and to give them habit patterns of thinking and acting that keep erotic and aggressive impulses always deeply hidden. Such people are grim, serious people, usually good workers, precise, punctual, reliable and dependable, but unemotional and unexciting, compared to the hysterical personality. Whether an individual will develop a compulsive personality and remain "compulsive but normal" or whether he will develop the crippling symptoms of a compulsion neurosis depends on whether at some point in his life he has had a degree of freedom to impulsive conduct that he is unable to integrate into a controlled pattern. Our patient might have avoided her illness had her father lived: he might have scolded and supervised her into a pattern of social conduct that would have had a great deal of duty in it, if lacking in love. He might, on the other hand, merely have postponed the breaking out of her neurosis, the symptoms appearing at the age of forty instead of thirty. Such powerful and undisciplined instinctual urges as she gave vent to—so poorly integrated with love and altruistic social feelings—were likely to give trouble some time in some form.

This case as presented represents compulsion neurosis at its simplest. It might sound as if the sequence of events resulting in the conflict indicated would be easy to resolve. In actual practice it is not. Many people with compulsion neuroses become slaves to their ritualistic defenses. Their families, friends and doctor who do not understand their severity may say, "Just don't worry about those things. You don't need to keep on thinking the way you do or go through all those motions to protect yourself and others." But the pattern goes on until the patient can feel he is a good and loving and nondangerous person in a dangerous world. An intelligent patient-friend of ours who expresses herself unusually well on these matters puts it as follows:

"Much of the difficulty in a compulsive neurotic is a fear of an instinct or impulse within himself of a murderous, hostile, or destructive sort. Now an impulse is a *very real thing* (to my mind) and can produce *very real results in the outer world.* As a matter of fact, if anything is characteristic of instinct, it is its tendency to discharge itself in the outer world. I am convinced that every compulsive neurotic senses his danger and that his whole system of defense is an attempt to overcome the destructive outgoingness of these tendencies.

"I maintain that the danger is real for two reasons that may be hard for me to express with lucidity: first because I postulate the reality of instincts and second because instincts *predetermine* action—and where one has a hostile or destructive trend, there is *potentially,* at least, the danger of inflicting harm. Every neurotic fears something within himself which may get the best of him—in fact, which he feels positively would get the best of him if he did not take the most elaborate precautions against it. To go into this, and how it works out in my case, in a little more detail, let me say that I always feel everything would be all right if only one of two things could be different. In the first place, if these awful things (that sometimes seem like frightful inner explosions) did not take place in me—very, very real things, subjectively speaking—then what a wonderful world it would be, because then I could go near all the most dangerous things in the world without the least fear—for there would be no *dangerous thing in me* to link up and *make* any use of many *dangerous things in the outside world.* Or, on the other hand, even granting I had the most murderous and destructive of impulses, it would still be a wonderful world if there was *nothing in the outside world* that was in the least dangerous, because, let me feel as hostile as Hades, if it were outwardly a perfectly safe and innocuous world, one could still be safe notwithstanding what went on inside of one. But unfortunately neither the structure of the world nor the structure of the personality is as I would wish it. People do have hostile feelings (and I maintain that these feelings are always potentially dangerous because there is always a chance that they will explode and discharge themselves and use something of like nature in the outer world); and also the outer world is full of its own strongly destructive forces, mechanical and chemical and germicidal. This realization is something which I find it impossible to deal with adequately. Somehow I simply cannot live properly with this knowledge, knowing how potentially dangerous I am and how many things there are in the outside world through which this potential danger could operate."

Many types of neuroses profit by the undertanding of unconscious mental functioning furnished by Freudian psychoanalysis; it is usually the *only* treatment that helps compulsive neuroses and even then treatment should be started early and kept up generally from eighteen months to two years. It takes time and patient work on the part of the analyst to win the patient away from his conviction that he is dangerous and convince him that the outside world is not full of dangers also. The average physician, through explanation and reassurance, can bring some *relief* to the compulsive neurotic, but efforts at *cure* should be in the hands of a specialist.

NEUROTIC CHARACTER

There is a group of people whose behavior is such that they are classified in one of several ways. Unlike the neurotic personality, they have few, if any, somatic symptoms, and then only under unusual circumstances. Unlike the psychotic personality, their behavior is never quite bizarre enough nor the disorganization in their thinking and behavior quite serious enough to warrant commitment to a mental hospital. Nevertheless, they are very sick people so far as society is concerned. Because of their behavior they get into difficulties with the law so that their cases need handling outside the family, either by correction in an institution or through moral restraint. People who get into difficulty with their families, the community or the law are called *psychopathic personalities*. They have also been called *psychopathic inferiors* and *constitutionally psychopathic inferiors,* and sometimes the term *moral insanity* has been applied to them, but there is coming to be an increasing tendency to call them *neurotic characters.*

These people are prone to act out their primitive impulses without regard to the rules and regulations laid down by society. Their attitude toward the group seems to be lacking in that ethical feeling which would lead them to better conformance with the demands of society. Largely because of this lack of feeling for ethical ideas and traditional ideals, they are unable to learn and cannot profit by experience.

There are many types of behavior in this group. There is the over-sensitive, unadjusted troublemaker who always feels himself picked upon or discriminated against, who criticizes those in authority or who may be jealous of those in authority, or who may be a zealous crusader for what he regards to be fair play or morally right. The result is that in an office, busy organization or shop, he will have too much to say or he will tattle to the boss or he will play one employee against another and otherwise be a troublemaker. In other words, he seems a master at making strife and contention. It would *appear* that he enjoys this; actually he does it without realizing he is doing harm. Usually when confronted with the nuisance of his behavior, he sets himself up to be a humanitarian with the welfare of everyone at heart.

Fairly close to the normal group, and often getting along with the normal group, is the man or woman who has little ethical feeling for family formation. Usually such people adapt poorly to marriage. If they do marry, the situation becomes full of strife and contention and may include alcoholic indulgence. They may be somewhat lacking in honesty and become involved with the law through neglect, for instance, of their premises or of regulations concerning their automobile. They may work irregularly at any employment and be truculent or quarrelsome with fellow employees or embezzle money which, if the family is sufficiently wealthy, is covered up. The result is that they are problems to everyone. Relatives and friends say, "He must be crazy," but they can neither institutionalize him nor reform him. There seems to be nothing to do for him (or her) but to let him go his way. One or two or more of these people are in every community.

From these milder problems the cases progress in severity to those who come in severe conflict with the law. The class called kleptomaniacs steal but feel extremely remorseful after and have a moral attitude of their own toward their behavior; but there are those who steal and think it is perfectly proper and have no moral attitude toward it whatsoever. When one of these latter takes a pocketbook or a car, the owner is rarely concerned whether the perpetrator has an obsession or is delinquent;

the results are very much the same in both cases and punishment is demanded. There are people who forge checks and when out of jail make it their lifework. When things do not go their way, they may even use a gun or some other instrument to commit murder. There are also pyromaniacs who like to cause excitement by setting fires.

Whatever the behavior that brings these people in conflict with the law, the fact is that their primitive, childish impulses are expressed without restraint, without remorse, without much or any feeling for society. It is partly this absence of conflict that keeps these people from developing body symptoms as in the other neuroses. They seem to have little or no moral sense and a poor development of that part of the personality we call the superego or conscience.

These people can be products of any type of family: they do not necessarily come from underprivileged homes; often they come from wealthy homes. In any case, they come from homes in which there has been an absence of interest in their welfare and where the parents either through accident or design have been unable to make the children feel happy with the conventional standards of conduct, and unable to inculcate in them any sense of responsibility toward others in their earliest years. In other words, the parents have been unable to help the children bring their primitive impulses under control and in line with what society expects. Many of these cases come from broken homes where the mother, father or both have been irresponsible in some way, or where a misfortune like death, accident or war has occurred which deprives the child of a correct upbringing. However, these people can also come from homes where the parents live with the children all the way to adulthood but who somehow do not have the ability to give the children what they need emotionally and ideationally in order to live considerately and constructively.

An example of the neurotic character is seen in the case of a man whose father deserted his mother a few weeks after he was born and who was sent to live with his grandparents for a while. They did not want the child because they had never approved of the daughter's marriage in the first place and hence could not approve of the child. His life was not a happy one. At seven years he had begun to be unable to take care of himself and at thirteen he was placed in a foster home, by which time complaints were coming in from the school and from the neighbors that he was breaking windows and committing other misdemeanors. Then he took part in a holdup with two or three other boys, for which he spent a period in a reformatory. Upon release, he participated in a series of robberies. After the fourth robbery he was put in jail for life. In talking to him one got the feeling that he had the idea there was nothing else he could do, that it was perfectly natural for him to have gone along with his friends and to have taken money to live by in this way. Such a person has the attitude that children are prone to have: if a man has a store, there is a lot of money in the till, and it will not matter much in the man's life if some of the money is taken.

We saw him after he had completed his fourth crime and asked him why he had not been able to realize that there was something wrong with his way of living. He said, "I thought I would make enough in this last bank robbery to settle down and go straight." In other words, the idea of going straight depended on his doing so with stolen money.

The thinking of these people is immature and childish. When confronted with a crime such as robbing a bank, they answer with reasoning like this: "A lot of people have their money there. No one would have suffered much. It would have meant only a little from each one. Besides, the money was insured, so if the bank was robbed, nobody would lose anything." They never realize very strongly that society is being harmed, or if they do, they don't care very much. They just feel that they need something, and so why shouldn't they take it? Why shouldn't society give it to them? Fortunately, there are not many of these people, relatively speaking, but enough to give us concern.

In talking to them for the first time, the physician often finds them surly and bitter. They say, "I never had a decent break." That reaction is unconsciously given, and as far as their behavior is concerned, to them it seems reasonable. They do not realize how bitter, resentful and hostile they are underneath their actions; it is only brought out when they are arrested and they can feel hostile toward society. With many of them treatment can be carried out only while they are under arrest or serving time, when their symptoms or hostility are evidence to them that something is wrong.

Treatment of the Neurotic Character

The treatment of this group is somewhat discouraging, though it must be said that for the most part when they are in jail they are being dealt with as expediently as possible. However, those in charge have the feeling that because they are not sick in body they are therefore not suffering. Of course, with the necessary restraint that is being imposed upon them they do sometimes have pains and aches and so become conscious of conflict, but while they are on the outside they usually think things are going well with them. Since they do not suffer, they are allowed to go their own way unless they come to harm others to such an extent that they must be put in jail.

Treatment in institutions is not easy because it is felt that their stay is temporary and less serious than the illnesses of those in mental institutions. However, ideally they should be treated intensively, because those who have received too little warmth and friendliness in the beginning of life have a hard time finding it later. It is extremely difficult to put a feeling of goodwill into a person who has had no such feeling to begin with, and when it is possible for the psychotherapist to do so, it requires a long, tedious process and much resourcefulness on his part.

During the course of the next five hundred years we may come to consider the problem of the delinquent and his hostile attitude toward society, but at present there are so many other social problems which many feel should come first that we are not giving much thought to the neurotic character. The child who grows up and behaves in a delinquent way soon gets a bad name and becomes unpopular. The attitude seems to be to "put him away where he can no longer harm us." It took society a long time to reach the point where it could see the problem of the mentally sick person, and it is still a difficult matter for a family when one of its members must be put away. The family complains about the state hospital, declares that the patient is not treated very well, that he is not helped enough, which in many cases is true enough. Since the community at large is *only a little* interested in our mentally sick or in trying to understand the causes that produced their illness or in making an effort to help them, it is plain to see that it would be even less interested in treating people who set fires, rob stores and banks and commit other crimes.

Society by no means feels that these are *sick* people. It takes the attitude that they are *bad* people and should be punished, and that is all there is to it. Society is resistant to "pampering" these delinquents. Just as soon as a rehabilitation program for delinquent boys, girls or adults is started that consists of social work, psychiatric therapy or a re-educational program for reformatories, immediately the men and women responsible for its financial support begin to show a great resistance to spending the necessary money. Merely teaching a trade, while having its merits, is a too superficial approach to the problem. Until we have a more widespread understanding by society of these people who give frequent expression to their undomesticated impulses, the result will be that nothing constructive will be accomplished.

At the present time we might as well be realistic and think of treating these people expediently. That means that as physicians the most helpful thing we can do for a family that includes a chronic delinquent is to point out the fact that he is incorrigible, or relatively so, as the case may be. That may not seem like the constructive thing to do, but actually if the situation is recognized early enough and corrective measures taken, the neurotic personality might be helped; whereas by allowing him to wait until the community and family are completely exasperated, he is not helped—rather, his attitude becomes one of great discouragement and of retaliation, with little of a constructive element left in the situation.

This need to recognize the problem when it arises applies particularly to children and adolescents, when they can be put into institutions for psychiatric treatment or into some other organization that will help them. For children *do not grow out of their asocial behavior*. They have to be treated—and early. The attitude of first shielding such a person until the age, say, of twenty and then turning around and saying "Put him behind bars!" is not help. Our plea is to let him feel that he is a problem as soon as he becomes one, to correct the attitude "We mustn't tell him he is a problem—it might shock him," and not to wait until he has to be put into jail.

It is well in this context to recall that in adolescence there are three main problems to solve: (1) that the adolescent must take responsibility and learn to think and plan for himself, (2) that he must choose a vocation and be able to earn his own livelihood, and (3) that he must make some satisfactory solution of his love life so that he can have personal friends and a community altruism. To help the adolescent solve these problems adequately is to reduce the number of neurotic characters.

BIBLIOGRAPHY FOR CHAPTER XIII

Alexander, F., and Healy, W., *Roots of Crime,* Knopf, 1935.
Alexander, F., and Staub, H., *The Criminal, the Judge and the Public,* Macmillan, 1931.
Beard, A., *A Practical Treatise on Nervous Exhaustion,* 1880.
Deutsch, Helene, *Psychoanalysis of the Neurosis,* International Psychoanalytical Library, No. 23, Hogarth, 1932.

Eichorn, August, *Wayward Youth,* Viking Press, 1935.

English, O. Spurgeon, and Pearson, Gerald H. J., *Common Neuroses of Children and Adults,* Norton, 1937.

Freud, Sigmund, *Totem and Taboo,* translated by A. A. Brill, New Republic, 1931.

Horney, Karen, *The Neurotic Personality of Our Time,* Norton, 1937.

Menninger, Karl A., *Man against Himself,* chap. 3, Harcourt, Brace, 1938.

Chapter XIV

NEUROTIC PATTERNS

ALCOHOLISM

IT HAS BEEN estimated that there are over one and a half million people in the United States who are social problems by reason of the excessive use of alcohol. This is a large number of people, and they constitute a tremendous social problem. Everyone is familiar with the proverbial alcoholic who spends all his money on liquor, leaving his family without food or clothing and often physically abusing them as well. The picture is truer to life than we like to realize.

Every person with an alcoholic problem has a personality difficulty—a neurosis. Every alcoholic is an immature, insecure, oversensitive and anxious person who is suffering from marked feelings of inferiority, unable to meet and enjoy people socially or unable to get on with his work without the support of alcohol in fairly large quantities. This sounds like a serious indictment against the alcoholic, but with rare exceptions it is a true one. The reason we do not as yet generally accept it as true is because we often see the alcoholic at his best rather than at his worst. We see him before he has drunk too much, when he is genial, friendly, often full of compliments, telling jokes and amusing people with his wit. But after he has a little more to drink his wit becomes monotonous and his stories cease to hold the center of attention, whereupon his sensitivity comes to the fore, he drinks some more in order to cover up his feelings of chagrin and finally he becomes so objectionable that he has to be removed from the scene.

The use of alcohol in large quantities is an indictment against society and shows a lack of maturity in that society. Undoubtedly too many people need alcohol to produce friendliness and a state of mind suitable for social intercourse or for carrying on their work, which means they are not fundamentally strong enough or friendly enough to carry on these functions without alcohol.

Drinking together, no matter what the beverage may be, is a symbol of friendship and goodwill and has a place in our civilization. Just as drinking and eating mean so much to us when we are very young, so they continue to have their place throughout life. As hosts we serve tea or coffee or wine or a soft drink as an evidence of friendship. The drink produces a pleasant sensation within and we feel emotionally warmer toward each other. This custom has a definite place in our society. However, as time goes on, either because life grows more complicated or because it makes more demands, people seem to need more alcohol in order to be friendly in the company of others or in order to get work done.

Why do people have to drink excessively in order to help their personalities accomplish what they are supposed to accomplish without any such help? A regression to an oral activity takes place in the alcoholic. The habit of drinking—having something go into the mouth and down the throat—has a great deal of meaning for these people. In infancy we were warmed and made comfortable by drinking milk and being nursed by the mother. And in the same way that these attentions quieted the anxiety of the infant, so does drinking liquor fulfill the alcoholic's present need. Alcohol acts as a narcotic; it affects the brain and deadens for the moment the painful impressions of unhappiness that have been built up with the years. For instance: A man enters a roomful of people. He feels strange, awkward, out of place, unwanted and uncomfortable. He is reluctant to get into conversation with anyone for fear of being regarded as silly or dull or stupid. Then he has a drink or two which dulls his anxiety and lo! a miracle occurs: he begins to feel interesting and important and worth while and to achieve a greater sense of comfort and well-being. He says to himself: "If two drinks work so marvelously, six will make me practically a genius." And so he continues, always hoping to reach the point of genuine ecstasy and well-being—of inner security. But he never achieves this happy state. He just gets drunk instead.

As we have already pointed out, the alcoholic personality has had early life experiences of great deprivation so that he or she (for there are women alcoholics) grows up feeling insecure and unable to cope with responsibilities. He reaches a point where he says, "Nothing ordinarily seems worth while. It is only when I am drinking that life seems bearable." If our experiences are pleasant and satisfying enough, we do not need to lean too heavily upon alcohol to make us feel buoyant and able to function from day to day.

Let us look at the matter of the personality of the alcoholic from the standpoint of sexual development. We have already said that the alcoholic is immature and that he seems to have strong oral trends. This grows naturally from the tendency to keep children dependent. Many parents fear that if the child is allowed to be aggressive and curious and has his curiosity satisfied he will grow up to be a problem in management or will leave parental authority too soon, and so he is kept frightened and dependent. It is a little like Hitler's idea of the "New Order"— tell them nothing; teach them nothing; do not let them know what the world is all about; and they can be managed. Because of this mistaken attitude, young people are kept from knowing the facts of sexuality and from developing into self-reliant individuals. All of which makes child raising easier (in the early years at least), but with disastrous results to the child's personality, to his social development, and to his genital level of functioning—which is the goal of life in successful home and family formation.

Grown people cannot remain dependent in attitude if they are to be successful with life's problems. It is that attitude of dependency that is present in the relation of the alcoholic who marries a maternal type of woman. He senses she is going to excuse him and take care of him. He works for a year or two, drinks more and more and enjoys her less and less. His interest is only in the bottle, and he neglects his obligations. After every drinking bout his wife excuses him and thinks, "Poor fellow, it is too bad." If anyone objects and tries to make him a responsible person, his wife smuggles liquor in for him, condones his behavior and gives no co-operation.

Such a wife may complain about her husband's behavior and seem to want him cured, but actually she wants to continue to indulge him. She does not want to make him stand up and be a man for two main reasons common to most human beings. One is our tendency to indulge others in those things that are important to them because we would like to be indulged ourselves. The other is the fear of arousing the other's hostility and reproaches when something is taken away from him. However, if the wives and families of alcoholic men want to help them, they should not mind reproaches.

When men come to indulge themselves more and more in the oral gratification of drinking, in the association of others who are likewise heavy drinkers, and in the mistreatment of their wives, they show themselves to be sick sexually and to be immature, acting like babies rather than like men who have an adult genital attitude toward the world. We were once asked by the court to examine a man who had been drinking.

He was married and "doing very well at it," as he put it. We pressed him with questions about his attitude toward his wife and his marriage and when he finally saw what we were driving at he said, "If I had to choose between a woman and a bottle, I would take the bottle every time."

To summarize: First, the alcoholic is made to feel warm, comfortable and glowing inside with the alcohol, partly through the physical activity of drinking and partly through the physiological reaction within him. Second, the alcohol reacts upon the mind so that it becomes possible to fantasy more pleasantly. Third, it deadens some of the pain of anxiety and depression and makes the task of socializing temporarily easier.

The more the alcoholic uses alcohol, the more he is going in the direction of all drug addicts, becoming more and more dependent upon it— be it a narcotic, a sedative or anything that gives him a "lift." He neglects to concern himself with the satisfactions to be gained through contacts with human beings and from his work. The final result is that alcohol is the only thing that satisfies him and the getting of it his chief concern—like the infant whose chief concern is obtaining milk and being nursed.

The question arises with friends, family and doctor—what shall be done about this condition? A specific case in this regard is a man of thirty-three who was the youngest of five children. His mother was a sensitive, empty, narrow-minded person who had little to give the children and who as she grew older became extremely bitter about life; by the time this youngest son came along she had only bitterness and criticism for him. Her chief pleasure seemed to be in making sarcastic remarks and in driving the children to a point of confusion—whereupon she would give them the worst verbal berating she could think of. She rarely left the house but stayed at home and complained about the neighbors and her husband, quarreled with the children and had almost no motherly feeling toward them, and particularly toward this boy. The father was a fairly capable businessman whose wife was too much for him. He sacrificed the children, and particularly this boy, to her mental state, and instead of standing up for the children and defending them against her, he always took the attitude, "Let's keep the peace. You know how mother is."

In spite of this atmosphere the boy got through high school and wanted to go to college. His mother disapproved, and again, instead of backing up the boy, the father said, "You know how your mother is. Let's keep the peace because mother will make it too hard for us if we don't." This, on top of all the other disappointments he had had, made the boy so bitter, resentful and dissatisfied that he took to drinking in increasing quantity. While under the influence of alcohol he would become irritable and pugnacious because his irritability and hostility toward his mother came forth. He had been brought up in such a hostile family environment that he could not feel friendliness anywhere. He held a job for a short time but gradually worked for shorter and shorter periods. Now he is in a state that requires a long period of rehabilitation; that is, if it is possible to cure him at all, because alcohol may be the last support a potential psychotic holds onto before going insane. Some people are mildly alcoholic all their lives and are fairly successful. Others go downhill rather rapidly when the underlying neurosis or psychosis is severe, and they may go all the way from apparent success to complete failure in three or four years.

Various attempts to cure alcoholism were made at one time with the use of drugs, whose purpose was, on the whole, to make the taste of alcohol obnoxious. Another attempt that is still sometimes used is to put a drug into the alcohol which will make the drinker sick and in this way an association is built up between alcoholic indulgence and feeling sick and miserable which will induce the person to leave it alone. Although these drug therapies were regularly advertised in all the household magazines and many families sent for them, they have resulted in only occasional successes because the personality difficulty in alcoholism is the crux of the matter.

To help an alcoholic, he must first be made to understand himself and his reasons for drinking. He has to be shown why he is failing with life itself, and then helped to be more of a success. This may be done by the doctor working with the patient alone, in private practice or in a sanitarium, or by contact with an organization called the Alcoholics Anonymous. Those sanitaria that have been most successful with alcoholic cases are the ones where individual attention is given to the patient not only in regard to a physical program but also to his personality problems. His anxieties, fears, and anything in the immediate environment that makes him feel distressed and which he cannot face are discussed with him. Then an effort is made to trace these anxieties back to the original situation that created them, and patient and doctor set to work to correct them as far as is possible.

Recently we heard an alcoholic who had been in a great deal of trouble say, "I have not a friend in the world. I do not trust anybody and I can tell you in a fairly short time why I have come to feel this way." He went on to relate experiences where he felt his friends had let him down. The point was that in all these experiences he was unduly sensitive to what was done and said. Furthermore he did not have enough goodwill in his own makeup to forgive these things and to realize that he was not being turned down so completely after all. People who come to sanitaria for the treatment of alcoholism feel they have been badly treated. If one word is said against them they respond by feeling justified for having used alcohol to try to find a little happiness in a world that has been neglecting and mistreating them for so long. They have to be shown that it is not the world that is so bad but their sensitivity and fear of the world.

Another favorable factor in sanitaria lies in the fact that there are others there who are also alcoholics. When patients find others with similar problems, they are more willing to work and struggle with their own. It is easier for them to find that they can get along without alcohol. This self-respect and loyalty to family and friends increase, and they leave the sanitarium with new ideas and a new perspective of themselves. Their success is often due to the fact that attention has been focused sharply on their personality problems. The best of these sanitaria have the atmosphere of a fraternity, where fraternal feelings are carefully cultivated. A strong personal entreaty is made to stay on the wagon, and staying on the wagon is made to look as attractive as possible. Also, the appeal to stay on the wagon is made for the sake of the sanitarium itself. And so patients leave with the feeling that they cannot fall into old ways because of loyalty to the sanitarium and to the doctor in charge.

Many have been helped by the organization called Alcoholics Anonymous, branches of which exist in many cities. It might be of some value to doctors to see how the organization is run and how it aims to help the man who is drinking. At their meetings the general problems of alcoholism are discussed. In addition, the drinkers themselves may get up and discuss their personal problems. This group feeling is vitally important. They feel that they belong to something and someone, and that feeling acts as a sustaining force through the week between meetings.

Each utilizes his concept of God and religious action in his own way. They are asked to take an interest in and help each other, and thus reduce the great degree of egocentricity that is so characteristic of them. Together they learn to function effectively without alcohol. Nearly everyone who has difficulty with alcohol has to stop drinking entirely. He cannot drink even a little. He cannot drink beer or ale with its small alcoholic content, for before long he will reach the whisky stage again. The only thing to be done is to leave it alone entirely.

Alcoholics sometimes attempt psychoanalysis, which involves intensive work on the personality and seeing the patient as frequently as every day. The doctor, on the other hand, who treats the alcoholic in his usual office practice should not be surprised if he is not successful, for the patient may not keep his appointments for long. It is not of much help to send alcoholics to a large mental hospital to stay for a while, for very little is accomplished, and often the only benefit derived is that they are without alcohol for a time and that their families are temporarily relieved. Mental hospitals are filled with psychotics and others suffering from severe personality disorders, and alcoholism is so subtle and so difficult to treat in a mental hospital that these hospitals do not relish taking alcoholics as patients. We trust we have indicated the need of those associated with the alcoholic to recognize his personality sickness, to recognize it early and to take an effective therapeutic attitude toward it.

IMPOTENCE AND FRIGIDITY

An age-old problem is that of couples who are unhappily married or who go so far as to seek separation or divorce because they are "mismated" or sexually "incompatible." These and other terms are used to denote that they are unable to enjoy the sexual relationship. It is important that married couples enjoy the sexual relationship for many reasons. In a culture making ever increasing demands upon the individual for tolerance and patience and interest in things outside himself, it is important that he be able to derive all possible physical and emotional satisfaction from marriage. The marriage relationship, coming on at the time of increased social responsibility, offers through the opportunity of a close physical relationship with the opposite sex a chance thereby to recapture some of the sustaining satisfaction that the child found so useful and enjoyable in the mother. The value of touch in human relationships should not be underestimated. From the time the child becomes too proud to be rocked in the mother's arms he does not have the pleasure of close touch again until he arrives at some of the petting of adolescence. Later in marriage *each* person can be the giver. Neither has to be wholly parent, neither wholly child, but each gives to the other in the play of lovemaking and in the sexual relationship.

The complicated arrangements preceding marriage and the strenuous events of the wedding are not conducive to a good start in sexual adjustment. The emotional tensions incident to shopping, dressmaking, invitations, being on display, calming distressed relatives and so on are definitely deleterious to that calm and relaxed state of mind which should accompany the initiation into sexual relations.

The genital organs are the executive organs of much of the pleasurable exchanges in the relationship. But often they cannot execute their function. They refuse to participate in the love act. We say the male is *impotent* when he cannot achieve an erection, or when he is unable to maintain erection long enough to effect entrance into the vagina and make at least a few coital movements before ejaculation occurs. We ordinarily speak of the woman as being *frigid* when she is disinterested in coitus or when, participating in coitus, she is unable to obtain any pleasure from it. A more specific description of the relative degrees of impotence and frigidity would be as follows:

MALE

1. Impotence complete with no interest in coitus.
2. Impotence complete but interest retained in coitus.
3. Premature ejaculation or excessively retarded ejaculation.
4. Inadequate or partial erection.
5. Interested in coitus but cannot always have erection when desired.
6. Potent but coitus had under protest.
7. Potent but coitus lacks pleasure.

FEMALE

1. Dyspareunia and vaginismus.
2. Vaginal anesthesia with aversion to coitus.
3. Vaginal anesthesia with no special aversion to coitus.
4. Mild pleasure in coitus but without orgasm.
5. Only occasional orgasm.
6. Occasional failure to obtain orgasm.
   (All usually accompanied by some lack of vaginal secretion.)

Thinking over these various degrees of emotional disturbance will enable the physician to estimate the severity of the case in question. Though not always true, it is certainly more likely that the woman who has had a great deal of pain and distress with coitus would tend to have greater psychological difficulty with subsequent sexual experiences than the woman who has achieved some satisfaction in the relationship. The man who has no interest in sex relations whatever is, by and large, the most difficult case to treat: his impotence being a psychological disturbance, the physician will have just that much more work to do with him in order to bring about improvement in this feeling. The man who retains his interest in coitus but who is completely impotent may be more easily helped because of the fact that he has some feelings and some ideation centering around the subject of intercourse.

Premature ejaculation is not usually thought of as impotence but the results can be just as serious because the man has difficulty in having sexual pleasure and in giving sexual pleasure to his wife. If he ejaculates before intromission, he will be unable to bring about pregnancy in his wife. When ejaculation is unduly prolonged, the result may be very fatiguing to both parties and the pleasurable spontaneity of coitus is absent. The man with an inadequate erection is suffering from a very disturbing symptom that affects both partners, depriving each of pleasure and frequently causing humiliation and feelings of inferiority in the man.

The man who is interested in coitus but cannot always have an erection when desired has considerable capacity for the sexual relationship at all times but the capacity is of short duration. The man who has little difficulty in getting an erection but who feels and believes that sexual intercourse is debilitating and will do him harm and has intercourse under protest, worries about the result to his health and how it will weaken his vitality; such an attitude is naturally not conducive to conjugal happiness. Some men have little pleasure in coitus and give a history of having intercourse once or twice a month, sometimes as infrequently as once a year. If the wife is sexually normal, she is bound to find incompatibility in such a marriage.

Ordinarily we think of the frigid woman as having no feeling of pleasure; in addition to this lack there may be an actual feeling of pain in the vaginal muscles with attempt at entry, so that they are thrown into spasm. Such a woman is usually much sicker emotionally than the one who can at least go through the act of intercourse without these handicaps. As in impotence, there are varying degrees in frigidity also. The woman who has no feeling and does not want to be approached sexually usually also has the feeling that she is being exploited and uses excuses like the fear of pregnancy and menstruation to avoid coitus. The woman who has very little feeling of pleasure in coitus but who, as she says, "does not mind it," usually feels she is quite normal and that she is very lucky not to have an actual aversion to the act. When such women are asked if they have sexual satisfaction, they often answer "yes" because they have never given much thought to the ecstatic pleasure of orgasm and, since intercourse is not distasteful to them, have taken it for granted that they have experienced all there is to enjoy.

Then there is the woman whose pleasure never reaches the point of orgasm which is the end point of complete pleasure and is accompanied by varying degrees of involuntary muscular movements ending in relaxation and satisfaction. Some women accept the lack of orgasm as normal for their sex while others recognize that it is not and seek some improvement in their status. There are women who have orgasm once in every three or four acts of coitus, or who have great difficulty in achieving orgasm and only under special circumstances.

Finally, there is the woman who occasionally fails to have orgasm. She is not likely to come to a physician or seek his counsel, yet she may, since less prudishness about sex is causing young couples to seek a better sexual adjustment than the preceding generation demanded.

Before going on we would like to make clear the difference between impotence, frigidity and sterility. These terms are often misused. Sterility in the woman means she is unable to become pregnant and sterility in the man means he is unable to bring about pregnancy in his wife. Yet there may be *no* disturbance in the capacity of either to have sexual pleasure in the sexual relationship.

The sexual organs and the pelvic region should be energized and sensitized for the achievement of sexual pleasure. Yet there are many forces at work in society that stand in the way of its achievement. Threats, admonitions and ideas imparted from childhood onward tend to dam back the flow of psychic energy which would energize and sensitize the pelvic organs for sexual pleasure. In fairness to parents it must be said that they do not realize how much harm they are doing in frightening children and young people about sexual relations. Parents do not realize that they may cause the children to lead a fearful, unhappy and perhaps childless existence as the result of these extreme attitudes. They should be told this fact, and in many cases it is the doctor who is in the best position to tell them.

Causes of Impotence and Frigidity

1. Fear of disapproval or punishment:
   (*a*) Fear of criticism or ridicule.

       (b) Fear of bodily injury from some disapproving person other than the partner.

       (c) Fear of pregnancy.

  2. Hostility toward the partner:

       (a) A general resentment toward members of the opposite sex with desire to do them harm.

       (b) The woman resents what she considers domination by the man.

       (c) The man is envious of the woman and her role in life and refuses to give her pleasure because of this envy.

       (d) A fear by one of the partners of injuring the genital organs of the other.

  3. Conflicting loves (usually unconscious):

       (a) The man loves some other woman and is unconscious of it (mother, sister); or the woman loves some other man (father, brother) and cannot accept husband sexually.

       (b) Latent homosexuality; i. e., persons of the same sex are loved rather than persons of the opposite sex.

       (c) Too much self-love. Love of another person is an overflow from self-love. In these cases there is no love left for the sexual partner.

Fear of disapproval is strong and deep in every human being. There are people who seem to be very much at home with the subject of sexuality and who tell jokes about it yet somewhere in their makeup still retain a great deal of prudishness, prejudice, disgust and fear of ridicule about anything having to do with sex. A great many people feel sure they are in love when they marry, which ought to mean the presence of a great deal of tolerance and acceptance. Yet when it comes to the matter of sex relations, the woman is very much afraid her husband will criticize something she might say or do in the course of sex play—and the same is true of the man. They may have this fear so strongly as to prevent sexual pleasure or sexual functioning. From childhood onward it is extremely common for grownups to tease children about their friendly overtures to each other. This leads to pain and embarrassment, feelings that are difficult to get rid of later in life.

The shortest definition of impotence and frigidity is the inability of a man or woman to have sexual pleasure. In order to understand the definition it is necessary to break it down into its various components and discuss them separately.

The fear of bodily injury applies to the person who, after entering marriage, still feels that he or she is going to be punished for doing that "bad thing." In other words, the marriage ceremony has not been able to break down the fears of being punished for sexual activity which such a person has carried with him all through life. He *still* fears punishment.

A young couple's sexual relations were going very badly. They were living in close quarters with the wife's parents. They were so conscious of this fact that when they got up in the morning they felt embarrassed about facing the parents when they went downstairs. They felt the parents knew of their relationship and as a consequence might punish or ridicule them. The thought made them unable to have sexual pleasure. They were about to move to their own home and we advised them to hasten that move, after which their sexual adjustment improved.

Fear of pregnancy may be quite a serious factor in sexual pleasure. Many women still hold the erroneous belief that pregnancy will not occur when there is no sexual pleasure or orgasm. Thus women who fear pregnancy will inhibit sexual excitement, thinking to escape pregnancy in this way. Such old wives' tales have been in existence for centuries. In many cases neither the man nor the woman has a knowledge of contraceptives or they are ashamed to seek it, which fear interferes seriously with their sexual pleasure.

Hostility is another factor that frequently exists in marriage. It is assumed that only people who are in love marry and that the love they hold for each other is going to carry them along through life and solve all of their problems. Yet often people marry who are not in love as they think they are. Instead of acting from strong positive feelings toward the opposite sex they dutifully go through the social conventions. In a great many instances there exists a deep and unconscious fear of the opposite sex which in a subtle way prevents their obtaining sexual pleasure. There are also those, particularly women, who feel passionate for a few weeks or months and enjoy sexual relations. Then it disappears and they wonder why. Actually their sexual desire was weak in the first place. It started out apparently normally but soon diminished in intensity when hostility in the form of "grim seriousness" caught up with them. Hostility is an important factor to be dealt with in helping people with their problem of impotence and frigidity.

Impotence and frigidity result from an identical personality disturbance in both the male and the female. Despite the difference in anatomy, the cause is practically identical, being the lack of feeling in the sexual organs which prevents their functioning with pleasure.

With respect to hostility toward the partner, we will first consider resentment toward the opposite sex with desire to do him harm. Resentment and hostility are fairly general attitudes and the physician cannot find out whether, for instance, the husband and wife hate each other by asking them directly or even by asking whether they beat each other. A better way to find out about a patient's internal hostility toward other people is to ask him how many friends he has or how many people he likes or how well he does in positively relating to people. This is a surer way to get at the truth, since few people want to admit they have active hostility. A great deal of hostility may actually exist in those married couples who boast that they never quarrel or say a cross word to each other. What they say may be true—because they never speak to each other! Many, many couples have hostility toward each other which is not recognized and cannot be admitted. The doctor may sense it but find it quite a task to make the patient consciously aware of its presence.

In one type of hostility the woman resents what she considers domination by the man, and the man is envious of the woman and her role in life and refuses to give her pleasure because of his envy. Men and women are envious and jealous of each other. It is accepted that women are envious and jealous of men but it is not so well understood that the same holds true for men and that men are often envious and jealous of the role of women. One amazingly simple reason explains why this can be so. As children are growing up they are not told in a positive way what their role in life should be. For instance, to talk to a female about her role in life means to talk about motherhood and childbearing, and that is taboo in many homes. To talk to a boy about his role means to discuss family life and fatherhood in addition to career, and that, too, is taboo. In order to keep the whole subject of sex away from the minds of young people, parents do not prepare them for their respective roles in life, and as a consequence any pleasure and satisfaction that might be obtained from these roles are withheld at the same time. They grow up without being positively related to the role they should play, without being enthusiastic about it, and instead are being envious and jealous of a member of the opposite sex. Attitudes of this kind are not close to consciousness, and in order to make them clear, the physician must use tact and understanding. Sometimes a woman overcomes frigidity after the birth of her first child. Through having a child she comes to see herself as being "as good as the man." She has finally obtained a substitute for the envied penis—the child.

Fear of injuring the genital organs of the partner is quite a common feeling. There is hardly a man alive who grows to the age of twenty-one without sometimes having been told about the harm that will come to the genital organs through intercourse with women. Also there are few women who have not heard stories about the pain and distress of intercourse. Thus both men and women grow up with strong fears within them of the harm that results from the sexual act and specifically related to the genital organs. This again is usually an unconscious attitude. One of its most conscious forms is the fear of venereal disease. In many people this fear is so marked as to be crippling to wholesome sexual functioning.

Conflicting loves (usually unconscious), where the man loves some other woman or the woman loves some other man, are much more common than is supposed. Young people are brought up to love their parents and to feel positively toward them and often are warned not to have any emotional bonds with anyone else because to do so is to be sexually tinged and "wicked." In other families, where the sexual aspect is not so strong, it is regarded as disloyal and even sinful for a boy to become interested in a woman other than his mother or sisters. He feels a general disapproval when he makes dates or goes out with other women. The result is that when such a person, man or woman, marries (and some do not marry because this complex is so strong) a great deal of his emotional investment remains in his family instead of in his marital partner. He actually remains in love with or devoted to his mother or feels guilty that he has left home and married another woman whom he supports or with whom he sleeps. He feels this guilt every day. Some men are always attempting to relieve this feeling of guilt by visiting home frequently, giving money to a mother or sister that is not needed or necessary, or asking advice of one or the other—all of which may be very annoying to the wife. Likewise there are women who never can seem to have a proper attitude toward their husbands. They not only cannot be tender or affectionate, having been taught that to be so is wrong, but they also cannot be loyal or have any respect for the husbands' opinions or desires. They refer all matters to the father or brothers to decide. These attitudes grow out of an improper and inadequate solution of the Oedipus complex, which is the emotional tie that exists between the female child and her father or between the male child and his mother.

We emphasized earlier that these emotions are not only present but necessary and acceptable during a certain period. All we ask for healthy development is that people do not remain fixed at that childish level of loving but finally get away from loving their own family and become able to love someone outside of it.

Fears of harm to the genital organs are remnants of a strong castration complex—a complex that exists in spite of the skepticism of some people. Some males unconsciously feel that the vagina is a fearsome cavity in which the penis will be lost, or squeezed, or bitten off. As boys they hear the untrue and fantastic story of the couple who became stuck together by reason of some unexplained contraction of the vagina, and the penis had to be amputated in order to effect a separation. Women hear of the pain that can be suffered in intercourse. Both fear harm to the other by way of venereal disease. As children they are warned not to touch each other's bodies—that to do so results in harm. Working with patients will in time convince those physicians who are skeptical that these constellations of ideas are important to understand and that parents should be made aware of them so that they can be handled adequately in childhood and not persist into adulthood and create the many problems that physicians see in daily practice.

Latent homosexuality is a condition of emotional immaturity. Remember, we do not love the opposite sex exclusively. There is some capacity for loving the same sex in everyone and this should be so for any desirable social functioning. The emotions of some people, however, have been so completely steered away from the opposite sex and such a wall has been erected between them and their ability to love someone of the opposite sex that they are what we call latently homosexual. This does not mean that the person actively participates in a homosexual relationship but that he is emotionally attached to the same sex to a greater degree than to the opposite sex, and that this feeling may result in impotence in the male or frigidity in the female.

Too much self-love is another condition of immaturity. There are people who grow up being so self-centered and demanding that they have nothing left over to give to anyone else, either in a sexual relation or in any other social relation. It is important to be able to function adequately sexually, to make someone happy in the sex relationship, and as a human being to be able to be interested in the feelings of another. This lack does not necessarily come about through what we call "spoiling." When the word spoiling is used we think of a person who has been "loved to death" and given everything he ever wanted from birth onward. Actually that is not necessarily the case. When it is the case the person comes out spoiled because no one ever trained him or requested him to think of others, to do things for others or to consider their feelings.

However, some of the most self-centered people are not necessarily those who have received a great deal. They are also the people who have had too little, who have lived in great emotional deprivation, whether in rich homes or poor, and the result of this emotional deprivation is to make them anxious and fearful. They are anxious and fearful because they feel that if they become too much interested in someone else, they will "lose out," they will "miss something," or they will suffer in some way. These people can never compromise or make plans that include the convenience of another. They can rarely say a kind word or rarely congratulate another person. Their conversation revolves about themselves, what they are doing and would like to do. A thought of making anyone else happy rarely enters their consciousness unless by chance it happened to make them feel good at the same time. Such people have been brought up to feel that they *give away* too much through participating in sexual relationships and as a result can easily be impotent or frigid.

Treatment of Impotence and Frigidity

Since most cases of impotence and frigidity (aside from a few resulting from demonstrable organic disease) are caused by disturbances in emotions and ideation, then the cure must aim toward modifying the feelings such people have toward each other and modifying their ideas about sexual functioning. Other approaches have been tried, based on theories of causation. There is, of course, the very prevalent idea that impotence and frigidity are due to a lack of glandular substance and therefore supplying this lack would naturally have a good effect upon the condition. In the first place, very rarely does a person suffering from impotence or frigidity show any glandular deficiency and very rarely does the giving of a glandular substance have a favorable influence. It used to be thought—and still is by some—that frigidity in the female is due to adhesions around the clitoris. This again is rarely if ever true. Operations that consist of grafting a glandular tissue substance to the male have been tried with limited success. When we come to evaluate the therapeutic effects of operation, we must not lose sight of the high degree of suggestibility associated with this form of treatment.

Therefore, if we are going to approach this subject from the psychological standpoint, we must take a very careful history of such persons, with particular emphasis upon the sexual side of their personality development, and try to bring out certain points. At the outset we want to know the attitude of the parents in the matter of sex. We have found that three general attitudes are taken in the home toward sex education. One is to enlighten the children in a sensible way as they come to ask questions, telling them as much as they want to know and no more, being prepared to tell them the answer to what they ask—not limiting the imparting of the information to any one day or age period and then with a sigh of relief saying, "That is over!" In other words, parents should be sufficiently at home and comfortable with the subject of sexuality to see the child's interest in it when it appears and enlighten him as he wants to be enlightened. The result will be that by the time the young person has reached twenty years of age he will have gathered the facts slowly, integrated them well, and feel comfortable about the subject of sex.

The second parental attitude so commonly seen is a more negative one. An effort is made to condemn everything pertaining to sexuality and to stress the dangers of sexual indulgence of all kinds; sex is called dirty and disgusting. Bad though this sounds, however, it is not the worst attitude that can be taken.

The third attitude, in which the whole subject is completely ignored, is the worst of all. Families who refuse to mention or discuss sex, who treat it as a subject not of this world, one that no decent, self-respecting person would think of, do far more harm in the end than those who take the attitude of condemnation, bad as that is. For fathers and mothers who emphasize the dangers of sex at least recognize and accept some thinking on the subject, and ideas germinate that can be corrected outside and that can through fortuitous circumstances be overcome. But in families where no thinking is allowed at all, where sex is not even dignified by condemnation, the children have a very hard struggle in making a sexual adjustment. Since no one in authority even touches upon the subject, these children may have a great feeling of guilt or many mistaken notions about sex which they harbor within themselves. They are the children who do not exchange ideas with other children, and hence grow up ignorant, emotionally and ideationally empty and with very little feeling about sexual functioning. They are the cases that are extremely difficult to treat because even when what the doctor says carries weight, he still has a difficult time combating twenty-one years or more of parental authority which has been saying that no right-minded person has any thoughts or feelings concerning sex. When the doctor starts to re-educate such a person he often finds nothing within the person that can respond to him and be utilized.

In questioning the patient, however, the doctor should ask specifically whether sexual matters in the home were regarded as disgusting, whether there was an effort made to separate the sexual function from the excretory function. He may ask whether there existed in the home a religious attitude strongly opposed to sexual thinking or functioning, whether love of the opposite sex and sexual expression were associated.

When a doctor begins to question people about sexual matters, they usually reply, "Everything was all right in my home," or "I had the average sexual education." Not until he questions them specifically is he able to help them to see in how many ways their thinking about sex was not average or normal. Even today there are many who believe that love is some pure ethereal feeling and that any physical expression of it is not a part of real love. The physician should ask whether fears were instilled over sexual expression, such as evil resulting from masturbation, the pain of venereal disease, or the shame and disgrace of illegitimate pregnancy. He should ask if sexual indulgence was pictured as hateful, frivolous, or dangerous. He should inquire as to whether the parents were in love with each other—a very important question—and also whether he ever saw demonstrations of affection between them.

The doctor should inquire into the parents' attitude toward other people outside the home who showed affection and ask whether there was any strong emotional tie to the parent of either sex. He may not get a very satisfactory answer to that question alone but by asking about the patient's behavior to the parent he will get a better idea of the emotional tie existing between parent and patient. He should learn whether the social and procreative roles of men and women were clearly outlined during growth and whether the patient has a strong attachment to the same sex. Thus will the doctor be able to define for himself and for the patient the wrong attitudes and feelings existing in the latter that need to be changed. He must be able to describe to the patient the new attitudes and feelings that must be learned if the patient is to create the proper attitude for sexual functioning.

The treatment for impotence and frigidity is not easy but a few cases respond fairly well. A woman had been married for three years without sexual pleasure. She had come from a home such as we described in the second group, where everything pertaining to sex was considered shameful and disgusting and where no one, particularly a woman, could take an active interest in sex or sex relationships and still be respected. The result was that though she was a woman of feeling and imagination, she took the attitude that in marriage the woman is to be used for the husband's pleasure and is never to make advances or take an active part in intercourse. After only two or three discussions with her, emphasizing the fact that women have as much right to sexual pleasure as men, as much right to discuss it and to make advances, she was able to participate to a much greater extent. In such discussions the doctor is sympathetically fulfilling the function of an authority—a function that should have been taken over earlier by the parent. All that was wanting was sanction for the sexual feeling and sexual activity.

There is another type in which some degree of impotence or frigidity is present and which does not need too much help. The husband or wife has become too preoccupied with his or her tasks, makes no time or opportunity for adequate sexual expression, feels that making a living or taking excellent care of the children and home comes first. The husband or wife is always tired, but regretful that sex relations are not what they were in the beginning, yet never gets around to taking any positive constructive attitude toward it. A discussion is usually needed for both husband and wife and suggestions made that they give some of the time and enthusiasm they are putting into everyday matters to plans for their lovemaking. In other words, they are expecting their love life to flourish without giving it any attention. It may not and rarely does when so neglected. In this very hurried, hazardous world in which we are living today, satisfactory sexual adjustment in marriage is not easy to maintain. We do have to give some thought and allow some time for it. If couples do not take an interest in an occasional trip, a show, a movie, a night out in order to put themselves in the frame of mind for lovemaking, they may suffer a partial degree of frigidity or impotence.

In a problem of this kind one or two discussions with the husband or wife are necessary first and then a discussion together. This is usually sufficient to improve their pleasure and ability for sexual functioning. When they learn that they cannot neglect giving some attention to their sexual relations, they usually take the doctor's suggestions and improve.

In a book of this kind we cannot go into all the factors surrounding marriage and sexual adjustment in detail. There are books on marriage that should be read by those having difficulty in marital adjustment. A book discussing the technique of coitus, for instance, might be very helpful for some. Such books are readily obtainable—the real problem is how to get people who need them to read them and *think about their contents*. We would like to close with the idea that in sexual adjustment —as in many other problems—kindness and thoughtfulness on the part of each human being involved will solve many problems. Both the mystery and the suffering connected with sexual maladjustment could be solved if each would have the generosity in his nature to be frank, listen to the other and try, *even though it hurts,* to be kind and meet the other's needs in the sexual as well as in the other relations.

UNUSUAL SEXUAL BEHAVIOR

In the teaching of medicine the subject of sexual perversion is usually left relatively untouched. The reason for this practice is probably due to the fact that the general practitioner does not often meet an individual who is behaving in a sexually perverted way. When he does, however, it is important that he know something about the patient's way of acting and that he be able to take an understanding attitude toward him.

Doctors are heard to express themselves most violently on this subject, saying they would have nothing whatsoever to do with a sexually perverted individual. We believe greater tolerance is necessary. There is no reason to reject a person completely because he has a problem of behavior in the sphere of sex. The best way to handle such a person is, first, to listen to his story and, second, to be able to tell him something about the ideas and attitudes that lie behind his behavior. The doctor may not cure the patient of his perversion but he can give him much reassurance, comfort and advice. And it is important for physicians to make themselves acquainted with the causes of sexually perverted behavior.

There are no fixed concepts about the normality of sexual behavior; it varies greatly from individual to individual and even in the heterosexually mature person. There are people whose behavior is such as to approach perversion, and sometimes is actually regarded as such by them. Among the various forms of perversion are the following: *fetishism,* which consists of deriving erotic satisfaction from loving things instead of people, such as a piece of a person's clothing, or hair, or shoe; *homosexuality,* obtaining gratification by practicing intimacies with a member of the same sex; *sadism,* obtaining gratification by inflicting pain and cruelty upon another person; *masochism,* obtaining sexual satisfaction by the opposite procedure—having pain inflicted upon the self; *voyeur-*

ism, obtaining gratification by looking at other people; *exhibitionism,* obtaining sexual satisfaction by exposing the self to the gaze of others; *bestiality,* obtaining sexual satisfaction by contact with animals; *pedophilia,* obtaining satisfaction by the seduction of children.

These behaviors are some of the more frequent of the unusual ways of achieving sexual gratification which come under the heading of sexual perversion. There is another phenomenon which lies in the realm of the normal love life of men and women: the tendency for one partner to bring the mouth in contact with the genitals of the other partner—called *fellatio* when it is the penis and *cunnilingus* when it is the vagina. This act may give pleasure not only to the one who actively carries it out but also to the more passive participant.

There are many definitions of a sexual pervert. The one we select is that a sexual perversion is a sexual activity that consistently defeats the aims of procreation. We prefer this definition to others because it seems to be a practical one and takes into consideration and allows room for certain occasional sexual practices out of the realm of what is called perversion. If we called all the things we mentioned above perversions whenever and wherever they occur, it would cause concern in a great many people. We cannot make any hard line between the abnormal and normal. However, if we call those acts perversions which consistently defeat the aims of procreation, then we have a broad, reasonable field of sexual perverse behavior that allows some of the deviations to be present in the life of the individual; he becomes perverse only if he does not eventually achieve a heterosexual adjustment.

Why does society become so upset about homosexuality or any type of sexually perverted behavior? The first important reason is that people feel it is unesthetic and conflicts with our idealistic values. The second important reason is that if all sexuality were carried out in perverse behavior, the aims of procreation would be defeated and we would soon die off as a race. The latter is only a theoretical possibility but it still alarms people.

Actually, we condemn sexually perverse behavior without knowing exactly why we do so. The truth is that people do lead their sexual lives in private, and how they conduct their sexual relations need be none of our business. Nevertheless, we have a great tendency to be upset about it, as if this type of behavior contaminated us in some way, and we act as though our condemnation could bring about its reduction. We would like to make clear that we can never bring about the reduction of perverse sexual behavior through condemnation, through punishment of the sexually perverse individual, by excluding him from our lives or from society, by bringing him into court and putting him in jail. These attempts do nothing to change him; he will go on with his perverse behavior just the same; we will never understand what caused it and hence will never cure it.

In a way we have no more reason to condemn the sexually perverse individual than we have to condemn an individual soldier for killing in wartime. For he is driven on by strong instinctual forces of which he is not aware—forces of which doctors and scientists have to be aware if they hope to alleviate the problem. The sexually perverse person is often hated, lonely and in conflict about his problem.

Homosexuality is only one form of perverse sexual behavior and is a character disturbance. It is indeed questionable whether there is any such thing as a constitutional homosexual. Furthermore, studies upon the glands do not give as yet any evidence that homosexuality is a matter of inherited glandular defect—with the possible exclusion of hermaphrodites who have remnants of sexual glands of both sexes. They—the hermaphrodites and pseudo-hermaphrodites—form a very small group; while homosexuals form a large group. Among homosexuals there are only a few who affect the mannerisms and dress of the opposite sex. The vast majority do not indulge in this conspicuous variety of behavior.

In seeking for the causes for the development of a sexually perverse individual, we find much the same ones operating as in the development of a neurosis, and we do not think it is stretching the concept of perverse sexuality too far to say it is a matter of neurotic conflict. A short definition of sexual perversion is to call it the persistence of infantile trends. Certainly voyeurs and exhibitionists are grownups experiencing a stage that all children go through. They are merely living out something they thought and wanted to do when they were younger but which they were not allowed to do; hence they live out these impulses later in life. There is also a great immaturity in the emotions of homosexual persons. The person who eventually becomes sexually perverse has difficulties in normal personality development. Certain important impulses have been frustrated, dammed back, blocked in their efforts toward the normal development of what we call the average well-adjusted personality. First, the homosexual had his sexual curiosity stifled as a maturing child. Second, sexual activity such as masturbation has been prohibited.

The normal aggressions, together with their ideas, have also been curtailed. The boy who wants to interest himself in masculine things and behavior is discouraged by his mother and becomes what is known as a "sissy"; the girl, too, is disturbed in her normal outlets and interests. This is clearly brought out in a book called *The Well of Loneliness,* in which the girl was started off by a father who was intent upon interesting her in boys' things and masculine interests. In these cases interest in the opposite sex has been shamed and discouraged and sexual play has been punished. They are unfortunate in their lack of opportunity to identify: the boy may have a weak, passive father; he may possibly have a dominating mother, who is very likely to thwart his curiosity and other efforts toward heterosexuality and also arouse in him a great hostility toward women. Hence he does not want to have anything to do with them later in life, and he finds more sympathy and understanding with men. Through his contact with his dominating mother he comes to fear and hate women and to prefer the company of men.

Then comes the matter of sexual seduction. We are putting this last because while it is true that a child might be seduced into homosexuality by someone much older, there are nevertheless many completely heterosexual people who have had some such sexual experience and who nevertheless remain heterosexual. In other words one or two experiences of this kind do not necessarily lead to homosexuality. It can do so only when the foundations for homosexual behavior and responding to it emotionally are already laid in the very early years of childhood.

Seduction is important in itself but by no means *all* important. It is much too superficial an explanation to say a person becomes homosexual because he or she was seduced at the age of ten by an older person of the same sex. One reason for condemning a sexually perverse individual is because he does not have the same responsibility toward a socially accepted form of conduct as the heterosexual individual does. He may be more public and indiscreet about his sexual activities and more ruthless in the seduction of younger children than the heterosexual individual. We have the right to require (whatever his sexual impulses are) that he at least control his activities to keep them in line with what is socially tolerable. Generally he does as well as he can but occasionally he does not have the feeling of propriety about sexual matters that the heterosexual does. The doctor may be able to help the sexually perverse person who is indiscreet in his sexual life. He may take the attitude that it is unfortunate he has this type of sexual expression but go on to say, "Whatever you do with it you owe it to society to be discreet. If you find people who are interested in sex expression that is similar to yours, what you do may be your own business, but I do not think you have the right to harm others with these impulses. You must hold them within reasonable control."

The cause of homosexuality is a sexual immaturity. Homosexuals do not progress toward a concept of heterosexual relations, which are concerned with marriage and family formation. We start life with sensual pleasures centered about the oral zone. Later, during the period of toilet training, come the pleasures associated with the activity of the anal and urethral area. Following that we must progress toward an interest in genital activity which carries us toward marriage, home formation and associated responsibilities. When people get delayed (fixated) at oral or anal activities, they tend to be neurotic, to be less constructive in their attitude toward society. Those who are not properly helped through these periods run some risk of becoming sexually abnormal or neurotic. Freudian psychology speaks of the *oral* years, the *anal* years and the *genital* years of childhood psychosexual development. The concepts that go with these words carry with them the broader ideas of *physiological-psychological growth* and are important for human adjustment.

There are homosexuals who lead constructive lives and make a contribution to society in spite of being homosexual, but they are in the minority. When people are homosexual there is a tendency for them to be immature in their reactions, easily depressed and discouraged, frequently frustrated and with a tendency to involve themselves in love affairs with their own sex which often end in jealousy, disappointment, frustration, depression and quite frequently suicide. They are less well-rounded personalities than heterosexuals, more emotionally unstable, and tend to be dependent. Some are actually delinquent. Associated with their great passivity they may be alcoholic or even involved in criminal activity. The most common types of activity displayed by the homosexual are mutual masturbation, fellatio or cunnilingus, and, in men, the contact of the penis with the anus. Any of these acts are possible means of gratification and some homosexuals will use one or more of them at various times. Male homosexuals usually prefer the company of men, and female homosexuals that of women; and each may prefer the things pertaining to the opposite sex rather than to the same sex. Homosexuals vary in degree all the way from those who merely like the company of their own sex and never engage overtly in physical homosexual behavior in their whole lives to those for whom homosexual activity is nearly everything. In other words, their need for physical sexual expression varies as it does in heterosexuals.

Sometimes homosexuals live together in order to have steady companionship and sexual expression and may accomplish it successfully for a fairly long period. But usually their emotional immaturity makes such stability impossible. A business woman of thirty-six had a childhood that was absolutely devoid of sexual education. She came to adolescence feeling herself to be awkward and unpopular. She never went to a dance or had any contact with sex. She had a good education. In her twenties she discovered that her interest lay with her own sex. She was a capable person and formed an attachment to a woman who was five years younger and who was just the opposite from herself, sensitive, passive, dependent, who was frequently ill and liked to be taken care of. The older woman was efficient and a good manager. She liked to run the apartment, do the cooking and take care of the younger woman. They lived together like mother and child even though they were only five years apart in age. They slept together and enjoyed homosexual relations.

The relationship continued for a year and a half when the more dependent woman became insatiable in her demands for the other's affection. She wanted her to stay home in the evening, go for walks with her, and became violently jealous of other friends. Moreover, she did not even want her to go to work. In order to enforce the older woman's enslavement she threatened suicide, which made the older woman extremely vulnerable. For when two women live together in a community, they know they are probably regarded as homosexuals. If one of them commits suicide, it causes consternation and makes the other a victim of gossip, morbid speculation and criticism. The older woman realized this and submitted. But what was originally love grew to be hate. She resented her restricted life but nevertheless did not want to break up the relationship. They were like the couple in the joke who held hands all night because if one were to let go the other would become homicidal. The result was a great deal of anxiety and unhappiness. Fortunately the older woman sought professional help. It was possible to talk to both and to point out how each was to blame, the older one overplaying the mother role and not calling a halt early enough on the younger one's childish demands.

We pointed out to the younger woman that if she was to be able to continue to enjoy the advantages of the situation that she had to allow her friend to carry on her work and not suck her dry with a very passive relationship, sapping the other's strength completely and ruining the relationship. Although she resented having to take a more mature attitude, she had sense enough to see the point of doing so. We offered her the choice of either being more reasonable or losing the older woman's friendship. She did not actually want suicide. She had too much to live for if she would do so in a mature way. The change in the situation is now quite satisfactory.

It is difficult to treat homosexuals, and extremely difficult to change them, for the problem is usually much too big for anyone to try to change radically. When well-meaning friends lecture a homosexual woman, for instance, and tell her she ought to be ashamed of herself and ought to get married, the practical question arises—where is she to find a husband? In the second place, think of all the emotional factors involved. She is not prepared to be a mother, does not want to live with a man if she could find one, nor is she able to gain any satisfaction from a heterosexual relationship.

We have to realize that homosexuals are seriously maladjusted persons whom we cannot cure but whom we can help by seeking to alleviate the emotional tensions in the situation. The homosexual problem is a large one; we can cure homosexuality no more easily than we can cure neuroses and criminality. Because of certain forces acting over a period of many years the homosexual has achieved an end point that is very difficult to change. He complains that society does not give approval to homosexual activity, yet at the same time he is quite satisfied with his means of gratification. When heterosexuality is offered to him—no matter how attractive it looks to us—he cannot adopt it. Furthermore, homosexuals do not come to physicians very often when in trouble because they cannot believe they will be understood.

The reader may be surprised that we discuss the case of homosexuality in terms of adjustment instead of in terms of change of attitude and behavior. There are two good reasons for our doing so. In the first place we must take a sympathetic attitude toward homosexuals, and in the second place we must accept the fact that there have been so many conditions operating that incline them in the direction of homosexuality that change becomes extremely difficult, perhaps impossible. For instance, the impulse to steal is very strong in some people and they cannot easily be converted to a life of honesty. They even go to jail repeatedly as a result of the need to steal. Also, a great many people have the impulse to use alcohol and have great difficulty in renouncing the use of it. In other words, we must realize that there are impulses in human beings that are very strong and that have to be worked out, and for which society does not possess a therapeutic program that can effect cure or change. There are times when we have to be "just practical" and accept the fact of homosexuality in certain people and try to help them live as happily and efficiently as possible. That is our task as doctors. It is tremendously important that as doctors we know what human beings are like, that we accept them as we find them, together with a certain good judgment in trying to help them get along by making the best of what we find in them.

Some doctors think they must make homosexuals change, that either they must cease the practice of homosexuality or he will have nothing to do with them. From a practical standpoint many questions follow upon advice of this sort. For instance, in most areas women outnumber men, and, in addition, a certain number of men reserve the privilege of not marrying. Hence when a doctor glibly advises two homosexual women to separate and get married, it might not be possible because they might not find the men. Even if it were possible for them to make marriages, they are not equipped emotionally for the relationship: they are not prepared to be wives and mothers of children, and the responsibility might easily result in symptoms of some kind. On the other hand, as long as they can function fairly well as homosexuals, they can at least get along. This may not be an "idealistic" viewpoint but at least it is workable and practical. We have to think of the physical adjustment of each person to the other and try to help both adjust to the circumstances as well as they can; try to make them accept this particular integration of their impulses as maturely as possible.

Some might ask the question, "Does this mean condoning the homosexual relationship, and if so by condoning it are we being a party to a perversion of the human body in its broader sense?" We think not. There are those who feel that sexual relationships even between married men and women are immoral. There are those who feel that masturbation is a perversion of the use of the human body. Most psychiatrists and educators accept the fact that masturbation is merely a step in human development and personality, which must be accepted as such in order to get the best results in personality development. In the same way, a homosexual, perverted use of the human body must be accepted as a certain particular trend in an individual and not necessarily having to do with morals. Homosexuals are doing the best they can with the personality integration that society, in the form of their families, has given them. If we *only* condemn the practice we do two bad things: we force these people to keep the matter secret and run away from an adjustment, from education and a certain amount of improvement of their lot, and second we close our minds to the nature of the problem and thus to preventing its occurring in individuals not yet entirely set in homosexuality but showing the beginning trends and in a state where they can still be helped. Therefore, if we are more accepting of sex and whatever manifestation of it we find, we are going to be better doctors in the end because we can teach people to know more about themselves and help each other grow up.

The problem of homosexuality does not lie in the physical practices that homosexuals carry out—in the "crime" as some call it—but in the fact that they are *unconstructive people,* and that is the important thing in the long run. A homosexual couple may occupy an apartment next door and thus disturb the esthetic sense of their neighbors. This is regrettable but not the disturbing issue. The important issue is that it is difficult in the long run for immature people to get along in the world. A homosexual is a person with a *neurosis* who happens to have a preference and longing for sexual contact with the same sex. We must turn our attention to spreading what information we have about the development of more mature personalities, and thus hope to avoid the incidence of homosexuality, instead of ostracizing and often punishing the individual homosexual.

BIBLIOGRAPHY FOR CHAPTER XIV

Ellis, Havelock, *Psychology of Sex,* Emerson, 1938.

Hall, Radclyffe, *The Well of Loneliness,* Blue Ribbon Books, 1928.

Lorand, Sandor, *Comments on Sexual Deviations,* Special Pamphlet. This article appeared as a preface to a book of 40 drawings by Arthur Zaidenberg called *The Emotional Self,* published by Claude Kendall.

Menninger, Karl A., *Man against Himself,* Harcourt, Brace, 1938.

Rado, S., "A Critical Examination of the Concept of Bisexuality," *Psychosomatic Medicine* 2, No. 4, Oct., 1940.

Sprague, George S., "Varieties of Homosexual Manifestations," *American Journal of Psychiatry* 92, No. 1, July, 1935.

Chapter XV

REACTIONS TO INEVITABLE LIFE
SITUATIONS

Reaction to Loss

SOME people have an extremely unpleasant reaction to loss, whether it be that of a relative, friend, money, home, job, position in the community or an ideal—or even, after an operation, to the loss of a part of the body. The person who has this unpleasant reaction to loss may show quite marked depression in spirits, lose interest in the people around him, be a joyless companion and refuse to take an interest in his work. He reacts in a rather helpless way, as if there were nothing left in life for him, and this feeling persists for a varying length of time. Some people take refuge under the concept of love and say, "I have to act this way. It is natural because, you see, I loved this person—or thing—that I lost." The implication is that he is a very idealistic person and, since he loved and lost, criticism could not possibly be leveled at him.

Let us examine this reaction of love, if it *is* love, as it pertains to the phenomenon of loss. We might ask the person, "What is the quantity or quality of your love that you can love only one thing, or one person, or one ideal?" We might find that his love was really not very great or we might find that he had unwisely invested it—or both. It is usually true that people who have a marked, even devastating, reaction to loss have a small amount of love and have put all this small amount in one place. We must remember that love is an emotion about which we know very little and about which we think very little, and an emotion of which we are very afraid.

Love has very humble beginnings. We begin to love as children because our parents are wise enough and kind enough to make us feel physiologically comfortable—because they make us happy and because they feel happy about us. They make us feel safe and accepted and, therefore, while still babies, we are able to mobilize a state of gratitude and pleasure in response to their thoughtfulness, which grows and continues to exist as long as we continue to be interested in and give of ourselves to others. In starting to love our parents, we come to like the things they like and to love the people of whom they approve.

In many cases, we come to love some of the persons and things our parents do not approve of. Unfortunately there are a great many parents who make it clear that they want their children to think as they think, to do as they do, to love only those whom they love. The children must not love a person of another religious faith, or race, or color, or political belief. All the while these same parents may be attending meetings whose aims are to promote a bigger and better postwar world in which all prejudice of mankind will be wiped out, not realizing the inconsistency between this attitude and the one they preach at home, which is one of great narrowness and limitation of love. Such an attitude toward life is unconstructive.

A mother of four children lost a grown son who was killed in a train wreck. From that day on she never appeared outside her home. She was bitter at fate, felt that she had been cheated, and became extremely morbid, taking no interest whatsoever in community affairs. This is an example of a pathological, selfish and inconsiderate reaction, and such a person cannot possibly take refuge under the guise of love for the boy who was killed. What feeling of love she had for the boy was only a small part of her reaction, which she called love. She merely became a problem to the rest of her family and succeeded in spoiling their existence. She was *weak*, not strong. She thought, "Many people will see my love is so great that when I lose someone dear to me I am devastated." We need to see through a reaction like this, and, if we have the opportunity, to point out to such a person that her behavior is not a mark of strength but of weakness. This woman had a weak ability to love anyone, and when fate took her son away, she had no love left for the rest of the family or for the world at large; she could only feel sorry for herself and indulge in what we call self-pity.

A salesman was earning about thirty-five thousand dollars a year and living in one of the more attractive communities in the outskirts of the city when the depression came and he lost his job. He had to take help from the community and go on one of the government work projects. His income was greatly reduced, which finally necessitated moving to another community. He and his wife did not take to this move to another community gracefully. They brooded and grieved over it, would have nothing to do with their new neighbors—thought they were a low type of people. They even restricted their children in their associations with the other children in the community, and spent their time reminiscing about the old days when they lived among wealthier neighbors. In other words, during most of the period when the children were in their teens the parents grieved and were pessimistic, which naturally affected the children.

In the process of growth, it is important that we learn that life is uncertain, that it has vicissitudes and that we need to invest as much of our interest in as many people and in as many things as we reasonably can. Samuel Johnson said that we must work at making friends and "we must keep our friendships constantly in repair." In other words, we should be prepared for loss, not necessarily dwell upon it or brood about it but be emotionally and ideationally prepared for it. There is no reason at all why we should not accomplish this attitude of mind with the proper training.

There are certain events that can be catastrophic for young children. The loss of a parent, especially the mother, can be expected to affect the development of the child's personality, and a suitable substitute should be made for the child until he reaches a reasonable age of maturity. Some young people will be quite integrated and mature at seventeen, others at twenty-six, but around the age of twenty, let us say, people should have had such experiences as to make it possible for them to tolerate loss and, after a certain reasonable period of mourning, be able to reinvest their interest in work, in old and new friendships and recreations, and go on with the business of living. Someone might raise the question that a philosophy of this kind conflicts with the concept of loyalty. We do not think so. We think that the progress of events is showing us quite clearly that if our concept of loyalty is too narrow, we shall come to grief. We cannot be loyal to only one person, to one family, or even to one country. Our concept of loyalty must extend to everyone if we are to be citizens of the world.

Christianity has always had inherent in it the concept of greater love, but few people have considered how much we should be loyal to ourselves and how much to all mankind. To date we have undoubtedly made the mistake of loving causes and concepts more than people. Unfortunately at present it seems that our loyalty to mankind is being developed through fear and force rather than through idealistic teaching.

Depression

It is a short step from these relatively minor reactions to loss to a pathological condition known as depression of spirits or melancholia. We all have disturbances in mood or mood changes from day to day and from hour to hour, and in the average person the changes are not extreme. In the psychoneuroses they are extreme. In the depressed phrase of the manic-depressive psychosis the individual has lost all interest in family and friends and work takes great effort. He often sleeps poorly, is selfish and temperamental; he feels worthless and also feels that the world is worthless. This feeling may be so extreme as to make him believe he would be better off dead. He may even commit suicide.

Such a person is merely reacting to loss in the most exaggerated way possible. Sometimes the thing he has lost is quite evident—money, or a relative or friend, or his position in the community—but in some instances it is not easy to find out what he has lost. What is clear is that he has gradually become disillusioned with life and can no longer take any interest in it. He has lost the mental picture of the goodness of life, or the pleasure of life, or his capacity to enjoy people, or his ability to enjoy work, and he cannot find it again.

A salesman of thirty-four began to lose interest in his work. His contacts with his customers "didn't mean anything." He began to fear he would fail and be discharged by his employer. He slept poorly at night and worried about finances and what would become of his family. He could not find anything entertaining any more. His wife and two children meant nothing to him. He could not enjoy a movie or contacts with friends. After three months he came for treatment. He was given six electro shocks over a period of two weeks. His depression lifted to a large degree and he became able to talk about himself and to try to understand how he came to reach this state of mind.

He had been an only child of a rather strict and emotional mother who was the head of the household and who directed the career of her husband, who was a more kindly but passive sort of man. She had few friends and was inclined to be critical of people generally, including her own relatives. Her thinking concerned itself mostly with being successful, and the pleasure of living from day to day was of minor importance. She drilled her son in the need for being clean, neat, punctual and doing well in his studies, so that most of his energies were directed toward becoming a successful man. The result was that he led a rather isolated life during his high school and college years, became an on-looker rather than an active participant in social life. He was attractive in appearance and actually did not lack for social opportunities, but, as he said, "As I look back I know I was just going through the motions of having a good time. I never seemed to feel like anybody else seemed to feel. There was a heartiness and satisfaction in their good times which I could never seem to capture."

At twenty-four he married a woman who though more gregarious than himself did not succeed in making him like or enjoy people. He preferred getting ahead in his work and looked forward to some kind of satisfaction from being a successful man. As he moved into his thirties he felt himself in a rut and began to feel that his efforts were not worth while. He gradually lost interest in the meager pleasure he had had in work and social life and his depression was the result.

Through psychotherapy he came to see that he had never let himself feel very strongly about people for fear of getting the same lack of response that his mother had always shown. He recalled that as a child he was always hoping that she was going to change and be happier herself and show more interest in him as a person. The psychotherapist was able to convince him that all people were not like his mother, that there was something important to be gained by his showing affection and believing in and accepting the interest that was shown to him. He came to alter his philosophy about life and to see that "doing things," while important, was not the be-all or end-all of existence, and that enjoying each day as it passed was important to maintaining his mental equilibrium.

Back in 1917, in writing on mourning and melancholia, Freud found that there is a temporary withdrawal of interest from the lost object, that a certain amount of work is required by the individual to re-establish this interest again, that he has to make substitutions, and that he has to replace the lost person with someone else and other things. He found that in the healthy individual the period of mourning is not long,—a matter of days or weeks, whereas in the person who develops a deeper melancholia—who cannot re-establish his interest in the world, cannot reinvest his libido in other people and things—remains in this depressive state for a much longer period, sometimes as long as eighteen months, or two years, or possibly more.

There is a tendency in all people with depression and melancholia spontaneously to *return to their previous personality* organization. However, it is rather a serious matter when a father or mother goes into this state of mind and remains there for a long period, becoming incapable of caring for her family if the mother or of supporting the family if the father. Such a person spreads a pall of gloom which is very hard to lift and which is potentially toxic and infectious to growing children. In this state of depression not only are the patient's interests in the outside world limited but also, being emotionally sick, he feels miserable in his body and will complain of fatigue, or indigestion, or poor appetite, or of symptoms referring to any part of the gastrointestinal tract. His doctor may be unable to recognize his condition, and the same may be true of his family and friends. He is diagnosed as having some organic disease and treated as such for many months without the true condition being recognized—namely, as one of emotional disturbance, a depression, a mental illness. It is important that people know more about the emotions and depression of spirits in order to avoid wasting time, and not treat as organically sick people who are actually emotionally sick.

In the past two or three years depression of spirits of long duration has been treated with electro shock, which is given by an apparatus that modifies the house current and is applied to the head by electrodes. A current is passed through the head which renders the patient unconscious and gives him a severe convulsion, fully as severe as an epileptic convulsion. It is painless and fast, and during the shock and convulsion the patient is carefully protected so that he does not injure himself. Electro shocks are given two or three times weekly until eight to twelve have been applied. They will cut short the depression in four out of five cases.

The electro shock treatment is a drastic treatment for a drastic condition. We do not know how the electro shock works. It grew out of the insulin shock treatment for schizophrenia, at which time it was observed that unconsciousness and convulsions seemed to give good results. So the medical profession searched for a procedure to render the patient unconscious and to give a convulsion. For a time metrazol (a cardiac stimulant) was used intravenously for this purpose. But electro shocks are more easily administered and regulated, and it is the treatment now preferred.

Electro shock is not a specific cure for depressions and is not the end of the matter. We still realize that depression of spirits is a personality disorder and grows out of the wrong kind of personality development.

Depressed people have the wrong kind of standards and values, an inadequate integration of thinking and feeling and hence live in such a way as to suffer great deprivation and miss thereby the strengthening force of human contacts. Some people have only one period of depression in their whole lives, but the tendency is to have three or four. The attacks usually do not come on before the age of twenty, often after thirty. At times depression of spirits may be substituted by great activity —euphoria, the manic phase of the manic-depressive personality. Theoretically the manic-depressive person is so called because there is potentially in him a tendency toward overactivity as well as depression. When he is overactive his aggression is freer, but the depressive phase is regarded as the more basic illness.

Most psychiatrists feel that in addition to electro shock treatment, which usually changes the personality rapidly, the patient should have psychotherapeutic treatment as well. In other words, the patient should be helped to understand his feelings more fully, and should be taught better modes of relating himself to the people around him in order to build up a different relation to life and avoid future attacks. This is being done in as many instances as possible.

Menopause

Just as the activity of the sexual glands comes on gradually at puberty, so it recedes gradually during menopause. The age at which this decrease in the activity of the sexual glands occurs varies between forty and fifty, forty-five being the average. The terms *menopause* and *climacteric* are both applied to this period. Critical events are always arising in people's lives. Puberty, adolescence, marriage, parenthood are all critical events occurring to both active and inactive people, and the menopause—and the changes associated with it—is just another event that has to be met.

In the past our thinking has not been very clear about the menopause syndrome. We have incorrectly ascribed to the cessation of glandular activity practically all the symptoms of the menopause. In discussing puberty we said that the onset of menstruation in the girl should be accepted with equanimity; that we should not expect this natural physiological function to interfere in any great degree with the woman's activities or with her emotional life, and that when we do not expect difficult menstruation, it generally will not occur. That is not quite so true in regard to the menopause, for women who have lived unwisely between the ages of twelve and forty-two can build up a great many regrets over which to be irritable, depressed, remorseful, bitter and pessimistic when the menopause appears. In addition to these mood disturbances, symptoms often occur in the menopause such as hot flushes, cold shivers, sensations of alternating heat and cold accompanied by perspiration, dizziness, cardiac palpitation, headaches, anxiety attacks, nausea, fatigue, insomnia and loss of appetite. These symptoms may be either mild or severe, sometimes severe enough to necessitate going to a mental hospital.

Studies of the personalities of those suffering from severe menopause neurosis or psychosis reveal similarities in personality makeup. Such a woman tends to be sensitive and to live a rather isolated social existence. She has not been warm and gregarious but one of those women who proudly declare they never visit around much but stay at home and mind their own business. In other words, she has made a virtue of the fact that she was afraid to associate with people or that she did not like people sufficiently to be friendly. Usually she has been strict and pedantic in training her children, often excessively religious, meticulous about cleanliness, many times the excellent housekeeper in whose home no one can be comfortable. She has been sexually frigid, ungenerous and prone to be critical. Such women take little from and give little to the world, so that by the time menopause is reached they not only have no more activity of the sexual glands, but they likewise have become emotionally and spiritually impoverished.

It is felt that the personality plays a larger role in the whole symptom picture of the menopause than the cessation of glandular activity itself. The physician and the family used to think that any symptom that occurred around this period of life was due to a deficiency in the ductless glands, and the remedy was a prescription for an ovarian glandular preparation of which every drug house has at least one to three products. It is important to remember that a certain number of women go through the change of life without any distressing symptoms. Dr. Pratt of Chicago undertook to treat women suffering from menopausal symptoms by using two preparations, one oil with theelin and one oil without theelin. He asked his colleagues to send him patients suffering from the menopausal syndrome for him to treat with a glandular preparation while his colleagues made observations and reported the patients' progress. Dr. Pratt found that just as many women improved with the sterile solution—that is, the oil without theelin—as did with the solution that contained ovarian substance. Benedek and Rubenstein made studies of the menstrual period in an effort to determine whether a correlation exists between glandular activity and the accompanying psychology. Daily studies were made both of vaginal smears and basal body temperatures and of psychoanalytic observations of the emotional life of the patients. When the findings were compared, it was found that certain types of thinking are associated at the various phases of the menstrual cycle. It is significant that in the first ten days after menstruation a woman's ideas about heterosexual activity and impregnation are much more active than they are in the last part of the menstrual period, when she is inclined to be much more passive and disinterested in sexual activity, more inclined to take care of herself than to want to undertake motherhood.

During the period of menopause some women become panicky with the thought that the energy which leads to sexual pleasure, romance, children and motherhood is leaving them, and believe it can be replaced artificially by an injection. This feeling is true to the extent that the body has been producing a vital ovarian substance since the age of twelve and is now ceasing to produce it. But if a woman has not found love, romance, a happy marriage, enjoyment in her children and interests to have made life worth while before she reaches forty-five, she is not likely to get these satisfactions from an injection of a glandular substance now.

The same thing is true of men and their desires to find strength, joy, happiness, or youthful vigor through ductless glandular preparations. Nature does her best and provides people with the source of life (as sexual glandular substance is looked upon as being). However, one of the inconsistencies of human nature is that man erects many anxieties, fears, prohibitions, and prejudices, and deprives himself (or herself) of happiness until he is forty-five, and then, finding it disappearing, runs around madly trying to find a doctor with a syringe who will inject the means of happiness into him. If he had not found happiness and romance before forty-five, his chances are much more limited of finding them after.

In a problem of the menopausal syndrome the personality factor that has produced this menopausal symptom should be treated, and the doctor should not depend upon ductless glandular preparations too much, whether out of a bottle or a syringe. Women who are not enjoying bringing up their children, who are working too hard and taking life in deadly seriousness should have it pointed out to them that if they continue this course, they are almost certain to be tired, disillusioned people at fifty. Doctors should give them a word of warning and thus help to prevent this serious emotional disturbance that comes with the cessation of menstruation.

A woman of forty-two began to suffer with irregularity of menstruation, headaches, indigestion, insomnia, nightmares, weakness and fatigue. She was given replacement therapy for months without any change in her condition. The uterus was curetted to relieve the menorrhagia, but relief was only temporary. She grew more anxious, depressed and sleepless all the time, and finally became bedridden. When seen psychiatrically she said her most distressing symptoms were the terrible dreams (nightmares) and the palpitation, sweating and terror that accompanied her awakening, which resulted in her remaining awake for hours afraid to go to sleep again. Her history revealed that she had a very rigid childhood training in both toilet and sex matters. Her life as a child was, as she put it, "a nightmare in regard to things like that." Her dreams were almost always related to these two functions: she would be in a public place and need to go to the toilet and be unable to find it and in panic would wet or soil herself or the environment; or she would be in a toilet and the bowl would overflow, soiling the floor, and she would be anxious about the possible punishment; or she would be in public partly clothed, and in a panic that she would be seen; or she would be chased by an ugly-looking man who she feared would assault her.

We explained to her the origin of these dreams and the ubiquitous nature of the conflicts, reassured her about losing her mind, got her to look upon sex and toilet training with less seriousness—with the result that her sleep became more restful, she ate better, her strength came back, and in two and a half months she was able to be up and about her work again after two years of suffering from what we regarded as an anxiety neurosis, rather than any glandular deficiency.

Since this is a book on psychiatry and since replacement therapy is a highly specialized treatment in itself, we refer the reader to any good current textbook on endocrinology for directions as to the careful study and management of cases that actually need endocrine treatment.

Reaction to Advancing Years

Whether men undergo a change of life similar to that of women is a question that has been raised in the past and that is still being argued pro and con by medical men.

We do not feel that there is anything in the man comparable to the menopausal syndrome in the woman. The cessation of glandular activity in the female is relatively rapid, usually taking place in two or three years. We have no evidence that sexual glandular activity in the male undergoes any similar sudden decline or cessation. The process in the male is much more gradual and goes hand in hand with all other evidences of aging. Consequently men do not have to undergo any of the discomforts of a too rapid readjustment of the ductless glands; nor do they have to face a particular crisis in their ability to reproduce such as women do with the cessation of menstruation.

It is true that at various ages men after forty can have *symptoms* akin to those of the woman at the so-called change of life. Like women, they can experience anxiety, irritability, depression of spirits, insomnia, digestive disturbances, headaches, tingling sensations in the extremities, but these disturbances are psychological in origin. They conform to the neuroses of other age periods; to treat such a syndrome in a man with replacement therapy—which means giving ductless glandular substance by mouth or hypodermically—and ignore the personality and the life situation would be to practice medicine incompletely. When replacement therapy relieves a man of his symptoms, such relief is largely obtained on the basis of suggestion. For the large number of persons who would not respond to such therapy, the symptoms are liable to become worse because the diagnosis induces anxiety in such a person and produces unnecessary conflict. If he is not undergoing any crisis in the ductless glandular system, particularly in the activity of the sex glands, such a diagnosis may start him worrying. He may feel he is weak, become discouraged and imagine his is a hopeless case. Men can be very sensitive to any implication that anything is wrong with their sexual power.

A man of fifty who was going through one such period of neurotic disturbance came to the doctor. He complained of insomnia, headache, inability to concentrate, depression of spirits, indigestion, worry over the future, and a great reluctance to mix with people, with a great desire to be by himself. His history revealed that he had a high-strung, irritable father and a more placid mother, and that he never liked school or mixed well. Later at work he never tried to make friends, always thinking he could get along without them. Instead of trying to cultivate friends, he kidded his colleagues and engaged in sharp arguments and criticisms with his friends when out socially. In this way he thought he would be "different, outstanding and not one of the average mob." As a result he was not very popular. Now he felt people disliked him for this, yet he was afraid to be quiet and reserved in a group. He had to try to take hold of the conversation and "kid people," as he put it, in order that he be regarded as clever. In business he never asked a customer about his family or recreations but attended strictly to business and—strangely enough for a salesman—never told a joke. In other words, he never indulged in the kind of casual friendliness that goes with living and working. He considered it a waste of time and felt that he did not need to resemble other people in this regard because he would be outstanding in his own particular way. He planned to work hard and retire at fifty. Now he *is* fifty and he cannot retire. The stock-market crash of 1929 interfered with his plans and he has never recovered financially. Even if he could retire, it would not solve his problem. He would not know what to do with himself because although he likes to work hard and keep to himself, at the same time he has the fear that he is going to lose his mind or that he is going to end in the poorhouse. This man has come to grief because he has lived a life that has led to emotional impoverishment, and not because he is undergoing any so-called change of life.

To get well he has to be taught to take a different attitude toward people and seek his cure in better social and family relationships. His difficulty in concentrating, forgetting people's names, is merely an exaggeration of his tremendous lack of interest and indifference to what is being said to him. It is not something new: he has been leading up to it for twenty-five years. He never cared about the thoughts and feelings of other people but only about furthering his own ends. Now his attitude is a little more exaggerated and he finds that it actually interferes with his work. His inner feelings, his misery, headaches, indigestion, are secondary conversion symptoms of his upset emotional state. These syndromes appearing in men, similar to the menopausal syndromes in women, are neuroses and not an outgrowth of any change in sexual glandular activity.

Retirement

For various reasons men and women may come to a point in later life when they must undergo retirement. Before the war, at least, business organizations, universities, and so on were enforcing increasingly strict retirement rules, usually at the age of sixty or sixty-five. The need for retirement may come about through a gradual exacerbation of such chronic illnesses as heart disease, cardiovascular disease or kidney disease. Some men undergo a self-imposed retirement because a son becomes old enough to take charge of the business and the father feels ashamed to carry on when it is more logical that the son should take over. Sometimes if a man is not doing well in the business organization, his colleagues insist upon his retirement.

There are some men who refuse to retire from business—thus making a great problem for their children. It is a difficult matter to combat. It can probably only be combated by the sons and daughters being sufficiently farsighted to choose their own careers. But if such a son should cast his lot with the father, he should be sufficiently courageous and businesslike to make a working arrangement that balances practical business logic with sentiment, thus assuring himself some protection if the father in his blindness or selfishness should tend to exploit him. This problem of older persons being unwilling to give way to the younger will be greater as medical science increases longevity.

Married women, having raised a family, may be forced to retire from home activities because of illness or because the children grow up and leave home one by one, leaving them with nothing to do. Such people, whose minds are not active and resourceful enough to turn to other interests, can be a great problem to themselves and an even greater one to those around them. The remark is often heard, "Mother has not enough to do. She is so restless, so difficult that she is nearly driving us all crazy." This situation should not exist to the extent that it does. As a nation we are poorly equipped to cope with the problem of retirement. In the first place, Americans have always put a high premium upon unaided individual effort. Prestige is attached to being a success and making money. In order to do this, men have applied themselves with extreme diligence and concentration, have avoided hobbies, recreations, reading, and artistic pursuits. As a result, they may be able to call themselves, at fifty or fifty-five, financially successful but when they have to stop working and have to live with themselves they are at loose ends and quite unable to entertain themselves, or come to depend too much upon living in their children.

In a subtle way the feeling exists that if a man takes any time from his career for hobbies, recreations or for otherwise deepening his personality, he is somehow being immoral or, at least, will come to economic ruin. For instance—unless medical students have changed since our day—the fellow who takes an evening off while the majority of the students are studying becomes the target for remarks that imply he will flunk out. Unconsciously the more conscientious students are jealous of his good times, and they try to make him feel guilty and uncomfortable. The same attitude is prevalent among business and professional men, and the result is that everyone tends to work hard, stay on the job and keep up consistent effort in order to make as much money as possible.

In the same way a woman may take an unusual pride in being a good housekeeper, in doing a good job with the children, and criticize the woman who goes out too frequently. In many cases such women are making a virtue of a symptom, which is that they are actually afraid to go out. They feel anxiety when they go downtown in crowds or feel uneasy in a group of women. They may feel, for instance, that they should belong to the parent-teacher's association, but disliking crowds and feeling conspicuous in them, they stay home and clean house and compliment themselves upon their diligence and ability to lead the busy home life. Diligence and work are important but, with nothing else to balance them, people can come to grief later on because of a lack of more diverse emotional satisfaction. The wise course is to blend work and application with social intercourse, with hobbies and with studies, so that when old age and retirement come, people will not be like fish out of water, not knowing what to do with themselves and becoming a burden to those around them.

Prophylaxis is the best treatment for this situation, and once the situation has appeared the family doctor may be considerably limited by what he can do about it. Insurance agents keep reminding people to make financial investments for old age or an emergency or an illness. In the same way doctors can help people by reminding them, before they come to the age of retirement, to make emotional and ideational investments for later life. When the doctor is caring for the new mother it would be a good idea for him to discuss the matter with her, to say, "Do you realize there is a time coming when your children will be grown

up and go away from you? What are you going to do when you're
older to entertain yourself or keep from being distracted because you
have too little to do?" She may be a little startled at such a question and
probably laugh the doctor off and say, "There is a lot of time for that!"
Nevertheless, it is important that young people think about the time
when they can no longer work, when society for some reason or other
will not allow them to work at their usual routine.

Just as people at twenty-one feel they are the finished product, so do
people in middle life have this same attitude toward adult education.
Adult education has had a new impetus in the past few years, but there
are many people who resist it. They say, "Oh, I am too old. I could not
think of going to school again." Or they may be more concerned with
whether the people will be nice enough to associate with than with
learning some new skill. In the course of our clinical practice we have
seen many people who would have profited by learning something new,
by having new thought outlets, yet who would bring up a dozen excuses
for not participating, even, in some cases, saying that they could not
bear to go alone and thus showing that they were suffering from the
same anxiety at forty that they had at five when they went to school.

We must help people to keep their eye on the future and to plan in
some small way to have something to do when the retirement period
comes. When there has been no preparation the family may have a suggestion to offer to the mother or father. If the parent spurns the advice
because it *is* given by his own children, the family doctor can usually make the same suggestion with better results. It will carry a great
deal more weight because of the respect and prestige accorded to members of the medical profession. The doctor should not feel anxious if he
is still young and a great many years lie between him and the older person, for often older people will take advice well from younger people
in authority. He should be emphatic in his advice: make the older person take a hobby course, tell him how much good it will do to have his
mind occupied, even going so far as to say it will be something to take
him out of the way of that daughter-in-law for a few hours; he should
point out that it will be very good for his health and insist that he do it.

Around sixty some people have definite organic changes in the brain,
atrophy of cells, an actual diminution in the size of the brain, and some
degree of sclerosis in the vessels of the brain, which tends to cut down
the nourishment to that organ. As a result of these changes, an exaggeration of personality characteristics may occur. We say they become child-

ish, which means that they are more demanding than usual, more irritable, more likely to talk and hold the floor and disregard the presence of other people. Men may become romantically interested in much younger women, and occasionally women show a like interest in young men. Many families have the problem of an older person who monopolizes the conversation, talks on endlessly of trivial matters, reminisces about his early life and seems to fail to appreciate the setting in which he finds himself. He is oblivious to the wishes and desires of the generation of his sons and daughters, and even more so to that of his grandchildren.

Whether the problem is a minor one connected with retirement or a major one resulting from changes in personality and physical condition, a point always comes in the family situation when the younger members can no longer bear the situation. This varies because some daughters and sons are more tolerant of older people and can absorb more of their idiosyncrasies and peculiarities than others, but still, if there are too many changes in the older person, a point comes at last where something must be done. The older person is inclined to interfere in the affairs of the younger members of the family, criticize the servants, give orders, try to manage the children and the running of the home. If the older person is a woman, she is likely to want the home and kitchen to be run the way she ran hers, forgetting that changes have taken place in the course of fifty years.

If the situation becomes so bad as to warrant placing such an older person in an institution, a home for the aged or, possibly, a mental hospital, the doctor can be of considerable help in guiding and advising the family, which may need moral support for this step. For though a querulous, irritable, fault-finding, irresponsible old person can greatly interfere with the happiness of a married couple and almost ruin the lives of their children, most people feel a loyalty to their relatives and fear being reproached for putting such a person into an institution, no matter how comfortable it may be, and therefore are greatly helped by the doctor's support. Unfortunately, there are young people who are in too much of a hurry to get rid of the older person and at the slightest provocation want him to go to an institution, when with a little tact and understanding they could solve the problem for at least a year or two.

Children and people in middle life need to be free of such impediments in order to strengthen them for the work that is ahead. Therefore doctors should be decisive and able to help in this problem of the older individual who comes to late life without the emotional and ideational resources to meet old age. Character changes of extreme degree are not necessarily inevitable as old age appears. Whether they appear or not depends largely upon two factors: first, on the rapidity with which degenerative changes are prone to take place in a particular family and, second, on the strength of personality integration as a result of home and environmental training.

BIBLIOGRAPHY FOR CHAPTER XV

Benedek, Therese, and Rubenstein, Boris B., "The Correlation between Ovarian Activities and Psychodynamic Processes," *Psychosomatic Medicine* I, 1939, 245–270.

Freud, Sigmund, "Mourning and Melancholia," *Collected Papers* II, Hogarth Press, 1934.

Lawton, George, ed., *New Goals for Old Age,* Columbia University Press, 1944.

Pratt, J. P., discussion of an article entitled "A Syndrome of Estrogenic Deficiency" by Philip J. Schneider, *American Journal of Obstetrics and Gynecology* 31, 1936, 782.

Chapter XVI

TREATMENT

THE TREATMENTS of psychiatry can be divided into several types. One of these is institutional treatment which is used when mental illness is so severe that the patient can no longer live comfortably outside in the community. Various treatments used in the hospital are hydrotherapy, electro shock treatment, insulin shock treatment, surgical therapy and occupational therapy. These treatments are usually given in cases of psychoses. For neuroses, certain psychoses, character disorders and various psychosomatic diseases the treatment of choice is psychotherapy and is usually carried on as office treatment.

Psychotherapy includes anything that is said or done by the physician which is aimed at favorably influencing the thinking and feeling of the patient and helping him toward happiness, efficiency and health. Under this broader heading of psychotherapy we should include what is called re-educational therapy, also bioanalysis and distributive analysis. These terms have been coined to describe a special form of re-education. The word *bioanalysis* refers to a study of the events that take place during the growth of the individual; in other words, it is concerned with the life history. Both bioanalysis and distributive analysis refer to the use of the history in helping the patient to understand himself and modify his thinking and feeling for the real life task before him. They are terms that are in use among that group of psychiatrists who were trained by Dr. Adolph Meyer at Johns Hopkins and who utilize his theories and treatment plan in this work. Psychotherapy includes the techniques of suggestion and persuasion as well as hypnosis, which is a special form of suggestion.

In re-educational psychotherapy time is spent with the patient in a face-to-face discussion and relatively little effort is made to emphasize the phenomenon of transference, little effort, likewise, to utilize the ideas and concepts belonging to the unconscious, such as the incestuous trends, the castration complex and latent homosexuality. In re-educational psychotherapy little effort is made to work these concepts out through transference, as is done in psychoanalysis. The non-psychoanalyst rarely believes these concepts exist and the Freudian psychoanalyst practicing a face-to-face therapy does not try too hard to make them conscious because he knows that it takes a long time for people to accept these trends in themselves, even when present in great degree and causing much trouble. Re-educational psychotherapy is carried out less frequently than psychoanalysis, once or twice a week, or once in two weeks, and in some cases once a month. The foundation to be used in all conscious psychotherapy is the life history of the patient which reveals that he is functioning in certain ways at an immature level.

Certain people do not want psychotherapy and may even resent the idea that it is needed, the reason being that before very much re-educational psychotherapy can be given, the individual has to accept the fact that he has a fault, such as fears, anxiety, jealousy or selfishness, to a more than average degree. Psychotherapy requires the co-operation of the patient, and the doctor generally gets it because the patient is suffering and he wants to feel better in his body or mind or he wants to be a more successful or a more effectual person. Wanting these things he is generally willing for the doctor to point out his immaturities and to make some effort to overcome them.

Psychotherapy is not a popular treatment. There are a few people who do not mind being reflective about themselves and having their difficulties pointed out. Such people want to learn and they are sincere about it, but they are in the minority. Most people, however, have what they call pride—a sense of importance and of their own completeness—and when the doctor makes any implication that they are childish, that they are reacting to life in an immature way, that they are emotionally weak, that they ought to do better in some way, the medicine is not easy to take. In applying it the doctor has to do so with a great deal of tact, understanding and kindness. Very often in a social setting after a person has been behaving in an immature way and has left the room, someone will say, "I know what is wrong with him. I know what he needs." Sometimes a best friend or a doctor will directly tell a person all that is wrong in the short space of fifteen minutes. Telling people too much about the part of them that is immature and socially unacceptable may have a rather unfortunate result and may merely turn people against the informer. To get good results this state of mind should not be aroused. Good psychotherapy tries to avoid this rejection on the part of the patient. The doctor does this by taking care never to give too much of the truth at once. The patient can take it and use it when mixed with a good deal of kindness and understanding.

An important part of treating the psychoneuroses and the adjustment problems of human beings is to understand human personality, how it forms and the possible paths or deviation from the average it may take. This means a study of the life history of the human being, a study of social pressures and demands and a knowledge of the varieties of traditional and conventional conflict, which we have discussed in the preceding chapters. A psychotherapist must have some ideas of the average in human conduct, a kindly but objective point of view as to what is fair in the relationship of parent to child, husband to wife, employer to employee, etc.

Many serious young medical people have an interest in and a sympathy for the specialty of psychiatry but hesitate to go into it because they do not believe that human beings can be changed—and that therefore they could not charge a fee for a service which brought no change.

First, let us say that there is no question about the fact that people can be changed, some more rapidly than others it is true, but they *can* be changed. Opinion is a stalwart thing but it can be favorably affected. Moreover, the person in trouble, the person who has suffered pain and distress in mind and body, is going to want to change if it means a restoration of his happiness or health or both. More and more people are becoming willing to consult the psychiatrist when necessary and to utilize what psychiatric understanding and therapeutic ability is possessed by the family physician.

History-taking Procedure

Just as the chapters of this book have given an ontogenetic study of man's emotional development generally, we must in treatment use history taking as a rapid means of studying and knowing the particular individual, his needs, how he has met them and his resulting conflicts.

To aid in history taking, the following outlines can be used and modified, as the case demands and time permits.

FAMILY BACKGROUND

1. Age, birthplace and occupation of parents.
2. How would you describe the temperamental traits of your parents, individually, with the following as a guide: depressive, cheerful, irritable, conscientious, indifferent, prudish, tolerant, optimistic, pessimistic, unfeeling, affectionate, understanding?

3. Would you say they had a broad or a narrow outlook on life?
4. Did they encourage you in your plans? Did they praise and reward your accomplishments?
5. Would you consider that you had come from a well-adjusted family?
6. Did their attitude foster any feeling of inferiority?
7. Did their attitude foster certain of your recent ideals?
8. Is there any history of epilepsy, migraine, alcoholism, psychosis, neurosis or invalidism in your immediate family?
9. If so how do you look upon them—with tolerance, shame, indifference, or with what emotion?
10. Do you feel that their presence has produced any effect upon your career from a psychological standpoint or otherwise?

PERSONAL EARLY DEVELOPMENT

1. What has been told you of your progress in nursing, weaning, walking, talking, dentition, feeding, bowel and bladder training?
2. What has been told you of early developmental incidents, such as thumb sucking, breath-holding spells, tantrums, bedwetting, spasms, night terrors, idiosyncrasies as to diet, fears, etc.?
3. Did you have any illnesses during childhood that have left a residual physical or psychic change or both?

ATTITUDE TOWARD FAMILY

1. Did you have any special attachment to father or mother?
2. Did you have any timidity before or antagonism toward either parent? If so, when and why did this come about?
3. Have you been on a frank or formal footing with your parents?
4. Are you an only child? If not, what is your position among the siblings? Age, occupation, success or failure of siblings in chronological order.
5. Are you aware that this factor has made a difference in your career?
6. Are you on friendly terms with siblings? If not, on what grounds is there difficulty? On the other hand has an older sibling been especially friendly and a source of inspiration?
7. How did you take births and losses (by death or separation) in the family?
8. Do you feel you are emancipated from home and parents?
9. Along what lines do you still turn to the home for advice and decision?
10. What person, inside or outside the family, has been the greatest influence in your life this far?
11. Have your grandparents, uncles, aunts, cousins, or any friend of the family played an important role in your childhood or later life? How did this come about and by reason of what characteristics in the person mentioned?

SCHOOL ADJUSTMENT

1. Did you have any difficulty in school attendance because of illness, unwillingness to attend, actual truancy, or other reason?
2. Was there any one year, or period of years, that you failed or made consistently low grades, in marked contrast to your usual ability? If so, can you assign any reason for this?
3. Did you have any special educational disabilities, such as inability to memorize, inability to use figures or to calculate, etc.?
4. Was there any one teacher during your school career to whom you were unusually devoted? Was there one whom you particularly disliked? If so, of which sex was this teacher? How do you account for the intensity of feeling?
5. Would you say any teacher had exerted a marked or permanent influence upon your personality? How?
6. During school age were you often involved in neighborhood mischief or actual delinquency, such as stealing, setting fires, etc.? If so, was this your own trend or due to gang influence?
7. What was your ability to mix? Were you an active member of the group? A leader or follower, or did you entirely dislike and avoid group activity?
8. How were you regarded by the other children? Were you teased and belittled, or admired and looked up to?
9. Was your school life a satisfactory balance of social, athletic and scholastic attainment? If not, do you now see any ways in which it might have been made so?

SEXUAL DEVELOPMENT

1. Trace the evolution of your sex life as far as possible in terms of concrete situations and reactions, with the aid of the following questions.
2. At what *ages* and on what *occasions,* and from what *sources* have you acquired sex information?
3. Has your environment given opportunity for sex orientation?
4. How much active interest and curiosity have you shown?
5. Have much misinformation and misinterpretation been involved?
6. Are you conscious of much shame and secrecy about sex?
7. How was it acquired and how has some of it been lost?
8. At what age did you become aware of your sex organs and their functions?
9. How did puberty make itself felt in your case?
10. What sex preoccupations or sex adventures did you have *before, at* or *after* puberty? How were they initiated and what do you estimate to have been their effect upon you?

11. Has masturbation been a special problem for you?
12. Have nocturnal emissions ever been a source of worry to you?
13. Did any special *person, event,* or *group* influence your sex trends?
14. Through what change of theories and views regarding sex have you passed?
15. How frequently are you preoccupied with sex fantasies? Of what type?
16. Have you many dreams concerning sex matters?
17. Have you had any sex experiences with your own sex, or any sex experiences of any sort whatever which you would consider abnormal, or any inclination toward such?
18. What situations give rise to sex tension and what method or methods have you attempted for relief and regulation of tension?
19. Has any part of your sex activity given you a sense of guilt?
20. What is your present sex code or goal? Do you think it differs from that of the rest of your family?
21. Does sex tension interfere with your work?
22. To what extent has the concept or urge of family formation entered into your sexual preoccupations, if at all, and at what age did it appear?
23. To what extent do *affection* and *broader human interest* enter into your sex preoccupation?
24. What in your opinion are the outstanding social sex problems?
25. What is your attitude toward them?
26. What is your conception of an ideal adult sex life?
27. What is your attitude toward monogamy?
28. Do you feel that you have any sex problem at present?
29. What is your attitude toward these questions of your sex life?
30. What should be the ideal attitude toward the sex topic, especially indiscretions or sexual perversions in patients?
31. Do you believe children should receive sex instruction, and at what age?

MOOD REACTIONS

(It is realized that an evaluation of these reactions can, in many instances, be only approximate. Try, however, to make your answer as specific as possible.)

1. Are you naturally cheerful or inclined to depression or worry, or is this variable with you?
2. Are you usually aware of what produces the changes or do they seem to come from a clear sky?
3. Are you optimistic or pessimistic?
4. Have you a good sense of humor? Are you stubborn?
5. Are you serious-minded or inclined to be frivolous?
6. Do you get sullen or sulk, or hold resentment? Can you be cheerful or gay at will?

7. How do you react to disappointment, to trouble, to competition?
8. Are you irritable, impatient, fault finding? If so, what conditions any of these traits? Can you relate them to particular topics?
9. To what extent are you influenced by the emotions and moods of others, and if so, how?
10. Do you think we can expect to modify moods, and if so, how?
11. What does the word "sentiment" suggest to you? What are your most important sentiments?
12. Are you fearful of the outcome of your projects, and do you indulge in forebodings, or are you usually confident?
13. Are you easily frightened? Are you quick-tempered?
14. Are your feelings easily hurt?
15. How do you react to success in others? Is it easy to congratulate them?
16. Can you work steadily for hours at a time, or do you feel concentration difficult?
17. Under what circumstances do you work best—i. e., by schedule, impulse, under pressure, or how?
18. Have you always the energy you wish for, or does this fluctuate?
19. Are you benefited greatly by rest periods or vacations?
20. How do you spend occasional holidays?
21. Is your attention easily distracted?
22. Can you make judgments easily or are you vacillating?
23. Does your performance during a day keep pace with what you have planned, or do you find performance lagging behind plans?

SOCIAL ADAPTABILITY

1. Are you timid, shy or tongue-tied in the presence of the opposite sex?
2. Are you at ease in the presence of older people?
3. What is your reaction to authority? Do impolite or unkind remarks of people in minor official positions upset you?
4. Are you independent in thinking and making your own decisions, or do you like to have help from others?
5. Are your decisions *impulsive,* due to *circumstances,* or *well thought out?*
6. What is your type of friendship—many or few, lasting or changing, warm or cool, reserved or confiding, protecting or dependent?
7. Are you married? Are you engaged? If not, when and under what circumstances would you contemplate marriage?
8. Are you interested in being a parent of children?
9. To what extent are you conscious of egoism or altruism in yourself? Has this ever been brought to a real test?
10. How do you take advice or criticism?
11. Are you inclined to seek sympathy or to pity yourself?
12. Are you overmodest or overconfident?

13. Do you often feel at a disadvantage compared to others?
14. Are you satisfied with the way the world has treated you thus far?
15. Do you dislike adapting yourself to new surroundings?
16. Are you able to co-operate well with others?
17. Are you tactful? Are you ingratiating?
18. Do you have a conviction that you are always right?
19. Are you a good loser? Do you like to talk of your accomplishments? Do you seek or shirk responsibility?

SENSE OF REALITY

1. Are your plans for the future clearly or vaguely outlined?
2. What factors caused you to choose your career?
3. To what extent do you think success depends upon effort, and to what extent upon chance and circumstances?
4. Do you rate yourself as imaginative, idealistic, visionary, practical?
5. Do you like or dislike responsibility?
6. Are you superstitious?
7. Are you frank and honest with yourself; i. e., can you acknowledge a mistake and attempt to correct it?
8. Have your plans up to now worked nearly as you would have liked or have you felt yourself thwarted or disappointed?
9. Do you plan well? Can you direct others? Is your advice frequently sought?
10. What is your attitude toward money? Are you saving? Do you spend wisely? Are you generous? To what extent is making money your aim? How do you react to economic uncertainty?

HEALTH

1. Illnesses, operations, accidents and circumstances leading up to them.
2. Length of convalescence.
3. Age at which each appeared.
4. When was physical health last checked up?

NEUROTIC TENDENCIES

1. What circumstances bring out uneasiness or blushing?
2. Does physical comfort mean a great deal to you?
3. Is food an important item to you?
4. Have you any special sensitivity to certain foods, either esthetic or symptomatic?
5. Have you a special fondness for alcohol? Is this related to a mood disturbance?
6. Do you take medicine or drugs?

7. Do you suffer from constipation?
8. Are you much affected by unusual sights, odors, or sounds of either a pleasant or disgusting or unpleasant nature?
9. Have you any unusual demand for system and order? Does disorder in your surroundings or interference in your plans or routine annoy you?
10. Have you any special fears, anxieties, or compulsive ideas or actions?
11. Are you overconscientious? Are you superstitious? Are you overfond of gambling?
12. Do you have any specific acts, habits, or thoughts which are a source of worry, doubt, or remorse to you?
13. How do you react to being ill or to inquiries about your health?
14. What games and sports interest you? Have you indulged intensively in any particular ones?
15. What type of reading do you like? Do you consider yourself well read?
16. Are you interested in politics, sociology, art, music? What is your favorite diversion?
17. Have you any special religious interests? How does this compare with your early training in religious matters?
18. Have you any special interest in any cult, philosophy, occultisms, etc.?
19. Have you any special interest in the factors at work in the development of mankind, such as history of race with regard to civilization, literature, language, and thought?
20. What are your concrete interests in sociological problems?

PRACTICAL TESTS AND SYNTHESIS

1. Do you feel that your personality is well harmonized, with a suitable distribution of energy into work, play, relaxation, fantasy, art, literature, religion, philosophy, science, and concrete life?
2. What have been your greatest difficulties and handicaps? To what extent have you been able to trace their origin to early experiences?
3. Do you have any sources of comfort during disappointment or discouragement? How do they act?
4. What means of adjustment have you tried, either upon yourself or others? With what success?
5. State one or two concrete difficulties you would like to adjust in the next year as an example and test of *what* is possible, and under *what conditions* it may be possible.

When the history has been taken we must be able to pick out the factors of significance, weigh them carefully in connection with the physical and laboratory findings and arrive at a diagnosis. If there is an absence of structural pathology or pathology revealed by laboratory study then psychotherapy should be the treatment. To use drugs, physical therapy, or surgery on a neurotic illness is contraindicated. It sometimes gives temporary relief but symptoms return and each time are harder to cure even if psychotherapy is later instituted.

A case that illustrates some of the things regarding psychotherapy is of a girl of nineteen who woke up one February with an anxiety attack. She woke up fighting for her breath, with her heart palpitating, with sweating, with a sense of constriction in the throat and with nausea. She felt as if she were going to die. A doctor was called who after administering treatment said, "It is a good thing you called me because a certain number of people with this ailment die before they wake up." Since she had eaten pork the night before it was assumed she had been poisoned by the pork, which was of course a possibility.

However, emotional storms that set up an anxiety attack, hard breathing and disturbances in the gastrointestinal tract can cause violent symptoms without the presence of poisoned food at all. At any rate these attacks continued. From February to August she had one almost every day. She saw about ten different doctors, each of whom said she had no organic disease and that she was "nervous." She got no better. In fact she grew worse and began to build up in her thoughts theories of what was wrong. She could picture that the nerves in her body were curling around her heart and that in one of these attacks the nerves would be so affected that they would constrict her heart and she would die. Another theory she had was that the poison from the pork had not gone entirely out of her system and that that which remained was causing the attacks. She did not believe she was nervous at all but thought she had a disease that the doctors could not discover.

She finally came to the accident dispensary. The medical resident was called and he spent some time with her. He recognized the fact that she had an anxiety attack and he told her what it meant. He said, "Your illness arose in the following manner. You know when anyone is afraid the heart beats faster and the person may have some difficulty in getting his breath. This fear can also make people sick to the stomach and cause other even more bizarre sensations. *That* is what you have and that is *all* you have, *nothing else.*" Of course she had a physical examination and laboratory work was done but the nature of the attack made the resident feel that the real pathology was an anxiety attack and that the girl needed reassurance and the cause of the symptoms explained. In other words she needed some education about the nature of an anxiety attack which no one heretofore had given her. All that the doctors had said was, "You are nervous. Go home and do not worry about yourself." The result of this twenty minutes' talk with the resident was that she went home and had a full night's sleep, the first in several weeks. Although the reassurance had not worked completely and had not cured the condition, talking to her in this way gave her enough reassurance for the time being to persuade her that she did not have the conditions she had been imagining and hence that she did not have an organic disease.

However, the resident realized that a person suffering from an anxiety attack has quite a lot of personality difficulty and so he referred her to the psychiatric department. We learned that she was the second child in a family of three: herself, a sister three years older, and a brother five years younger. The father was a fairly cheerful man who had been a policeman at one time and who told the children all the dangerous things he met in his work. He used to tell his daughter about the dangers of a girl going about a big city and how a girl must watch out against boys who would only deceive and betray her. "Never trust a boy until you are married to him," he said. The mother was also a fairly cheerful, optimistic type of person with considerable friendliness and gaiety in the home and especially with the patient who was an attractive child. Very little was expected of the girl and everything was made easy for her. She was dressed well and was the showpiece of the family. Her sister was a little envious and jealous of her and said, "I do not see why everyone likes her better than me. I guess it is because she laughs so much and is never irritable."

Stories used to be told in the family about such things as the world coming to an end. When our patient heard them she would hide under the stairs and think of the house falling in and people dying and being imprisoned. When she got to school she talked among the girls and they told her how disgraceful it was that many girls had illicit sex relations, even getting pregnant and sometimes dying in childbirth. Acting on instructions from her teachers, her older sister would go through considerable handwashing and tooth washing as a prevention of disease. Our patient saw this and did likewise.

When she became seventeen years old she met a young man three years older than herself and they began going together. Finally they decided to be married without telling either family about it. They went to a magistrate, went through a ceremony and supposed they were married. Marriage was a very difficult thing for this girl because she had been brought up in a home where there had been much discussion about the fear of pregnancy. It would have been difficult enough if she had had an open, accepted marriage with the approval of both families but the secrecy of the marriage did a great deal to make her feel anxious. In addition she had married a man who had an attachment to his mother. He could not bear to tell his mother that he was married. If he even hinted at it his mother became quite excited and talked down the idea so that he did not dare tell the truth. After a year they found out that something was wrong with the marriage papers and that they were not married at all. Thirty days later the girl had her first anxiety attack, after which a great change took place in her disposition. From being a cheerful, buoyant, happy girl she became moody, had temper outbursts and even scratched and bit people. From her first attack until she came to the hospital six months later she went through a most difficult time. It was then that the resident saw her and reassured her and thus effected a reduction in anxiety and an improvement in symptoms.

However, reassurance alone is rarely enough to cure neurotic symptoms of this type. It has to be followed up by re-educational therapy which helps to re-educate the patient in more mature ideas and feelings for living. We have said that two things tend to make people anxious —fear of harm and fear of the loss of love and affection. Our patient had been a "good girl." She had repressed many sexual and aggressive impulses. Yet she had been taught very little about the facts of life, her home life had been made very easy and now, at nineteen, she was faced with a great deal of responsibility. She was brought to the point where she had to use her personality assets, assets that had not been very well developed. First, she had to face the prospect of an adjustment to a man sexually. Second, she had to face the possibility of an immediate pregnancy, and everything she had ever heard about these matters had been unpleasant and fearful. Third, she had actually to wrest her husband away from his mother. If she revealed the marriage both families might make a row. Wanting approval herself she yet had to put herself in the position of having to petition her mother-in-law and to face the fact that she might get a "beating" from her for stealing her son. Fourth, she had to face the responsibility of planning a home. All during the so-called marriage she had managed to stay well. But when she learned that the marriage was not valid, that she had been living in sin, and that if she had any feeling for her husband at all she would have to go to the mother-in-law to try to take her son and bring about a satisfactory ceremony, she was faced with a situation that she was completely incapable of handling. It was in this setting that she had her first anxiety attack and the ones that followed.

Re-education

Our patient's anxiety attacks were not accidental. An anxiety attack is *never* accidental. It means that there has been a long period of faulty living and that re-education is required. Re-education in this case means, first, to make her feel comfortable with the sexual problem and, second, to give her help with her normal aggression so that she will be able to step forward and deal with her mother-in-law and utilize her aggression in a mature way. The question of marriage will have to be discussed with both families, a ceremony satisfactorily performed and help given in setting up a home. She has to be able to say to her mother-in-law, "I want your son for myself." Up to the present time her husband has only been half hers, the other half catering to his mother's whims. She has a great deal to work out for herself and little courage to do it with. No acceptable utilization of aggression has been cultivated in her. She has been babied and petted, and at no age trained to face responsibility or to anticipate the responsibilities of the twenties, thirties or forties. She has to be educated to meet them.

When such a patient comes to a doctor he must have her continue to visit him for psychotherapy. Even though the symptoms of anxiety attacks are sometimes brought in abeyance a case of anxiety neurosis is not made *well* quickly and the patient should come to the doctor at stated intervals, at least once a week. When he or she comes for treatment the doctor should not examine the heart, or take the reflexes or the blood pressure just to make an impression. Instead he should concentrate upon how the patient is living and how managing his or her personal problems. In the case of our patient, for instance, he must ask how often she has seen her husband during the past week, what his attitude about the marriage has become, how far they have progressed in discussing the problem with both families, if she has seen her mother-in-law and what she is doing about the latter's disapproval. He should discuss with her some of the childish incidents that made her a timid, anxious girl, as well as more current material, and point out to her how her present fears of her husband's mother are the fears she had as a child for her parents and teachers. If the husband and his mother are so emotionally bound together that he cannot take the interest in her that a mature man should, then she had better face this fact and accept the fact of living alone for the present and making other plans for the future.

Many people need help over a critical situation like this. They often remain in a bad social situation which gives them no pleasure and satisfaction, only grief and frustration, but they cannot, without help, make the decision to move out of it. A physician doing psychotherapy must be able to help a patient test out the positive and negative aspects of his real life situation and if the positive ones indicate that they can furnish sufficient ego gratification then they must be utilized to their fullest extent. If there are not enough positive factors to keep the personality alive and thriving then a change in direction must be taken. Too many people live on from day to day and week to week never being able to mobilize their aggression to the point of asking for what is needed to keep them happy and healthy.

In the case of our patient it is most important for her peace of mind and health that the husband have the capacity to emancipate himself from his family and take the patient as his wife with full resolve. For this reason an interview with him would be necessary in order to find out his intentions toward the patient, his sincerity, his maturity of outlook. If he should seem the type that could make her a home and appreciate her as a woman she would have a strengthening force available and the doctor could utilize this force in his discussions with her, pointing out that anxiety being born of insecurity can be neutralized when security appears in one's life. By discussing with her the difficulty in managing her life and offering at the same time the interest and guidance of a friend, the doctor strengthens her emotionally and prevents any further recurrence.

Anxiety symptoms can be most incapacitating. In the six months before seeing us our patient not only had these attacks and other symptoms (such as dryness of the throat and irregular menstrual periods) but also ideas of having been permanently "poisoned" by the pork, of having a "nerve constrict her heart to death," which are actual delusions in the making—and delusions which once fixed make the personality more difficult to approach and help. Ideally such a person should have psychoanalysis, for when a breakdown occurs so early in life, a great deal of interest and re-education in ideas are needed to stabilize her and make her strong and a good mother. She needs a great deal of thinking about herself, a great deal of help to do the various things that are necessary if she is to become capable and stay well. However, psychoanalysis is a long, expensive treatment and sometimes the best we can do is to utilize what psychoanalysis teaches us in the direction of what we call re-education.

As it turned out in our case the husband was interviewed and he was able to love the girl and ignore his mother's demands upon him. They had another ceremony, took an apartment, and our patient became free of symptoms.

The successful psychotherapist must get into the lives of emotionally ill patients—not by taking them to a ball game or by paying the rent but by asking them enough questions about themselves to find out what they need for emotional security and then showing them how they can get it, and sometimes helping by seeing other members of their families who may hold the key to their happiness and security.

Transference

Everyone, whether he has a neurosis or not, is in need of friendship and help in working out a happy and successful existence. If the parents have tried to do this, even though imperfectly or unsuccessfully but with the child's interest at heart, he will transfer a desire for help, friendship, guidance, emotional support and interest. Such transferences are called *positive*. If during his early development the parents have not had his interest at heart but have been cold and indifferent, have disappointed or frustrated him, then he has probably developed a corresponding unfriendliness and suspicion and distrust. As one might expect, the more positive the transference the more quickly and easily can help be given, whether it be in the form of enhancing the patient's sense of well-being or correcting false ideas. When the transference is negative then part of the work of the psychotherapist is to help the patient understand the origin of his negative feelings and work toward making them more positive. Improvement in a neurosis of a permanent nature is dependent upon an increase in the capacity for satisfying personal social relationships.

Suggestion—Persuasion

Suggestion and persuasion are inherent in all psychotherapy. Suggestion applies to the tendency in all human beings to submit to and conform to ideas put forth by others with little question or resistance. The suggester expects a response and very often both the suggester and the one who responds are unconscious of what is going on between them. Persuasion, on the other hand, is the use of facts, figures and argument in order to bring about a response. Suggestion implants new ideas by indirect means, while in persuasion the attack is more directly conscious.

For example, if a doctor finds a patient free of organic pathology and says, "I find no evidence of disease of the heart and henceforth we shall look into the emotional factors that are causing this symptom," he is making a positive suggestion that the patient no longer concern himself with tissue pathology in accounting for his symptom. If, on the other hand, he says, "I see no evidence of structural disease and your electrocardiographic study is entirely normal but you had better stop in after six weeks and be checked over," he is still making a suggestion but a negative one. He says in effect, "Even though I do not find any disease of your heart I feel it may appear soon and the next examination will probably reveal it." There are some physicians trained only in the structural cause of disease who will make negative suggestions of this kind, which increase the anxiety and do great harm to the patient. The use of persuasion would be to utilize the facts of the examination to convince the patient he is not organically ill. To go further and show the patient the relation between his emotional conflicts and his symptoms is re-education.

Hypnosis

A special form of suggestion is hypnosis. In this form of treatment it is suggested to the patient that he go to sleep. A certain number of patients can do this at the suggestion of the physician and hypnotist. While in the sleeping state suggestion can be given to remember forgotten events, to dispense with certain symptoms, or to get rid of a troublesome condition. Hypnosis has always been and still is a difficult therapy to control and though one of the oldest of the psychotherapies, it still awaits development. Freud began his psychotherapeutic work with hypnosis but abandoned it in favor of free association in the waking state. The results of occasional cases treated with hypnosis are dramatic, but it has limitations—imposed by a *resistance* present in all human beings against allowing any large amount of affect-bearing material to emerge at one time from the unconscious. Once unhappy situations are over and done with the patient does not wish to live them over unless entirely necessary and he must be given time or some other alleviating force to help him. Hypnosis has always been an interesting phenomenon, containing potentialities for good, and has never fallen into discard. In fact it is being utilized with good results by several psychiatrists, one of the best known being Dr. Milton Erickson of Illinois, who has written extensively on the subject. It is also being tried at the Menninger Clinic in Topeka, Kansas, and its use in a case of anxiety hysteria was reported by Brenman and Gill. The technique is not easy to master and good results are obtainable only by a few. Theoretically it has psychotherapeutic possibilities but it has to be further developed in order to be more generally applicable and give better results.

Narcosynthesis

Narcosynthesis is being used extensively in the war theaters as a combination of drug therapy and psychotherapy of various psychoneurotic states following combat. A barbiturate drug, sodium pentothal or sodium amytal, is given intravenously at a slow rate until a seminarcosed state is induced, during which most patients are able to relive the traumatic battle experience with release of powerful and intense emotions. With the aid of the psychiatrist the patient is able to synthesize the emotions and memories that have produced symptoms. With each treatment an additional quantity of emotion is released and through utilization of the psychiatrist as friend and substitute for his childhood family and service buddies he is able to establish a working relation with reality again. This treatment is reported to be strikingly effective in reducing the permanent crippling effects of neuroses and in enabling many men who would otherwise be completely incapacitated to take up some activity again. It is indicative of the advances of psychiatry over the period of the last war to see so much emphasis put upon the crippling effects of fear and of psychologically traumatic experiences and to see the widespread importance that is being put upon psychotherapeutic treatment, which is replacing punitive, mechanical and electrical treatments.

Just how effective narcosynthesis will be in facilitating the treatment of civilian psychoneuroses remains to be seen, but we can surely look forward to the fact that the experiences with war neuroses will add greatly to our knowledge of psychosomatic conditions.

Psychoanalysis

Of the various psychotherapies employed, psychoanalysis is the most intensive psychotherapeutic treatment we have. Although not everyone in the field of psychiatry would agree that psychoanalysis is the most effective treatment, we think they would all agree that it is the most intensive.

Psychoanalysis was originated in Vienna about fifty years ago by Freud. It grew out of work on conversion hysteria by Freud and a colleague named Breuer. These two men began by using hypnosis. Under hypnosis the patient was able to recall events of his early life which he could not remember in his waking state, and to some degree the part he could remember under hypnosis he was able to integrate into his existing personality.

Treatment under hypnosis was difficult to control and so Freud eventually abandoned it and adopted the technique of free association. In free association the early experiences of the individual, his deeper attitudes and ideas, are gradually revealed to himself and to the doctor through a process of saying whatever comes to his mind and continuing that process at regular intervals. Thus psychoanalysis was carried out in Freud's time and still is today unchanged as to procedure. Once the diagnosis has been made and doctor and patient have agreed that psychoanalysis is the therapy of choice, a treatment program is made according to which the patient comes to the doctor's office frequently—that is, four to six times a week at a stated time. The patient lies on a couch, with the doctor sitting behind him at the head of the couch, and the patient proceeds with the technique of free association, saying whatever comes to his mind without being concerned about the relevance of his ideas but just allowing his mind free play and expressing whatever thoughts, feelings and ideas come to his mind. No limit is put upon the patient regarding what topic he may discuss or concerning whom or what he may talk about. What comes forth may seem rather meaningless for a few days. Soon, however, the patient's main problems begin to take shape. Under this kind of treatment and with the doctor's aid the patient comes to learn more and more about himself.

This technique of psychoanalysis has been used during the past fifty years by an increasing number of physicians who have studied the technique for the application of psychoanalysis. It has been followed in England, Germany, Hungary, Switzerland, the Scandinavian countries, India, South America and Japan. Although this form of treatment has spread very widely throughout the world it has been met with considerable resistance. Yet in spite of all condemnation, it has come to gain more and more respect from the medical profession. Doctors do not always like its ideas but they have come grudgingly to respect its uses as a therapeutic tool.

To practice psychoanalysis a doctor has to have a medical degree, two or three years' experience in psychiatry in a state hospital, with a knowledge of all types of mental illness, and undergo a personal psychoanalysis himself. In addition he has to attend seminars and lectures on the theory and practice of psychoanalysis for a period of two years, part of which can be done while he is having his own personal analysis. Finally he must analyze two or three cases under the instruction of an experienced psychoanalyst. The preparation needed to train a psychoanalyst takes a long time. Therefore joking references to the effect that a psychoanalyst is able to find out all about a person in two minutes are ridiculous. The shortest time needed for any investigation and readjustment of emotional trends which could justifiably be called psychoanalysis would be six months. Usually it takes from one to two or four years and may even go on longer. This may seem on first thought to be a fantastically long time but when a person considers how difficult human personality is to change he must realize that any re-educational therapy would *have* to take that length of time.

In this treatment one has to take into consideration certain phenomena: (1) the importance of childhood experiences in determining later personality reactions; (2) the fact of the unconscious mind (by that we mean experiences that take place early in life, remain as impressions in the mind even though no longer consciously remembered and exert a force in determining the reaction pattern); (3) the ability to make the patient able to be well must come through his awareness of the unconscious forces within his personality so that he may bring them into line and direct them properly for his own happiness and efficiency. This last, of course, presupposes that the person who can be psychoanalyzed is one who has a certain amount of healthy personality. Consequently certain insane people cannot be analyzed because they do not have enough healthy personality left to understand what is going on and with which to effect a cure.

Finally, in considering psychoanalysis, the phenomenon of transference must be taken into consideration. Transference is the tendency in every human being to relate the emotions and attitudes that have developed during his growth to those people in his immediate environment. A simple example of transference would be that of a fussy, petulant, domineering boy who becomes a fussy, arrogant, domineering husband or father or becomes a businessman who displays those qualities. Every human being behaves in the way he knows best and he will of course continue to behave that way in his work, in his home or in the psychoanalytic sessions.

Continuing with the example of the arrogant, domineering man, his childish pattern may be covered up by an air of humility when he comes to the doctor. However when people are given a chance to lie down and speak their minds the tendency is for them to expose their real selves. This is important to the patient and likewise to the psychoanalyst who is sitting there watching. Once people start free association and begin talking about themselves they find out that they are more petty, more childish, more selfish, more afraid, more inconsiderate than they ever imagined they were. As the treatment continues and the patient becomes increasingly aware of these immature trends in himself he naturally wants to correct them. We can safely go on the assumption that all human beings want to be better people if they are shown how. At this point the healthy part of the personality plays its part and enables the patient to make the resolve to be more courageous, more generous, to exert more goodwill, to renounce jealousy, to be more constructive and less self-centered. All the while psychoanalysis is going on the patient is becoming more aware of himself and at the same time making resolves to behave in a better way. If he is a fairly strong individual who is not too sick these resolves come of their own accord and little help is needed from the outside.

Let us take as an example an adolescent who has an idea of which his father, mother, or older friend disapproves. He goes ahead with it anyhow and it turns out badly. When it is over he sees the error of his ways. He might take the attitude, "Don't rub it in. I see what was wrong." In the same way in psychoanalysis, people who are not too sick become aware of the childish part of their personalities and can almost automatically correct it. Others see what is wrong but their resolves are weak and need support from the family and the analyst. They need more time and help to correct what is so evidently wrong in their reactions to life and the ways they relate themselves to people.

If the patient comes to the psychoanalyst with fear or headache as a symptom he soon finds he does not talk much of his fear or his headache but he concentrates on his relation to the world at large and to the people in his environment in particular and analyzes his emotional trends. Thus psychoanalysis is a treatment involving a gradual breaking down of the personality, a sort of catalysis and then synthesis going on at the same time. As the analysis proceeds, with the doctor's help the patient learns the structure of his makeup, his relations to his parents and others during growth become clearer, and his struggle to achieve a more altruistic pattern toward life has begun.

Most neurotic people feel very sorry for themselves and in their analytic hours may take the attitude that "nobody cares for me. I am miserable and no one tries to help me." Psychoanalysis has been described as the holding of a mirror to the patient's face. So when these childish attitudes predominate the patient has to learn what the nature of that childishness is and that such an attitude does not work well with people but causes them to turn away from him instead of helping him. He has to adopt a better and more mature reaction pattern, go out to people and do something for them instead of waiting in a passive way for something to be done for him. During this time he has the analyst's help in interpreting his character and the structure of his neurosis, and by his very presence the analyst helps him in his new resolution and with whatever he wants to achieve through the analysis.

Briefly that is how psychoanalysis takes place and what it accomplishes. To learn it thoroughly a doctor has to make a special study of it. It is a postgraduate course, and one that cannot be learned in medical school. A student may learn something of what it *does,* but to know how to apply it and to master all the little things that go to make up its technique take special study.

Dreams

The interpretation of dreams forms an important part of psychoanalysis and psychotherapy and is a part of the study of the human mind. Freud showed that dreams are an attempt on the part of the mind to live out its wishes and to solve its conflicts. It might also be said that dreams are a way of revealing to the dreamer, or to the doctor, what is going on in the unconscious. Mental activity goes on all the time we are asleep. When we can recall a piece of this activity we call it a dream; so a dream, strictly speaking, is one or more thought processes we remember after waking. We dream every night and may remember nothing of it, but mental activity goes on all the same. Sometimes the fragments of a dream seem fairly real or closely related to the events of the day before, or the week before, or even ten years before.

Dreams vary greatly in character. Understanding the dream can be a means of help in understanding the unconscious. For instance, a patient may insist on telling the doctor that he is a very friendly fellow, that he never quarrels with anybody, that he cannot think he has any aggression in his makeup. But on watching his dreams the patient may find that in them he is always quarreling with someone, that he may actually be hurting someone, even making an attack upon the person with a gun or a knife. Through dreams patient and physician see the other side (the unconscious side) of the personality at work. As another example, the physician may ask a patient if he is interested in sex and he answers that he never thinks about it. However in watching his dreams the doctor sees that they have a definite sexual coloring.

Most analysts do not feel they understand *every* dream perfectly or that every dream is significant to the patient's immediate problem. Even though we have worked over a dream for half an hour with a patient we may not understand it completely. The only way a dream can be understood is for the patient, once he has told it, to take its various parts and say what each part reminds him of. A part may remind him of something that happened yesterday, another part may be something he is wishing for, another part may reveal his feelings toward his employer, his wife or his doctor. When a patient tells what he thinks of the dream he is bound to be making a contribution even though he may not be able to integrate the various associations correctly. In the same way the analyst may see a meaning in a dream which he can pass on to the patient. The two pool their knowledge. The doctor says, "This seems to mean something about your deeper thought processes which I feel to be true." The patient may not be able to accept the comment at the time but later its truth becomes evident. We vary in our imaginative capacity and in our capacity to accept symbols. Dreams contain a great deal of symbolism and condensation of psychological material, and a proper utilization of the material requires an understanding of the mechanics of dream formation.

In dreams there is a tendency toward *condensation,* which is a bringing together within one dream not only of present-day events but events, emotions and fantasies out of past experiences.

Displacement is another mechanism of the dream, which may consist of either putting the greatest amount of feeling upon one of the least significant events of the dream or making an insignificant detail occupy the foreground of the dream while the main theme is relegated to a place of little importance. Man's important interests and emotions recur again and again, but because society taboos them, these objects and interests are expressed in symbols instead of directly. For instance, a man's aggressive, unbridled trends may be represented by a wild animal in the dream picture. Generally speaking, the more repression of feeling there is concerning any subject the more completely and subtly that subject will be symbolized.

Dramatization is the acting out in concrete visual imagery the thoughts and ideas that are latent in the unconscious. The making of this into a kind of congruous and partly logical story is called the process of *secondary elaboration*. This process seems to try to effect some mutual understanding between the unconscious and the conscious mind by introducing as many familiar elements as the repressive forces will allow. It is an attempt to bring about a rapprochement between what is known and understood by the conscious mind and what is striving to make itself accepted and understood from the unconscious.

A patient who was working on the matter of sexual adjustment had the following dream. He was afraid of everything pertaining to sex, was not very fond of women and yet was trying to get more out of life, act in a more friendly way and get over some of his fears regarding sexuality. While making love to a girl he had an ejaculation. As he went to the bathroom he touched the doorknob. Thinking about it later, he became fearful lest the girl might have touched the doorknob also, get semen on her hands and later inside her vagina and become pregnant—and he would be responsible. That night he had a dream in which a snake and a cat were on the ground together. Both the snake and the cat seemed to be behaving in a friendly way but he (the dreamer) was afraid. Since the snake was poisonous he thought that at any moment the snake might bite the cat and kill her. Anyone who has seen spermatozoa under the microscope might be struck by the resemblance of their shape to snakes. In this dream the snake represented spermatozoa, the cat symbolizing the woman and also the vagina. Some will accept this symbolism, and we suppose an equal number will reject it. The point is that during sleep the problems continue to be dealt with in a more or less disguised way. Some ask, "Why does the mind portray things symbolically?" and the answer is, "To avoid the anxiety of dealing with them more directly." It is only after a period of study of human beings and a period spent during which the doctor lives with and sees psychotic people, hears what they think, talk about and write, sees the embellishments they put on events and the symbolism they use in their dealings with the world that it is possible to realize the great capacity human beings have for condensation and displacement of feeling onto some object other than the problem with which they cannot cope.

We cannot enlarge too much upon dreams here but a knowledge of dreams and their mechanisms is necessary to a psychotherapist. With the dream as one of the means of understanding the unconscious mind, patient and doctor work toward an ever greater ability for the former to see himself, his personality assets and liabilities and the problems of life to be met. Thus, changing the perspective through psychoanalysis, the patient can come to make better use of his assets, and educate himself so as to diminish his liabilities. He comes to see the essential and the non-essential in a clearer perspective and withdraws concern over the latter and puts all he can into the former. This reduces conflicts, makes for happier, more effective living, and symptoms disappear because the energy that kept them active (anxiety) has been dissipated.

Sanitaria

Institutions, while generally thought of as being places for the seriously mentally sick, nevertheless have a place in the treatment of psychoneurosis of adults, in some of the problems of children, in cases of alcoholism, in certain psychosomatic conditions and in certain character disturbances. In some cases of children's neuroses it is better that—if treatment is to be most effective—they are taken out of the home and are placed in a completely sympathetic environment. In certain adult cases an institutional environment is necessary while the psychotherapeutic treatment is going on because they will accept routine and restraint upon their self-indulgence from strangers which they will not accept from their families or which they cannot manage while living by themselves.

Group Psychotherapy

As we acquire a greater knowledge of emotional maladjustment and learn how much suffering occurs as a result we see how woefully few psychiatrists there are to treat the vast number of people needing psychotherapy. This has led to efforts at treating people in groups, called group psychotherapy.

Such a procedure has its limitations but also its values. First the emotional needs and maladjustments of human beings differ greatly and hence only rather general explanations can be given to the group. As yet

it is not easy to get any large number of people in a group psychotherapeutic endeavor who are suffering from *exactly* the same symptom picture or who have suffered the same traumatic situations. Even if we
could assemble entirely similar cases they would still have difficulty in
giving expression to their most emotionally charged ideas in the group
setting. It is also hard for the group patient to get the same feeling of
complete rapport that is so necessary in psychotherapy. However, if the
neurosis is not too severe, if the patient is resourceful and is the type
who can take inspiration from a group leader and can appreciate being
part of a group working toward a common goal, he may derive much
from group work.

In other words, group psychotherapy is valuable for the person who
has not drifted too far from the ability to relate himself to a group. It
should be highly desirable in the case of maladjusted high-school and
college students, *provided* the student and his family accepted the need
for psychotherapy. Unfortunately, many young people struggle along
alone until they reach a point where intensive personal work is necessary. However, greater resourcefulness on the part of the physician will
increase the value of emotional re-education in groups.

Emotional Disturbances That Accompany Organic Illnesses

We can hardly leave the subject of treatment without touching upon
the problem of emotional disturbances in illnesses that are not psychogenic. In an earlier chapter we discussed the importance of the effects
of organic illness and operations on the emotional life of the child and
assume it is understood that it applies to adults as well. When an adult
takes ill with a serious or a painful illness he is confronted suddenly with
the fact that his body is not under his control, that he can be made uncomfortable by influences he cannot avoid, and that his life, of which he
has felt so certain, may come to an end. Like most human beings he has
spent his time avoiding facing the fact that *he* as a *person* can suffer pain
and death, and now when forced to face these facts as applied to himself, his self-confidence is rudely shaken and he becomes greatly frightened.

These fears—particularly the fear of death—overwhelm the sick person with a feeling of helplessness and make him look forward eagerly
and pathetically to the visit of his physician as if the latter held the keys
of life in his hands. The fact that the patient feels that an interpersonal
relationship is an important help in overcoming the fear of death indi-

cates that this fear is based to some extent on a dread of loneliness. Much
in the writings of poets and novelists—who, as Freud says, are often
closer to recognizing the unconscious than we are—expresses the loneliness of death. The fear of death is often responsible for the constant
and unreasonable complaints of patients, or for the dissatisfaction that
causes them to shift from one doctor to another, or for the exaggerated
respect they frequently show for their medical attendants, or for the
shift made by many persons with minor chronic illnesses from treatment
by the medical profession to various forms of faith healing like Christian Science, whose appeal lies in the supernatural denial of the reality
of death and pain. It motivates also in large measure the painstaking
search carried on by the medical profession for remedies that will cure,
as well as the too optimistic reports of panaceas in medical literature.

Fear has a disturbing effect on bodily functions and in certain instances can bring about death, as has been proven by the work of good
physiologists. Its presence must be taken into account by the doctor in
the treatment of any sick person. Physicians have their own ways of
dealing with the fear of death. Some deal with it by prescribing medicine. The patient's relief from his apprehension will be relieved whether
the medicine is colored water or whether it contains a drug really potent
against the disease process. It is as if with the ingestion of the medicine
the patient said, "I need no longer be afraid of anything because mother
has now fed me with milk." It is such a reaction that forms the motiva-
tion for the addiction of many persons to taking medicine, whether its
use is scientifically based or not. This is a childish form of self-comfort.
It is as if the patient said, "I do not need mother to protect me. As long
as I have something to put in my mouth I'll be all right." We suppose
that most successful physicians intuitively understand what will most
readily relieve the patient's fear of death.

In this connection the nurse is often the physician's alter ego. So much
of the nursing care essential to the adequate and rapid recovery of the
adult patient is a practical method of banishing the patient's apprehension. It is as if the patient said, "Now I know mother and father are
interested in me. I am sure they will protect me from death."

The handling of the patient's fear of death, which often shows its
existence only by a feeling of panic and discomfort, is part of the art of
medicine. It cannot be taught didactically; it consists of an intuitive understanding of the patient's needs. From a practical standpoint, however,

we believe the following suggestions are helpful in dealing with the situation.

First, the patient should be made as comfortable and free from pain as possible.

Second, the patient should be made as comfortable in his mind as possible. This can best be done by allowing sufficient time so that he can pour out his worries, fears and complaints. Too often we are too interested in ascertaining what is occurring inside the bodies of our patients, whereas we might be more helpful if we were more interested in learning what was in their minds. This outpouring itself is helpful and if we find that some of the worries are based on misconceptions it is our duty to correct them, for to do so will often relieve some of the patient's anxiety. Physicians frequently are loath to do this, perhaps because of the time required or perhaps because of a lack of understanding of the patient's needs, but they often employ a nurse for the same purpose where real nursing care to the physical body is not so necessary. The patient can express himself throughout each day to the nurse and she has the opportunity to correct his misconceptions. These so-called misconceptions are due either to ignorance or to the emergence of infantile ideas from the unconscious. In most cases there is some of both. One woman was disturbed greatly because she thought that therapeutic radiation would cause her to lose her body hair permanently. She felt ashamed of this worry and could not discuss it with anyone, meanwhile becoming more and more emotionally upset and nervous. Here the importance of the body hair was an emergence from the unconscious of a childhood anxiety.

Third, the patient should be taken into the doctor's confidence regarding his illness, the means that must be taken to make a diagnosis and to effect a cure, the time that these means will consume and the fact that recovery is not delayed but aided by the measures being undertaken. He should also be warned specifically of the possibility of new symptoms occurring so that he will not become panic-stricken if they should do so.

Fourth, the reasons for specific directions, such as staying in bed, etc., should be discussed with him. It may be argued that discussing physiology and pathology with the patient tends to center his mind on himself whereas he would be better off to think of other things. This is true as far as his relations with other laymen are concerned, but it is not true in the special relationship between himself and the doctor.

Many patients appreciate an opportunity to speak to the doctor alone without nurses or intern present. The doctor should be sensitive to this need and make such a contact possible in the case of a patient who may not have the courage to ask for it. Remarks to nurses and interns about the patient should be clearly made within earshot of the patient if he is intended to hear them. If he is not supposed to hear them they should be made out of sight and out of earshot. A murmured or whispered conversation about the patient near his bed is embarrassing to him and may cause him a great deal of needless anxiety.

All human beings have another fear besides the fear of death, i. e., the fear of being incapacitated. This fear is really the childish fear of mutilation which exists in all of us at all times. Any operative procedure calls it forth in full force. Time and again the physician is surprised—and he should not be—to hear an intelligent person state that the operation took out all his insides or some other grossly exaggerated statement. These statements represent the real emotional reaction of the patient to the operation, and because they make them they should not be ridiculed; instead the patient should be given the opportunity to express himself as freely as possible, knowing he is talking to a sympathetic and kindly friend who can and will correct his misapprehensions. In fact, the rules we laid down for pre- and postoperative preparations for children are also good rules to apply to adults. Explanations concerning what is to be and has been done, explanations concerning manifestations that may appear subsequently, as well as their relation and importance, should be given in even more detail. As with children, so with adults, operations on the nose, throat and genital organs produce more emotional shock than do other procedures and need more intelligent psychological management.

The symptom of bleeding is regarded by most people with great apprehension. Little children often become panicky at the sight of a small drop of blood oozing from a scratch, children who otherwise show no undue fear at a more serious but unbloody injury. Similarly adults tend to become panicky when they bleed. This is curious because bleeding to death is not very common and often the frightened adult actually has not known anyone who has done so. Perhaps this panic is a component of the fear of death (for in primitive thinking the life often resides in the blood) as well as the fear of mutilation, which could not occur without bleeding. It is well known that individuals who are upset at the sight of blood make poor soldiers, not because they are likely to see much blood, although they may do so, but because they are making a poor adjustment to their childhood fears.

Any doctor who has himself undergone a serious illness or who has been close to a loved one who has is in a better position to understand what the patient really feels and thinks. We earnestly recommend that any person who desires to deal with sick people reread carefully the chapters on the development of the child, with a realization that the desires, wishes, doubts and fears that we have described are still active and present in the unconscious minds of his adult patients, and that they have to be taken into consideration if he wishes to give them the best kind of help possible.

BIBLIOGRAPHY FOR CHAPTER XVI

Alexander, F., *The Medical Value of Psychoanalysis*, Norton, 1932.

Brenman, Margaret, and Gill, Merton M., *Bulletin of the Menninger Clinic* 7, nos. 5 and 6, Sept.–Nov., 1943.

Deutsch, Helene, "Some Psychoanalytic Observations in Surgery," *Psychosomatic Medicine* 4, No. 2, Jan., 1942.

Erickson, Milton H., "The Applications of Hypnosis to Psychiatry," *Medical Record*, July 19, 1939, pp. 60–65.

Levine, Maurice, *Psychotherapy in Medical Practice*, Macmillan, 1941.

Menninger, Karl A., "Polysurgery and Polysurgical Addiction," *Psychoanalytic Quarterly* 3, 1934, 173.

Sharpe, E. F., *Dream Analysis*, Norton.

Weiss, Edward, and English, O. S., *Psychosomatic Medicine*, Saunders, 1943.

Zilboorg, Gregory, *Mind, Medicine and Man*, Harcourt, Brace, 1943.

Index